AFRICA: *A Study*
in Tropical Development

By L. Dudley Stamp

A Glossary of Geographical Terms
A Regional Geography (in five parts)

Second Edition

AFRICA: *A Study*

in Tropical Development

L. Dudley Stamp
Professor Emeritus of Social Geography
University of London

John Wiley & Sons, Inc.
New York   London   Sydney

FOURTH PRINTING, JULY, 1967

Preface

Although it is less than ten years since I completed the writing of the first edition of this book, in that short space of time changes in Africa have been so fundamental and developments so rapid that a complete rewriting of many sections has become essential. In the first edition I divided the book into three parts. The first dealt with the continent as a whole, the second with its countries and regions, and the third, a single chapter, with current problems and developments. It was my intention to bring the book up to date periodically by expanding this third part, in the belief that the general picture of countries and regions sketched in Part 2 would remain broadly fixed. But such has been the hurricane of change induced by the rising tide of nationalism and self-determination that such a procedure has proved impracticable. In this edition I have, accordingly, eliminated Part 3 and have tried to present, strictly objectively, the African scene of 1962–1963 in the main part of the book.

The newly independent states which have arisen from former French, British, Belgian, and Italian territories inevitably derive much from their former status—a heritage of administrative, legal, linguistic, educational, and economic organization; hence, much of the historical background has been retained as helping greatly to explain the present position, though each of the new states has been accorded separate consideration. It is my hope that this second edition will thus fully justify the subtitle, "a study in tropical development."

I referred in the preface of the first edition to the need for much careful detailed study and interpretation before the countries of Africa can plan satisfactorily for their future. I referred in particular to the need for mapping existing use and nonuse of land along the lines laid down by the World Land Use Survey of the International Geographical Union. In the meantime considerable progress has been made, and many of the new countries are alive to the need for a careful stocktaking of their resources. The scanty literature on the basic geography of Africa has been enriched by a number of works. I would mention especially Professor G. H. T. Kimble's two-volume work

Tropical Africa, prepared under the auspices of the Twentieth Century Fund. Another noteworthy volume is the *History of Land Use in Arid Lands,* published by UNESCO in both English and French, with notable contributions on the arid lands of both North and South Africa. Southern Africa now has the two-volume work by Professor J. H. Wellington of Johannesburg and a lengthy treatise by Dr. Monica Cole. The considerable spate of detailed monographs and scientific papers, largely inspired by Africa's new universities in both East and West, is noted in appropriate places.

The broadsheet entitled *Focus,* published ten times a year by the American Geographical Society, New York, affords an invaluable means of keeping up to date. Each number is devoted to a single country or topic. Within the last few years many issues have been devoted to Africa: Angola (October 1956), Sierra Leone (December 1957), The Sudan (January 1958), Madagascar (May 1958), Mozambique (September 1958), Ghana (April 1959), South West Africa (November 1960), Algeria (February 1961), Gabon (October 1961), Mauritania (November 1961), Tanganyika (June 1962), Republic of the Congo, Brazzaville (October 1962), Rwanda and Burundi (February 1963) and Uganda (January 1964).

In the last ten years I have had the opportunity of revisiting many parts of Africa. Official journeys in connection with the development of higher education have taken me to Ghana, Nigeria, the Sudan, Uganda, and Kenya, scientific conferences to East and West Africa in both French- and English-speaking areas; there have been happy reunions with old students in Egypt and Ethiopia and other journeys to the Rhodesias and South Africa and to many of the island groups off Africa. New impressions have been gained by flights over Libya and the Sahara, over the Congo and the Veld. It has been my privilege to be "in at the birth" of two great national parks or nature reserves. I hope that the pages which follow have been enriched by these personal contacts.

I am deeply grateful for the valued help of many friends and colleagues, not only on these journeys but in correspondence, and I can only repeat that comments and constructive criticism are always welcome

L.D.S.

May 1964

NOTE. The spelling of African place names presents a lasting difficulty. The international convention is now to give precedence to the spelling used by the countries themselves, but it must be remembered that the majority of newly independent African states use either English or French as their official or international language. Where there is a well-established conventional name in English this has been used, since it seems pedantic to write Tombouctou for Timbuktu or Côte d'Ivoire for Ivory Coast, but the correct titles of countries have been given in the appropriate places. In Portuguese territories one should strictly use Portuguese spellings: Moçambique, not Mozambique, and Cunene, not Kunene, although "K" in such cases is usual elsewhere in Africa. It may be noted that Kamerun, Cameroon, and Cameroun are all correct, each in its appropriate context. I have tried to compromise by using what seemed to me the appropriate spelling in each case.

L.D.S.

Contents

PART 2 · THE COUNTRIES AND REGIONS OF AFRICA

PART ONE

The African Continent

CHAPTER ONE

African Highlights

Africa is unique among the continents. Although each of the great continental masses of the earth's land surface has its own distinctive features, there are points of comparison between some of them. North and South America, for example, are broadly alike in build, with a great complex of mountain ranges trending from north to south in the west, vast plains in the center, and old mountain remnants and plateaus in the east. Australia repeats some of these features, though reversed—plateau in the west, central plains and mountains in the east. Asia with its huge arid mountainous heart is quite distinctive, but most mountain ranges in Asia trend from east to west, cutting off northern lands very sharply from southern. The same is true of Europe; the east-west central mountains, such as the Alps, cut off the north and northwestern European lands from the Mediterranean.

But Africa in all its major features stands alone (Figure 1.1). In the first place it lies fairly and squarely athwart the equator and projects almost equally into both the northern and the southern hemispheres. It is very roughly the same distance (2580 miles) from the equator to its northernmost point (Ras ben Sakka just west of Cape Blanco near Bizerta in Tunisia), which is in latitude 37°21′North, as from the equator to its southernmost point in South Africa (Cape Agulhas), which is in latitude 34°51′South (2400 miles). True, the continent is much broader in the north than in the south, so that two-thirds of its area lie in the northern hemisphere, only one-third in the southern.

The bulk of its 11,700,000 square miles lies within the tropics—over 9,000,000 square miles, in fact—so that Africa is essentially the world's problem continent where development under tropical conditions is concerned. Africa's northern lands, cut off by the great Saharan deserts from the tropical parts, form worlds apart, fascinating in their own special problems and in their historical backgrounds so different from the rest of the continent. In the extreme south of the continent the milder climatic conditions of

Figure 1.1   The position of Africa. An outline of the Americas superimposed on an outline of Africa to show the relative position of some chief towns.

lands again outside the tropics have combined with historical circumstances to give South Africa over the last 400 years a history very different from the history of the main mass.

Africa is a remarkably compact land mass with no great gulf of the sea penetrating towards its heart. Figure 1.2 shows all those parts which are more than 250, 500, 750, and 1000 miles from the salt water of the oceans. This is in marked contrast to the North American continent. Yet the African continent has never really been a unit. The Mediterranean shoreland and the Barbary States of the northwest have always been part of the Mediterranean world, cut off from what may be called Africa proper by the great Saharan desert. Egypt has been linked throughout its history with either its Asiatic neighbors or the Mediterranean world. Off the west coasts, the Azores and Cape Verde Islands are stepping stones along transatlantic routes rather than African islands. The eastern shorelands of Africa have long been part of the Indian Ocean basin, indeed since the Hovas, allied racially with the peoples of southeast Asia, crossed the ocean and settled in Madagascar. The Arab traders and slavers for centuries ranged the East African coasts and penetrated considerable distances inland; they maintained the link with the other shores of the Indian Ocean and even imparted a veneer of Mohammedanism over the once extensive Sultanate of Zanzibar. Thus the "core" of Africa is intertropical Africa, south of the great deserts and away from the coasts. This, the true *Afrique noire,* has a considerable unity, even monotony of pattern. The absence of mountain barriers means that peoples and their cultures have flowed back and forth over its gently rolling plateau surfaces, and there is much to be said which remains true of east and west, north and south.

Africa is not quite an island. Its link with Asia in the northeast is a nar-

Figure 1.2   Africa, showing distances from the heart of the continent to the coasts.

row neck of flat desert land, less than 150 miles across, between the Mediterranean Sea and the Gulf of Aqaba, which joins the Red Sea. West of Sinai, between the Mediterranean and the Gulf of Suez, the isthmus of Suez is even narrower, less than 100 miles. Yet this isthmus of Suez has played a role throughout Africa's history out of all proportion to its inconspicuous appearance on the map. In the great days of world exploration in the fifteenth and sixteenth centuries, it forced the explorers' ships that were seeking passage to the Indies to circumnavigate Africa, and incidentally to discover America. When the isthmus was cut by the Suez Canal in 1869, it focused world spotlight on the essential link in a new world trade chain. Eighty-six years later the control and the protection of the Suez Canal precipitated a major crisis in world affairs.

Although, beginning with the voyage of Vasco da Gama from Portugal to India in 1497–1498, the continent of Africa had been continually circumnavigated, almost until the end of the nineteenth century Africa remained the unknown, the Dark Continent. Books with such titles as *In Darkest Africa* served by those very titles to underline the remoteness and the isolation of lands which so long remained unknown and unexplored by Europeans.

That the whole vast extent of Africa south of the Sahara should thus have remained unknown to Europeans for more than three centuries after its shores were charted is due to an interesting and fundamentally important combination of circumstances. Inhospitable desert coasts are succeeded quite abruptly by almost equally forbidding swamps and forested shores. Except for temporary use as ports of call for running repairs, water supplies, and the like on the route to India and the Far East, there was little to attract the European voyager. The scantily clad black inhabitants were all regarded simply as savages, and there were no fabulous cities with gold and silver treasure to attract *conquistadores* as in South America. Nor was there any reason why the native peoples should receive voyagers from afar with joy. For countless generations the foreigner had been identified with slave raiding; never had the stranger brought other than sorrow. Where, as on the east coast, alien traders—the Arabs—were established, they were far from friendly towards possible rivals.

The prevalence of various tropical fevers added to the unattractiveness of tropical Africa, and where the adventurous sought to penetrate inland, natural obstacles presented themselves. In the first place, the coastline of Africa is almost devoid of any major opening permitting penetration by sea into the heart of the land; indeed, even harbors affording reasonable shelter are few. Along great stretches of the coast there are offshore winds, and the great waves which break some distance out in a line of surf presented another formidable hazard. With no roads, often no tracks other than footpaths wandering from village to village, only human porters afraid to go far from their own village because of intertribal feuds, penetration by land was almost impossible. The obvious routes were up the few major rivers. It was found that in nearly all cases these routes were barred at no great distance from the sea by rapids and waterfalls which we now know to mark the descent of the rivers from the great African plateau. That great navigable stretches lay beyond these falls was not realized until much later.

Where the hinterland offered conditions more physically attractive in South Africa, the story of European interest and subsequent settlement and development, as we shall see later, has been very different. In tropical Africa there have been coastal trading posts and forts maintained by European nationals for the last five hundred years, but the "opening up" of the interior and the partition of Africa among the European nations have taken place almost entirely within the last century. It was in 1855 that Livingstone discovered the Victoria Falls on the Zambezi; it was as recently as 1871 that H. M. Stanley set out to look for the missing Livingstone and found him lying ill at Ujiji on the shores of Lake Tanganyika.

The story of the development of Africa in the last hundred years is a complex one. It is sometimes depicted as one of exploitation of the African by the white man, but, although there are elements of exploitation to be found, a more dominant motive was the suppression of the age-old slave trade.

The opening up of tropical Africa has brought a crop of problems, perhaps best described as the results of a clash of cultures. African tribal organizations and systems of law and justice have been brought up against Western concepts of democracy and European law. Jungle law—the survival of the fittest and might is right—may have been reflected in some aspects of the earlier European penetration, but is incompatible with modern concepts.

Africa has other claims to urgent world attention. By Western standards much of the continent is underdeveloped, with resulting poverty and misery to its inhabitants, and with a further consequence that resources of interest to the outside world in minerals and in agricultural and forest products remain unused.

We find two consequences of this position. One is the awakened conscience of the Western world, which to a considerable extent dates from President Truman's address to Congress in January 1949. Public memory is short, and it may be well to repeat the famous Point IV from which stems so much of the present policy of aid to underdeveloped countries. "Fourth, we must embark on a bold new program for making the benefits of our scientific advances and industrial progress available for the improvements and growth of underdeveloped areas."

The second consequence of the long-continued stagnation of African economy is the awakening and growth of political consciousness. It was inevitable that as Africans seeking higher education should come into contact with the Western world that they should return dissatisfied with the conditions in their homeland. In the period since the end of World War II, Africa has become a collection of independent nations.

On the whole, all those nations of Western culture which have had an interest in Africa have sought to guide the development of Africa's legitimate ideals and aspirations. When the first edition of this book was published in 1953, Africa could be described as the last remaining great colonial domain of the European powers, where Britain, France, Belgium, Portugal, and Spain had their chief colonial dependencies. Although each of the European powers may be said to have envisaged the eventual independence of these African territories, there were and still are marked contrasts in the mode and pace of progress toward that goal, and some may doubt Portuguese and Spanish intentions. There seemed then to be a three-cornered contest between nationalism, communism, and Western interests. Few could then have foreseen the rapidity with which nationalism would sweep through Africa, but many might have prophesied that the attainment of independence would bring unhappiness and chaos in place of order—which has, alas, proved to be the case in some areas, though not in others.

Although there is, in parts of Africa, considerable pressure of population on land resources, the continent as a whole is still sparsely peopled. In a number of territories no exact census has yet been taken. In some cases, such as Uganda, where a first census was taken after World War II, earlier estimates were found to be very wide of the truth. In many other countries the estimates were well below the actual figures revealed. In 1900, the population of the continent is estimated to have been 120 million; in 1920, 141 million; in 1930, 157 million; in 1940, 176 million; and in 1950, 206 million. By mid-1960 the Statistical Office of the United Nations gave a total of 254 million out of a world total of 2995 million, so that by mid-1963 it was probably around 270 million. If, however, one excludes the Moslems of the Atlas lands, Libya, and Egypt and the whites of South Africa, the population of Negro Africa is about two-thirds of this total—of the order of 170 million in 1963. The growth is now rapid: till recently Africa has been steadily losing ground in its relative world position. If an estimate of 100 million is accepted as the population in 1650, that figure would represent over 18 per cent of the world's population. By 1850, using Carr-Saunders' figures, an estimated population of 95 million would represent only 8 per cent of the world total.[1] Today Africa as a whole has about 8 per cent of the world's people, and Negro Africa rather over 5 per cent.

Although in some areas the population density may be the maximum supportable under existing conditions and existing economic systems, poten-

[1] A. M. Carr-Saunders, *World Population,* London, 1936.

tial changes are enormous. The spread of the knowledge of medicine and hygiene means greatly increased survival rates and greater longevity. The conquest of such pests and diseases—so often described as the real rulers of Africa—as tsetse fly, locusts, yellow fever, malaria, and hookworm means that enormous areas at present unusable may be thrown open to settlement and development. Increased control of water supplies will mean a maintenance of crop yields as well as an extension of irrigated areas; the spread of agricultural knowledge can only result in greater productivity. When cattle come to be regarded as sources of human sustenance rather than symbols of wealth, the carrying capacity of the lands in terms of human beings will be still further increased.

Some writers place the control of water as the foundation for all development, but others would echo the words of Lord Lugard: "The material development of Africa may be summed up in one word—transport."

All the signs are that Africa is on the threshold of a period of great population expansion coupled with economic and political development. The lesson of Africa, however, has been, over and over again, to "make haste slowly." The failure of some recent large schemes has served to emphasize this lesson.

The emphasis in this book is on Africa between the tropics. The monotony of the physical pattern over much of this vast area is matched by the sameness of human response. From the far west to the east coasts, the African system of shifting cultivation is found with little variation. Yet there are contrasts, and Africa today may be divided into four regions: Mediterranean Africa, which is part of the Moslem world; western Atlantic Africa, which is tropical Africa *par excellence;* eastern Africa, affected by large-scale immigration of non-African peoples, notably Arabs, Indians, and Europeans; South Africa, the white man's stronghold. Each has its own problems; each reacts upon the other. Not least among the problems is the contrast between the white settlers' outlook in South Africa and the attitude of the rest of the Western world.

From another point of view, Pierre Gourou in his *Pays tropicaux* draws a distinction between "tropical lands" with a rainfall exceeding 800 millimeters (16 inches) a year and "desert lands" occupying drier country, where the problems are different. Here again, in this book, the emphasis is on tropical Africa.

BIBLIOGRAPHY

Books dealing comprehensively with the whole continent of Africa in its geographical setting are few. First place must be given to the two volumes in the great French *Géographie universelle: Afrique septentrionale et occidentale* (Vol. XI, in two parts), by A. Bernard; and *Afrique équatoriale, orientale, et australe* (Vol. XII), by F. Maurette (1937–1939).

In English, *Africa,* by Walter Fitzgerald (New York, First Edition, 1934, many subsequent editions), is a general geography emphasizing the physical background and especially the major regions. There is still much of value in A. H. Keane's *Africa* (*Stanford's Compendium of Geography and Travel,* 2 volumes, Second Edition, London, 1907). When the problems of Africa were coming markedly to the fore an administrator with wide experience was commissioned to make a comprehensive survey. The result was Lord Hailey's *An African Survey* (Oxford, Revised, 1956). It is not a geography but a mine of information.

So rapidly is development taking place in Africa that many of the books noted in the first edition are mainly of historic interest as showing the trend of thought at the time. As a fine pictorial survey with careful commentary, R. U. Light's *Focus on Africa* (American Geographical Society, 1944) retains its value; so does the thoughtful, scholarly work of Pierre Gourou, translated into English as *Tropical Lands* and brought up to date in a third edition in 1961. But the great compendium is now G. H. T. Kimble's *Tropical Africa* (New York: Twentieth Century Fund, 2 vols., 1960) where the treatment is by topics, not by regions. Latest population statistics are available in the *Demographic Yearbook* (United Nations).

CHAPTER TWO

Unrolling the Map of Africa

The sea in the midst of the lands, the Mediterranean, if not the cradle of mankind, has seen around its shores the birth, growth, and decay of many great civilizations. Its Asiatic, African, and European shorelands have all shared in this early history—Babylonia, Assyria, Phoenicia, Israel, and later the Ottoman Turks in Asiatic lands; Greece and Rome in Europe; and Minos on the island of Crete. But perhaps the greatest of all these early civilizations was in Egypt, on African soil. Egyptian civilization flourished for some four millennia before the birth of Jesus Christ. In the great days of Rome, Carthage, founded by the Phoenicians in the ninth century before Christ in North Africa, was more than once a serious contender for world supremacy. In the eighth and ninth centuries of the Christian era, when Mohammedanism swept across North Africa, Moorish or Arab domains extended from Egypt across to Morocco and thence into Iberia.

Thus the long, well-documented history of North African lands is in complete contrast to the almost history-less story of most of the rest of the continent. What was the barrier which separated two worlds so utterly in contrast? It was, as it still is, the greatest arid waste on the earth's surface, the great desert known as the Sahara, stretching unbroken from the Atlantic coasts to the shores of the Red Sea, and nowhere less than a thousand miles wide (Figures 2.1 and 2.2).

The one natural routeway across the desert waste would appear to be the River Nile. But sailing up the Nile beyond Upper Egypt is impossible, for no less than six series of cataracts obstruct navigation between Assuan and Khartoum. Above Khartoum another obstacle exists in the form of great masses of floating vegetation, or sudd.

Thus, for thousands of years those who dwelt within reach of the Mediterranean had no direct knowledge of the lands which lay to the south of the great wastes. The nomadic tribesmen who knew the secrets of its waterholes took care to keep their knowledge to themselves, for their livelihood de-

Figure 2.1   The arid lands of Africa. Areas in black have less than 10 inches of rain a year.

pended upon the transport of a few rare commodities cheaply obtained in the south which the northerners valued.

In the Christian era the spread of Mohammedanism only intensified the barrier; the Christian who attempted to penetrate the barrier took his life in his hands.

For many centuries, indeed millennia, Negro Africa, as we may call those parts of the continent south of the Sahara, yielded but one product of major interest to the outside world: slaves. Slavery would seem to be indigenous in Negro Africa itself. There were Negro slaves in ancient Egypt; Ethiopian and Negro slaves were by no means unknown in Greece and Imperial Rome— Arab slave traders brought them across the northern deserts; Arab slave ships called in at ports down the east coast. The mistaken idea is widely held that Europeans introduced slavery into Africa. Nothing could be farther from the truth. Indeed, its suppression within Africa remained a problem long after it had been abolished elsewhere. It was about 1442 that the first Negroes were brought from West Africa by the Portuguese to work in Spain and Portugal, and it was from there that they were introduced into the New World— some to Haiti as early as 1502. In 1517 Bartolomé de las Casas, the celebrated Bishop of Chiapa, sought to relieve the sufferings of the native Indians of Haiti working in the mines by securing a license to import slaves. This was really the beginning of the systematic slave trade between Africa and America.

When the Portuguese were alloted by the Pope's Line the Brazilian shores

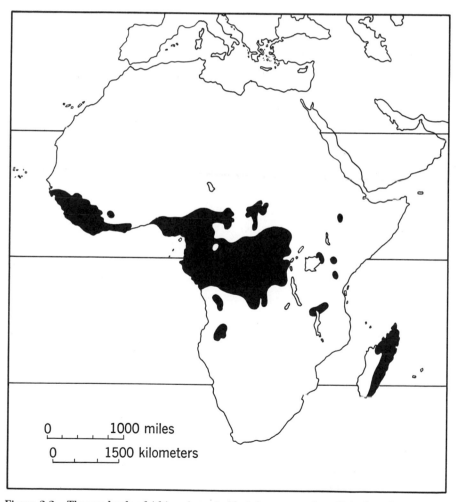

Figure 2.2   The wet lands of Africa. Areas in black have more than 60 inches of rain a year.

of South America, they did not find there the sophisticated Inca cities with stores of gold and silver such as lured the Spaniards in the western parts of the continent. They found instead land which could yield abundantly if only labor were available. This constituted another large demand for slave labor in the New World. Though the English Admiral John Hawkins, at war with Spain and Portugal, captured slaving ships and then sold the slaves to the Spanish settlements as early as 1562, it was not till 1620 that a Dutch ship sailed for Jamestown in Virginia and sold the first slaves to a British American settlement. As sugar plantations became established in the West Indies and cotton plantations in the American South, Britain developed the notorious "triangular traffic." Ships left Liverpool, Bristol, or Lancaster in Britain with cotton goods, cheap jewelry and other merchandise, or gold as the price of slaves. They took on their human cargo along the "Slave Coast," as parts of West Africa were long known, sailed across the Atlantic, sold the slaves, and returned to Britain with cargoes of sugar and raw cotton. Bad as were the conditions on the slave ships, the hardly won cargo was too valuable to lose, and the survival rate was high, about 85 per cent. On the coasts of East Africa conditions in the slave trade were infinitely worse; it has been said that sometimes only 10 per cent of the cargo of some Arab slave ships survived. The West African trade reached its height just before the War of American Independence when 192 slave ships, with a capacity of 47,000 Negroes, were sailing from these British ports. In 1790, during the revival of slave trade after the war, 75,000 slaves were landed in America by the British, French, Portuguese, Dutch, and Danes.

The slave trade conferred one lasting benefit on Africa. For the purpose of feeding the slaves herded together in the coastal barracoons awaiting shipment to the Americas and also for feeding the same slaves en route, the Europeans, especially the Portuguese, introduced many exotic food plants, since local foodstuffs were either too scarce or too perishable. In this way corn, peanuts, manioc, sweet potatoes, coconuts, bananas, and citrus fruits were introduced into Africa. The long-term results on African diets have been almost as revolutionary as the introduction into the Americas by the Spaniards of such European animals as the horse and cattle or such grains as wheat.

It may seem strange that this trade in Negro slaves continued for so many centuries. Why, for example, did not the Africans band themselves together to prevent it? It is necessary to form a picture of a continent inhabited by warring tribes. The hunters who depended for their existence on the chase wanted vast tracts of land in which to hunt; they resented any intruders. The nomadic cattle keepers and herdsmen needed vast open grasslands for their animals and resented any enclosures, though their animals appreciated succulent crops stolen from sedentary cultivators. Those who had adopted the settled life and systems of shifting cultivation were at pains to keep off the cattlemen. Almost any one of these groups would view the selling of an enemy as a slave a more profitable solution to his problem than killing him. Over this continent-wide pattern of incompatible economic elements were the ambitious empire builders, gaining wealth and power by selling their captives or betraying enemies. The Moslems from the north brought Islam to the Negroes along the Saharan borders but made little impression on the vast tribes of pagans, and it was clearly in accord with the will of Allah to rid the world of the infidels. So great was the drain on the continent that it is probable that its overall population was actually reduced from the sixteenth to the nineteenth centuries.

Mention of the early Portuguese participants in the slave trade brings us to consider the European exploration of African coastlands. The Carthaginian Hanno claims to have made a voyage about 470 B.C. through the Pillars of Hercules (Strait of Gibraltar) and along the west coast of Africa, with the object of founding colonies. He probably reached south of the Gambia River, but for many centuries his discoveries were forgotten. It was only after the decline of the Moorish power in Spain and the rise of Spain and Portugal to front rank among the nations that European exploration by sea of the African coasts was undertaken in earnest.

Prince Henry the Navigator (1394–1460) was the fourth son of King John (João) I of Portugal and his French bride Philippa the daughter of John of Gaunt. He established a school for navigation and an observatory, and one of his captains discovered the fertile island of Madeira. His ships sailed on past the inhospitable Saharan coasts of the mainland to the green lands beyond; hence the name Cape Verde ("Green Cape") and Cape Verde Islands.

Before the voyages of Columbus, the Portuguese had sailed along the coasts of Guinea, and Bartholomeu Diaz (1455–1500), without realizing it, had rounded the south of Africa into the Indian Ocean in 1486. It was the strong easterly winds which drove him back to the Cape of Storms, afterwards renamed by the King of Portugal the Cape of Good Hope.

These probing voyages of the Portuguese were prompted by a desire to reach the spice lands of the Far East by an all-water route instead of having to rely on the uncertain and expensive supplies brought to Europe overland.

Although the shores of Greenland, Labrador, and other parts of North America were undoubtedly known to early Norse voyagers and others from northwestern Europe, the discovery of America is usually understood to mean the first sighting of land by Christopher Columbus in the Bahama group in 1492. The voyage of Columbus the Genoese, financed by Spain, had been undertaken, it is generally believed, to find a westward route to the Spice Islands of the East Indies. There are, however, those scholars who consider that the North American continent had been discovered some years earlier by Portuguese sailors and that when Columbus sailed he already knew that his way to the west would be barred by a great continent. At a time when there was intense rivalry, indeed mortal enmity, between Spain and Portugal, it is difficult to understand why Columbus on his return voyage called at the Azores—Portuguese territory—and then went straight to Lisbon. It is difficult to believe that he was such a bad navigator that he struck Lisbon in Portugal accidentally instead of Cadiz, or some other part of Spain. In Lisbon he was certainly granted an interview with the King of Portugal and then allowed to depart unhindered for Spain, instead, as one might have thought, of being imprisoned or even executed. Was King John of Portugal his secret master? Was the object of the intrigue to draw the attention of Spain to the new lands of the New World while Portugal consolidated her interests in India and the Far East by seeking the Cape route? If so, it succeeded to an amazing degree, and we have fully explained the lack of Spanish interest in the early exploration and development of Africa.

If those are right who believe the Portuguese knew of the existence of the American continent before Columbus sailed on his first voyage, we have a reason for the ready acceptance by the Portuguese of the Treaty of Tordesillas in 1493. It will be recalled that this treaty gave lands discovered west of 60° West to Spain; lands east of that line to Portugal. Though this treaty is normally considered as applying to the Americas—it gave Brazil to Portugal before land in that area was even discovered—it clearly gave authority to Portuguese claims to *any* lands east of the 60° West meridian, that is, to all Africa. While Columbus and the Spaniards were concentrating on the New World, Portugal was certainly active in the search for the sea route to India. Vasco de Gama rounded the Cape of Good Hope in 1497 and landed on the well-watered, forested coasts farther to the northeast on Christmas Day; hence the name Natal which he gave to the area, and which has remained to this day. He reached what is now Lourenço Marques on Delagoa Bay on March 1, 1498, but farther north he was not welcomed by the Arab traders and settlers in the coastal towns. As it turned out, this was fortunate, for he secured a pilot who directed him across to India and he landed at Calicut, previously visited by Cavilhao traveling via Egypt in 1486. The way to India was won. The great spice trade was soon firmly in Portuguese hands, and the Spaniards could have America. A settlement was established at Mozambique in 1505; a fortified factory was built at Calicut in 1510 and established as a Portuguese settlement and trading post; Goa was occupied in 1510; the coasts of Ceylon were settled in the next few years, and Malacca on the coast of Malaya was captured in 1511. A little later, in 1557, Portuguese settled on the island of Macao off the south of China.

While the Spanish conquistadores were busy with the northern coastlands of South America, the Portuguese Cabral, taking advantage of the northeast

Trades on his way to India, found himself carried too far westward and off the coasts of Brazil. This was in 1500, and the land was promptly claimed by Portugal. In the following year, 1501, the King of Portugal sent out Amerigo Vespucci to follow up Cabral's discovery. He probably (though there is some doubt about his achievements) traversed the whole coast of South America from Cape San Roque to the Plate estuary, and then sailed on to South Georgia. Portugal thus gained interests on both sides of the South Atlantic, but it was the sea route to India which was of immediate importance. It is said that Algoa Bay (on which Port Elizabeth now stands) was the resting place "on the way to Goa," while Delagoa Bay in what later became Portuguese East Africa was the most convenient port of call "on the way from Goa."

In the meantime the Portuguese had penetrated well into the Gulf of Guinea. They observed the frequent thunderstorms around the norite mass which forms the Peak in what is now Sierra Leone and likened the noise to the constant roaring of lions, hence the name Lion Mountains or Sierra Leone. They founded their first permanent station at Elmina on the Gold Coast as early as 1481. The small quantities of alluvial gold brought down from the interior and exchanged for manufactures by the tribes of the coast originally made these lands of interest to Europeans. African ivory had long been famous, but it was slave trading that soon became most important. The Portuguese established a string of forts to guard their interests in the trade. British traders visited the West African coasts from 1530 onward, and it was as early as 1554 that the famous Captain Thomas Wyndham died in the creeks of the Oil Rivers, or Niger delta. It was not until the early seventeenth century that the British established their first trading post, a fort on the Gambia River. That century witnessed the ousting of the Portuguese by the Dutch; but the Dutch found themselves sharing interests with the British, while Denmark and Brandenburg also had forts along the coast (Figure 2.3). France was also interested in the Far Eastern trade. French interests in Senegal (West Africa) date from 1637, and the capital, Saint-Louis, was founded in 1658. In the Indian Ocean the French have held Réunion since 1643 and were masters of Mauritius (Île de France) from 1715 to 1810; Pondicherry, the oldest French Indian settlement, was founded in 1674.

It was not until toward the end of the eighteenth century that a profound change took place in the European (and by this time American) attitude towards Africa. On the one hand was the growth of the movement for the abolition of slavery; on the other hand, the urge toward exploration of the unknown African interior.

In Britain the abolitionists found a champion in William Wilberforce. Born in 1759, he was elected to Parliament at the age of 21 and was soon known for his forceful advocacy of many philanthropic causes. In 1787 he took on the leadership of the abolitionists and fought doggedly for 20 years

Figure 2.3　The Old Danish Fort of Christiansborg Castle, Accra. It is now used as the official residence of the President of Ghana. (Official Photograph.)

before his dreams were realized. In 1807 the British Parliament passed a measure for the abolition of the slave trade. This was, of course, an entirely different matter from the abolition of slavery and the emancipation of slaves, but Wilberforce lived to see this ideal realized too. He died in 1833, the year in which slavery was abolished throughout the British Empire. Even in the early days the abolitionists were not inactive. In 1787 they formed the Sierra Leone Company, with a trading charter from the British crown, but with the avowed object of resettling freed slaves in Africa. It was impossible to return slaves to their native places because these places were unknown. A tract of land, therefore, was ceded to the company by its native ruler in Sierra Leone. The task was a difficult one, but after early troubles progress was made, especially after the founding of Freetown in 1792. However, the company was glad to transfer its responsibilities to the British crown in 1808. Though it was not the oldest of the British Colonies in Africa, the origin of Sierra Leone, one of the oldest, as a home for freed slaves should not be forgotten.

American interests in tropical Africa have a similar origin. In 1821 the American Colonization Society selected Cape Mesurado (now Monrovia) as an area to which freed slaves could be sent, and the American-Negro colony was founded between 1822 and 1828 by the white American Jehudi Ashmun, some 30 years after the founding of Freetown. The name Liberia was given to the settlement in 1824 by the Reverend R. R. Gurley. Another settlement, like Liberia a republic, named Maryland, existed until the two were joined in 1857. Curiously enough, the United States did not recognize the new republic until 1862.

The early years of the nineteenth century were the days of Britain's struggle with Napoleon of France, a struggle which did not cease until the decisive victory at Waterloo in Belgium in 1815 and Napoleon's exile to St. Helena. Even then, the traditional British-French rivalry persisted. The abolition of slavery in 1807 rendered the West African forts of little value. By 1821 the number of British stations was reduced from twelve to four despite many requests from the Africans that Britain should take over the whole coast from Gambia to the Congo. By 1820 the forts, assumed a new importance as bases from which the British navy could operate against the remaining slave traders. The handful of traders who refused to leave the coast when Britain proposed to evacuate the whole area turned the scales towards a new growth of real trade.

Turning to exploration, we have an important name in the Scottish doctor, Mungo Park, who set out from the mouth of the Gambia in 1795 to find the great river known to exist inland and called the Niger. He traveled almost due east, and passed through country where he found strong, well-built Negroes engaged in cattle rearing and in burning the grass of the savanna lands in the dry season, which they believed improved the growth of succulent shoots later. When he entered the country of the Mohammedan emirates, he found hostility but persisted—as a Christian in danger of his life —northeastwards to the Saharan margins, where wandering pastoralists were still unfriendly. He reached the Niger at Segu and traveled down it some fifty miles before he decided to return. Despite great hardships (it was the rainy season), he had, on his return, a burning desire to solve the riddle of the Niger. In 1805 he set out again on a similar route. He was never again seen alive by white men; he was drowned at the falls of Bussa (now in the heart of Nigeria) after an attack by local tribesmen. So the outlet of the Niger remained a mystery until 1830, when R. L. Lander proved the "Oil Rivers" to be the delta of the Niger (Figure 2.4).

It is interesting to turn for comparison to South Africa, where the story of European interest and penetration was very different. In general terms the climatic conditions around the Cape of Good Hope are comparable to those in the pleasantest parts of California. The winters are milder, and the summers are less scorching than in Mediterranean Europe, but there is abundant sunshine in the well-watered coastal plains and valleys. Furthermore, there are some reasonably good natural harbors, especially the harbor of Cape Town under the shelter of Table Mountain. Though known to and used by the Portuguese ships en route to the Indian Ocean, Cape Town came into being as a regular halfway house when the Dutch ousted the Portuguese in the Far Eastern trade and established a settlement on the site of Cape Town in 1652. Though the Dutch East India Company was sternly against setting up a colony, it was convenient to allow old servants of the Company to retire there and grow produce and rear cattle for the benefit of ships which called

Figure 2.4   Reproduction of a map of Africa, 1821. This map shows the large areas of the interior then remaining unknown, including the Congo and Zambezi rivers, the true course of the Niger and the source of the Nile. (From *A New and Comprehensive System of Modern Geography*, by Thomas Myers, London, 1822.)

to rewater and revictual. Naturally farms were established at increasing distances from the coast, and the settlers came into collision with the native Hottentots against whom the Dutch company had neither men nor materials to defend Dutch nationals. The British occupied the Cape during the Napoleonic Wars to protect the sea route to India, and by the Peace Treaty of 1814 they retained the territory. By this time the Dutch farmers or "Boers" (*boer* = farmer) had become well established, but, as they expanded farther into the interior, they met increasing resistance not only from the Hottentots but also from the Kaffirs, as the Boers called the Negro peoples they found in Southeast Africa. This was not altogether the fault of the Kaffirs, for they were being pressed southward by other and warlike Bantu tribes sweeping southward from central Africa. The Boer farmers had in the past relied on slave labor, and tended to take the frontiersman's view that when there were signs of trouble a dead Kaffir was safer than a live one.

The British, on the other hand, had abolished slave trading and were seeking to abolish slavery altogether. They sought to replace the frontiersman's methods by peaceful settlements. Disagreement between the Boer farmers and the British government came to a head in 1833 when slavery was abolished and the Boers received eventually somewhat inadequate compensation for the loss of their slaves. In 1836 the Great Trek began; the Boer settlers set off with their great lumbering ox wagons, each with a "span" of sixteen oxen, into the interior. They crossed the Orange River and later set up the Orange Free State (Orange Vrij Staat). Others crossed the Vaal River, fought the Matabele, and established what later became the Transvaal Republic. In 1837 Piet Retief crossed the scarp of the Drakensberg into country occupied by the Zulus, but he and other leaders were murdered by the Zulu king in February 1838. Though the Zulus were defeated later the same year, the Boers found a British colony already established at Fort Natal. After a period of friction Natal was declared a British colony (1843), and the Boers left.

The British government was in a difficult position when the Great Trek took place. Should it try to follow the trekkers and attempt both to control and protect them, thus involving itself in a possibly endless war? Or should it let them go and risk their being overcome by the hostile Kaffir tribes? In 1852 the decision was made by recognizing the Transvaal as an independent republic, provided there should be no slavery. The trekkers of the Orange Free State were more doubtful about accepting independence if it involved losing protection. Nevertheless, the Orange Free State was declared formally independent in 1854. Thus in broad lines the four countries which eventually became provinces of the Republic of South Africa were established by 1854.

By this time the work of exploration from South Africa associated with the name of Dr. David Livingstone was already well advanced. David Livingstone, the son of a poor Scot, was born in 1813. Though he was working in a cotton mill at the age of 10, he had a burning desire to become a medical missionary to China. The London Missionary Society sent him instead to South Africa. He arrived at Cape Town early in 1841, proceeding at once to the mission station established by Robert Moffat at Kuruman in southern Bechuanaland. In 1844 he married Mary Moffat, who (sometimes with young children) accompanied him on many of his journeys until her death at Shupanja in 1862. In 1849 he discovered Lake Ngami, which has since partly dried up. In 1850 he reached the Upper Zambezi with his wife and children, but they fell sick and he sent them back to Cape Town (incidentally, they took nearly two years on the journey). From the Upper Zambezi he went north and west up the Liba to Lake Dilolo, arriving, exhausted from fever and ill nourished, at Loanda, on the west coast, on May 31, 1854. Nothing daunted, he returned in 1855 to the interior, determined to follow the Zambezi to its mouth. On this journey he discovered the Great Falls, which he named in honor of Queen Victoria, in 1855, and reached the mouth of the Zambezi the following May. After a sojourn in England he set off in 1858 on a second journey to Africa with his brother Charles and John Kirk. The expedition started up the Zambezi and its tributary the Shiré, but met the inevitable rapids; on a second attempt, light canoes were carried to the navigable upper reaches. The party had many other troubles, but when he returned in July 1864 Livingstone had explored the Shiré River, discovered Lakes Shirwa and Nyasa, and opened the eyes of the world to the horrors of the slave trade which still existed. Although Livingstone declared that he found exploring easier than writing, his diary[1] is fascinating reading. On his 1849 journey to Lake Ngami he spent some time among the Bushmen. By showing them how to irrigate their crops in this dry Kalahari country from wells in the dry season and streams in the precarious wet season he did much to ameliorate their hard life. In his 1855 journey he met with suspicion as well as demands for bribes from the native chiefs. He learned also of the many plagues of Africa: heat and drought; mosquitoes which were sometimes only annoying, at other times dangerous carriers of fever; the tsetse fly, which caused havoc among his cattle and pack animals and was capable also of bringing the dread sleeping sickness to man. Travel by canoe involved the hazards of attack by crocodiles and by the floating logs which resolved on approach into hippopotami capable of capsizing the canoes if only in play. Living entirely on the country meant killing antelopes in the savanna lands and subsisting on nuts and fruits in the forests.

In 1865 he started on his last journey with the object of finding the source of the Nile, an old problem. It cannot be said that he was treated overgenerously. The British government granted him £500 (then about $2500), and the Royal Geographical Society a like amount. While he wandered over vast tracts of country from Lake Nyasa to Lake Tanganyika he was lost to the world, and his fate for five years was unknown.

[1] *Missionary Travels and Researches in South Africa,* London, 1857. See also *Livingstone's Private Journals, 1851–1853,* edited by I. Schapera, London, Chatto and Winders, 1960.

The explorations of Dr. Livingstone and his revelations of the horrors of the slave trade which still existed had aroused intense interest in the United States, where slavery had been finally abolished in 1864. Mr. Gordon Bennett of the *New York Herald* translated into deeds the popular demand by sending Henry Morton Stanley with a well-equipped expedition to search for Livingstone. Stanley was an Englishman born in North Wales in 1841, who emigrated to New Orleans at the age of fifteen and sought adventure as a roaming journalist. Having already accompanied Lord Napier's Abyssinian expedition in 1867–1868 as special correspondent for the *New York Herald,* he was the obvious person to send in search of Livingstone. Reaching Zanzibar in 1871, later in the year he came upon Livingstone, ill with fever but indomitable as ever, at Ujiji on the shores of Lake Tanganyika. Livingstone refused to return, and, partly recovered in health, he and Stanley explored the northern end of Lake Tanganyika together. When Stanley reluctantly left him, Livingstone set off once again to seek the source of the Nile. His health deteriorated, and on May 1, 1873, his followers found him dead. He was at Chitambo's village on the Molilamo, actually one of the headstreams of the Congo. The love and confidence he had inspired in his African followers were well shown in the devotion with which they carried his body a thousand miles to Zanzibar, whence it was conveyed to England and buried in Westminster Abbey.

Before we review the later work of Stanley we must look at some of the earlier exploration in East Africa (Figure 2.5). Little is known of the early contacts between Egypt and the peoples to the south, including the ancient Empire of Ethiopia or Abyssinia. The Abyssinians proper or Amharas were converted to Christianity in the fourth century, and connection was maintained continuously with the Coptic Church of Alexandria, since the Abuna or Chief Bishop of Ethiopia had (until World War II) always been a Copt and appointed by the Coptic Patriarch of Alexandria. This did not, however, result in any direct contacts between Europe and Ethiopia. The first written record of a land exploration by a European is that of the Portuguese missionary, Father Lobo, who reached Ethiopia in 1622. Although he saw the deep valleys whose waters feed the Blue Nile he did not realize the connection, and it was not until 1770 that the Scottish explorer James Bruce (1730–1794), in the course of five years' journeying in Ethiopia, solved the riddle by following the Blue Nile down until it joined the main river, the White Nile, at Khartoum. Nearly a century was to pass before Speke solved the riddle of the source of the White Nile.

Exploration in East Africa was hindered, even along the coastlands, by Arab seamen and traders. Richard Francis Burton, born in England, educated in France, Italy, and at the University of Oxford, served as a young man in the Indian Army and as a surveyor before he made his famous jour-

WEST AND NORTH AFRICA

.... Mungo Park (1795-7)
—·—·—·— Mungo Park (1816)
————— Clapperton (1822-7)
------------ Lander (1825-30)
—·—·—·— Caille (1827-8)
—··—··—·· Barth (1850-5)
--------- Rohlfs (1865-7)
—··—··—·· Binger (1887)

EAST, CENTRAL AND SOUTH AFRICA

.... Bruce (1769-72)
--------- Livingstone (1841-73)
.... Stanley (1871-89)
----------- Speke (1858)
————— Speke & Burton (1857-9)
+ + + + + + Speke & Grant (1860-3)
.... Baker (1862-4)
—·—·—·— Nachtigal (1869-74)
————— Junker (1880-6)

🌿🌿 Swamps or marshes

Figure 2.5 The routes of certain leading African explorers. The routes shown are those followed by the explorers whose work is mentioned in the text, together with others who added greatly to the knowledge of the interior of the continent prior to 1850.

ney to Mecca in 1853 disguised as an Indian Pathan. He then turned his attention to Africa and was the first white man to enter the Somali capital of Harrar. He had time to serve in the British army, though never actually reaching the front, in Crimea before joining John Hanning Speke (1827–1864) when they set off in June 1857 from Zanzibar westward. They crossed the high grassy plateau abounding in game in what is now Tanganyika until they overlooked that great rift in the earth's crust, the East African rift valley, with the long narrow Lake Tanganyika at their feet. This was in 1858, and they reached the settlement of Ujiji where thirteen years later Stanley was to find the sick Livingstone. Burton was already seriously ill, and, leaving him at Tabora, Speke went on northwards alone. He discovered the great inland sea, which he named in honor of Queen Victoria, before returning to Burton.

With Burton's later journeys in West Africa, South America, and elsewhere we are little concerned, but Speke, accompanied by J. A. Grant, set off on a second expedition with the help of the Royal Geographical Society in 1860. They reached and were detained in the capital of the prosperous land of Uganda but were later released. Finding that the waters of Lake Victoria poured out over the Ripon Falls, they realized that at last they had found the source of the Nile. To confirm what must have been virtually certain they followed the river northwards until they had the good fortune to meet S. W. Baker (1863) who, accompanied by his long-suffering wife, had journeyed up the White Nile through the Sudd region. Speke published his findings in 1863, but his old companion Burton was not fully convinced. Speke accidentally shot himself the very day he was to meet Burton and defend his momentous discoveries.

Samuel White Baker (1821–1893), after eight years in Ceylon attempting to form an agricultural settlement on the English model, started his explorations of the Nile basin in 1861. He explored the Atbara and Ea tributaries and, after meeting Speke, went on to find Albert Nyanza (1864), which he showed contributed an important part of the waters of the Nile. In 1870 he was actually appointed Governor-General of the Nile Equatorial Districts by the Khedive Ismael to suppress the slave trade and open up the area to trade. In this post he laid the foundation for the work of General Charles George Gordon, his successor.

We must now return to H. M. Stanley, who set out on his second journey in 1874 with the main object of solving some of the great problems which the death of Livingstone had left unsolved. He circumnavigated Lake Victoria, passed down the Lualaba to where it becomes the Congo and then down that great river to the sea. It was Leopold II, King of the Belgians, who realized the enormous potential value of this navigable highway penetrating into the heart of Africa. On his behalf Stanley headed an expedition in 1879 which resulted in the establishment of the Congo Free State five years later. For many years, indeed until 1907–1908, this enormous area in the heart of Africa remained the personal possession of the King of Belgium. With its establishment the "scramble for Africa" may be fairly said to have begun. Partition was precipitated by the activities of the German explorer, Karl Peters (1856–1918). Peters founded the German Colonization Society at Berlin in 1884 and in the same year made an expedition to East Africa.

The chief ruler in East Africa had long been the Sultan of Zanzibar. After the abolition of slavery in the British Empire in 1833, Britain's policy was to influence this powerful ruler against slavery and to persuade him to undertake the necessary reforms, and to help him to do so. The first British consul at Zanzibar was appointed in 1840, but it was not until Sir John Kirk was appointed in 1873 and occupied himself with great skill for fifteen years that slavery was actually brought to an end and replaced by legitimate trading. At first the closing of ports to the Arab slavers drove them inland; then Britain supported the Zanzibar Sultan Barghash with arms and ammunition, and the sultanate began to grow into a real state (Figure 2.6). But Karl Peters had gained access to East Africa with three companions, all in disguise and using false names. They traveled around the country, obtaining concessions for the German Colonization Society from chieftains who were in fact under the Sultan of Zanzibar's suzerainty. In 1855 the German government backed up the claims based on these treaties with local chieftains and sent a fleet to anchor off Zanzibar, which they threatened to bombard. The British government weakly instructed Kirk to advise the Sultan to submit, with the result that he lost the bulk of his mainland territory, and German East Africa came into existence (Figure 2.7).

But for two circumstances the whole of East Africa might have become German. One was an Arab revolt which, though suppressed in 1889, occupied the attention of the German administration. The other was the formation of the British East Africa Company in 1888 with the primary aim of rousing British public opinion to a realization of the importance of East Africa and to act as an agent of civilization and good government in the regions entrusted to it. The company successfully contested the claim of Peters to Uganda until the British Prime Minister, Gladstone, was forced by public opinion against his own will to take over responsibility in 1893. The company similarly looked after the destiny of the territory later known as Kenya, until it surrendered its charter in 1895 (Figure 2.8). British East Africa became a protectorate under the British crown, and the construction of the Kenya-Uganda railway dealt a final blow to the slave trade. Zanzibar became a British protectorate in 1890.

The revival of French interest in West Africa was an indirect result of France's defeat by Germany in 1870–1871 and the loss of Alsace-Lorraine. To restore her prestige and self-esteem she turned her attention to West Africa, and had secured a firm hold by the time Germany became active in the same area. Various British trading interests had consolidated themselves as the United African Company in 1879, which became the Royal Niger Company in 1886. The vigorous policy of the company's chief, George Taubman Goldie, secured trading places and agreements with Negro authorities, thus forestalling the activities of Herr Flegel, who attempted the same methods that Karl Peters was using in East Africa. By the Berlin Conference of 1884–1885 (the "General Act" was signed on February 26, 1885) Great Britain's paramount interest in Nigeria was confirmed. German claims were

Figure 2.6 Africa, November 15, 1884. This map shows the spheres of influence of the various European powers prior to the Berlin Conference. It indicates also the footholds or trading stations. With the exception of two French trading stations in Senegal, European influences were entirely restricted to the coast.

Note. Figures 2.6 to 2.13 and 2.16 show the partition of Africa among European and other powers. Each of these maps has been drawn on the same scale and with the same key and indicates the rapid partition of Africa and the very small part of the continent (indicated by unshaded areas) which remained under African control until the rise of nationalism after World War II.

Figure 2.7 Africa at the end of January, 1885, after the Berlin Conference. The broad claim of the French to the French Congo is indicated by broken lines and the approximate area laid down for the Congo Free State.

restricted to the Cameroons and Togoland, both of which may be regarded as becoming German in 1884. It was also in 1884 that Germany annexed Southwest Africa.

Both Germany, from the west, and Portugal, occupying Mozambique on the east and Angola on the west, had plans for stretching inland across the whole of the southern part of the continent, which Portugal claimed but had neither explored nor annexed. But a strong man arose in the person of the British Cecil John Rhodes. In 1887 Portugal attempted to close the Zambezi, announcing that the interior belonged to her. Rhodes retaliated by securing in 1888 from Lobengula, the King of the Matabele, exclusive rights to work minerals in his territories, which lay north of the Transvaal. In 1889 he formed the British South Africa Company for the purpose. In 1891, the limits of the Portuguese and British spheres of influence being agreed upon, Nyasaland became a British Protectorate, whereas the bulk of the heart of the country was handed over to Rhodes's company, afterwards becoming Northern and Southern Rhodesia.

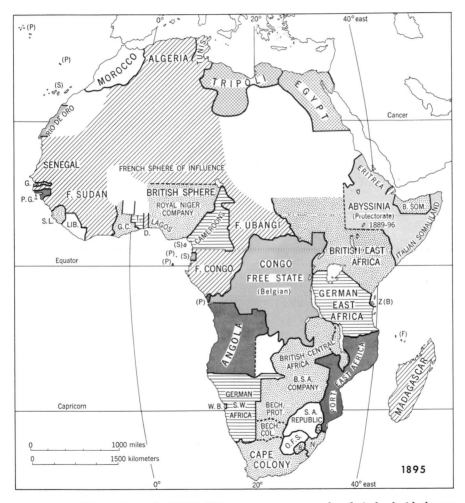

Figure 2.8 Africa at the end of 1895. This map contrasts very sharply indeed with the preceding one and indicates that practically the whole of Africa had within the short space of the ten years from 1885 to 1895 been partitioned among the leading European powers. 1895 was before the outbreak of the war between the British and the Boer settlers, whose two independent republics, the Orange Free State and the South African Republic, are shown unshaded.

In the meantime French interests in West and Equatorial Africa had been consolidated. In Equatorial Africa (long called French Congo) acquisition began on the Gabun River in 1841, and Libreville was founded in 1849. The coastal possessions extended along the coast for 200 miles to include Cape Lopez. Everywhere the story is the same: coastal settlements followed much later by extension inland. In West Africa, the British had failed to respond to requests—a natural result of the British Anti-Slavery Law of 1807—to take the whole coast under protection, and so had left the field open to the French. However, there was little activity by France till she recovered from the Napoleonic Wars. The French obtained rights on the Ivory Coast about 1842 but did not actively and continuously occupy the territory till 1882. In Dahomey the footing on the coast dates from 1851, but not till 1894 was the whole Kingdom of Dahomey annexed.

Along the Guinea Coast fragments remained to Portugal (Portuguese Guinea and the islands of São Tomé and Príncipe) and to Spain (Spanish Guinea and the islands of Fernando Po and Annobón). Although many boundaries were not defined until much later, it may be said that by 1891 practically the whole of tropical and South Africa had been parceled out between Britain, France, Belgium, Germany, Portugal, and Spain. Even the Republic of Liberia was alien, not African (Figure 2.9).

The story over the north of the continent was somewhat different. The Atlas lands of the northwest, long called the Barbary States from their Berber inhabitants, had formed part of the dominion of Carthage. Carthage itself was near the modern Tunis. After the fall of Carthage in 146 B.C. the Atlas lands continued to flourish under Roman rule; many cities were built and the land provided much food for the Roman Empire as a whole. After the fall of Rome the Moorish or Arab Empire extended right over North Africa, and in turn the Barbary States became nominally part of the Turkish or Ottoman Empire, which extended from Egypt to the Atlantic. Conditions were worst in Algeria, where Turkish and other renegades terrorized both inhabitants and traders, and along the coasts became notorious as the Barbary Pirates from 1650 onward. English, Dutch, French, Spaniards, and Americans all failed successively to check piracy until in 1830 the French bombarded Algiers into submission. Thus began the French regime in Algeria. Success was not immediate, and troubles lasted until 1883. In due course, however, Algeria came to be administered with but few differences as an integral part of France and the home of a million and a quarter Frenchmen, mostly born there and representing an eighth of the total population. Tunis or Tunisia was a kingdom whose ruler, the Bey, was descended from one who, a native of Crete, made himself master of the country in 1705 while acknowledging the suzerainty of the Sultan of Turkey. The obvious need of

Figure 2.9 Africa in 1910. This was the year in which the four South African Colonies united to form the Union of South Africa. The Congo Free State had been annexed to the Belgian Crown as the Belgian Congo and the Anglo-Egyptian Sudan had been established for more than ten years.

the French to protect law and order recently established in neighboring Algeria led to invasion in 1881 and the placing of Tunisia under the protection of France. This lasted till 1955–1956, when France recognized the independence of Tunisia, retaining only the naval base of Bizerta. The monarchy was abolished in 1957 and the country became a republic.

Although Morocco remained nominally an absolute monarchy in which the reigning sultan exercised both supreme religious and civil authority, the threat of German interference led to the establishment of "zones" of protection by France (the bulk) and Spain in 1912 and the subsequent recognition of the "International Zone" of Tangier by agreement with Britain in 1923. Unity and independence were restored to the country in 1956.

With independent Morocco to the west and independent Tunisia to the east, it was scarcely to be expected that the Moslem majority in Algeria would remain content for the country to continue as French territory. An unhappy period of internal strife culminated under the regime of de Gaulle in a referendum of which the result was a foregone conclusion. Algeria became an independent republic on July 4, 1962. The majority of the French—who had never had any other home—fled the country. It was estimated that in July 1963 fewer than 100,000 remained.

Between the Atlas lands and Egypt lies the country, largely desert, known as a whole as Libya. Part of the Turkish or Ottoman Empire, despite a certain measure of Arab autonomy, the area was a Turkish vilayet from 1835 to 1911. In the latter year a quarrel between Italy and Turkey, then the "Sick Man of Europe," led to Italian annexation.

The story of Egypt is much more complex. For long a part of the Turkish Empire, Egypt was at least nominally a vassal state of Turkey until the outbreak of World War I. From the latter part of the eighteenth century Great Britain had had special interests in Egypt. The old route from Britain to India was by ship to Egypt, thence up the Nile to a point where the desert was crossed to the Red Sea, and so by ship again to Indian ports. Egypt was thus a vital link in a vital Empire chain, and the strategic importance of Egypt's position was emphasized rather than diminished when the Suez Canal was opened in 1869.[2] The protection of the Canal became of first importance to Britain. In 1882 internal disorders led to British military intervention and the stationing of British troops in the country. When World War I broke out in 1914, with Turkey ranged among the enemies, a British protectorate over Egypt was declared, thus ending its status as a Turkish vassal. The protectorate ended in 1922, when Egypt became an independent kingdom, later a republic.

We turn now to the vexed and complicated question of the Sudan and northeastern Africa. Between Khartoum and Aswan the Nile follows a long course interrupted by successive rapids across 500 miles of waterless desert, effectively dividing the habitable parts of Egypt from the Sudan. The Nile water is the life blood of Egypt, so that there is an obvious importance in considering the water problems of the Nile basin as a whole. From about 1820 onward, the Egyptians began to extend their control over the Sudanese

---

[2] See below, page 223. Incidentally, the strategic value of Aden, the islands of the Red Sea such as Perim, and the ports opposite on African shores was also enhanced.

peoples and to claim the newly discovered equatorial lands. The Khedive Ismael of Egypt relied largely on collaboration with the British, and in 1870, as we have already seen, S. W. Baker was appointed governor of the Equatorial Provinces to deal with the suppression of the slave trade. The British General Charles George Gordon (1833–1885) was governor of the Sudan from 1873 to 1880, when he resigned after dealing successfully with the slave trade. Two years later came the great revolt of the Sudanese under Mohammed Ahmed, who declared himself the Mahdi. It was decided to abandon the Sudan, and General Gordon was sent in 1884 to undertake the difficult task of evacuating the Egyptian population. With only one English officer he and his faithful Egyptian Moslem band were surrounded and besieged in Khartoum for 5 months. There was fatal delay in sending a relief party, which reached Khartoum eventually on January 28, 1885, 2 days after Gordon had been put to death. There followed 13 years of tyrannically cruel, despotic rule by the Mahdi and his successor, the Khalifa. In 1896 an Anglo-Egyptian army commenced operations for the recovery of the lost provinces, culminating in the overthrow of the Khalifa in 1898 and his death in 1899. The convention between the British and Egyptian governments signed at Cairo on January 19, 1899, provided for the administration of the territory jointly by Egypt and Britain as a condominium, and lasted until December 3, 1955.

Among other foreigners in the service of the Egyptian government in the expansionist days of the seventies was a German, Eduard Schnitzer, who had been a medical officer under General Gordon, and who was appointed governor of the Upper Nile provinces (Equatoria). Known as Emin Pasha, he was isolated by the rebellion in which Gordon was killed, and no news of him caused anxiety. So Stanley, having founded the Congo Free State, was sent to search for him. Because access via Egypt was impossible, Stanley determined to travel up the Congo, and had a very difficult journey both by river and through the forest. He discovered Emin Pasha at Lake Albert in April 1888, happy and comfortable with his men and disinclined to leave Uganda for Europe. Emin's real object was to remain and to claim Uganda for his fatherland, Germany. A little later, while exploring, he was killed by Arab slave traders; otherwise the story of East Africa might have been very different.

Lying east of the great knot of Ethiopian mountains are the arid plains of Somaliland occupying the "Horn of Africa," with shores along the Indian Ocean, Gulf of Aden, and Red Sea. Near the entrance to the Red Sea the French acquired the port of Obok in 1862 but did not undertake its active occupation until 1884, when the territory was extended. In 1888 the French created the port of Jibuti and later constructed the Jibuti-Addis Ababa railway, for long the main outlet of Ethiopia. The Somali Coast farther east was administered by Egypt until 1884, when their control collapsed and the British Indian government administered the territory as a protectorate. Italian interest in these coastlands dates from the establishment of a colony in Eritrea whose boundaries were defined in 1889–1891. In 1892 the Sultan of Zanzibar leased certain Somali ports to Italy, selling them outright in 1905 when Italy assumed control of Italian Somaliland.

Between the momentous decade of 1880–1890 and the outbreak of World War I in 1914, changes in Africa were mostly of the character of consolidation of interests (as of the French in North Africa), further exploration; definition of boundaries; organization of administration and administrative units; construction of railways, roads, ports, and administrative centers; and the development of agriculture, commerce, and trade. There were inevitable clashes and minor wars. The one serious conflict involving two peoples of European stock was the Anglo-Boer War of 1899–1902, which will be considered under South Africa. The political map of Africa as it was in 1914 is shown in Figure 2.10.

With the outbreak of hostilities in August 1914 between Britain and Germany, things began to happen in Africa. German Southwest Africa surrendered to the forces of the Union of South Africa on July 9, 1915. Togoland surrendered unconditionally to British and French forces in August 1914; the Cameroons, in February 1916. German East Africa, renamed Tanganyika, was conquered in 1918. Britain, France, Belgium, and South Africa all accepted the jurisdiction of the League of Nations. Southwest Africa was entrusted under mandate to the Union of South Africa. This was a Class C mandate, which laid down that the territory should be administered as an integral part of the territory of the mandatory power, but made the mandatory power responsible for promoting the moral and material welfare of the peoples. Togoland was divided between Britain and France as a Class B mandate. Part became joined to the Gold Coast, part to Dahomey. The Cameroons (Class B) were similarly divided between Britain (Nigeria) and France (French Equatorial Africa). An important though small strip of German East Africa (Ruanda-Urundi) passed to Belgium, also under Class B mandate, and was added to the Belgian Congo, the main part became a Class B mandate under Britain as Tanganyika. It was laid down that Class B mandates should be separately administered, but again making the mandatory power responsible for promoting the moral and material welfare of the peoples. After World War II all these mandated territories passed under the trusteeship scheme of the United Nations.

Figure 2.11 shows the political map of Africa as it appeared shortly after the end of World War I.

The period between the world wars was marked by much economic activ-

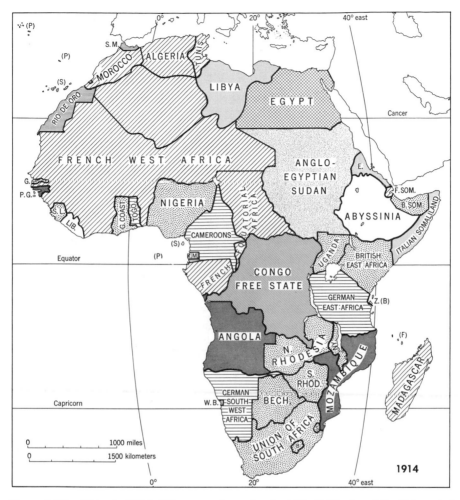

Figure 2.10   Africa in 1914. This was at the outbreak of World War I, and it will be noted that the Germans had so far extended their territory of the Cameroons as to split French Equatorial Africa into two separated portions.

ity—the building of railways and roads, the opening up of mineral deposits, especially in the Katanga, and the development of air transport, which has made such a tremendous difference to the accessibility of the heart of Africa. The British Colonial Office, following the tenets laid down especially by Lord Lugard after his experience in Nigeria, did much to develop indirect rule—to encourage the Africans to perfect their own administration based on tribal customs and laws under British guidance, so that the British officers interfered only when African customs were found to be directly opposed to Western ideas of right and justice.

Figure 2.11   Africa in 1930. With the defeat of Germany in World War I, German territory in Africa disappeared. Former German territory is shown as held under mandate from the League of Nations by Britain, France, Belgium, and South Africa. As a reward for Italian efforts, Italian Somaliland was increased in area by the addition of the country around the Juba River. (M = Mandated Territories.)

To this interwar period belongs the story of Italian expansion. With a restricted and overpopulated homeland, their need for elbow room was great. Libya, acquired in 1911, though large, was mainly desert; Somalia was no better. Eritrea had some good land but had nothing compared with the undeveloped resources of the ancient kingdom of Ethiopia. So Ethiopia, or Abyssinia, was invaded and conquered in 1935–1936. With Eritrea and Somalia it was reorganized to form Italian East Africa (Africa Orientale

Italiana) by the Act of June 1, 1936, under the dictatorship of Benito Mussolini (Figure 2.12). Italy declared war on Britain on June 11, 1940. British
Imperial forces invaded Ethiopia, and by November 1941 the country was
cleared of Italian forces and the Emperor Haile Selassie restored to his throne.

After World War II Libya, Eritrea, and Somalia were governed until 1950
under British Military Administration, replaced later by a British Civil
Administration. Libya was then granted independence, taking effect formally
on January 1, 1952. Eritrea became an autonomous state under the Ethiopian

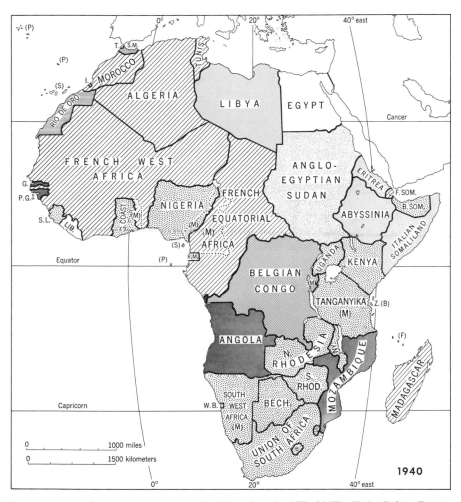

Figure 2.12   Africa in 1939 to 1940. At the outbreak of World War II the Italian Empire
had come to include Abyssinia as well as Eritrea and Italian Somaliland, together with the
enlarged and redefined Libya. Only two countries in the whole of Africa are shown in this
map as independent, Egypt and Liberia.

crown, and Italy was allowed, in 1950, to re-enter and administer Somalia (Figure 2.13).

It was the decade 1950 to 1960 which saw the really spectacular political developments in Africa. The postwar political instability of France which had resulted in a bewildering succession of governments, many lasting only a few weeks, was brought to an end by the recall from retirement of the wartime leader General Charles de Gaulle, who was given almost dictatorial powers.

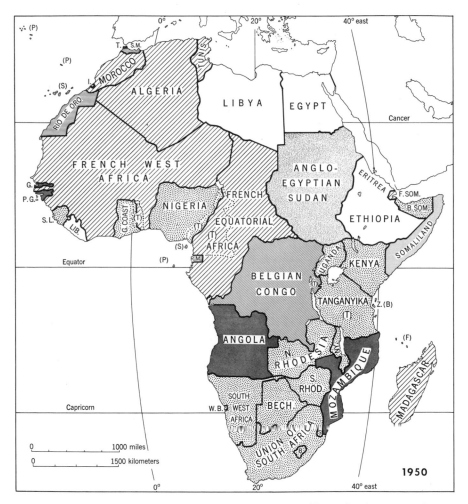

Figure 2.13 Africa in 1950. At the end of World War II the old mandated territories became trusteeships under the United Nations. The growth of nationalism in Africa is indicated by the reappearance of the independent Ethiopian Empire, now including Eritrea, and by the appearance of independent Libya, together with the old independent countries of Egypt and Liberia. (T = Trusteeship Territories.)

Under the new constitution, styled the Constitution of the Fifth Republic, and approved in September-October 1958, the French Union was replaced by the French Community (La Communauté), and overseas territories were offered three solutions: first, to keep their existing status; second, to become overseas "départements"; third, to become member states of the Community. According to an amendment to the Constitution adopted on June 4, 1960, member states can become sovereign independent states without ceasing to belong to the Community. One French territory in Africa voted at once in 1958 for complete independence and left the Community: this was former French Guinea, now the Republic of Guinea. By the end of 1960 the position was thus:

I   French Republic
   A   France (Metropolitan Departments)
   B   Algeria (Algerian Departments)   } became independent July 4, 1962
   C   Southern Algeria (Sahara Departments)
   D   Overseas Departments, including Réunion
   E   Overseas Territories, including French Somaliland

II   Member States of the Community
   1 Central African Republic
   2 Republic of Congo   } former French Equatorial Africa
   3 Republic of Gabon
   4 Republic of Chad
   5 Republic of Ivory Coast
   6 Republic of Dahomey
   7 Republic of Upper Volta
   8 Republic of Niger   former French West Africa,
   9 Republic of Senegal   continuing as a customs union
   10 Republic of Mali
   11 Republic of Mauritania
   12 Republic of Madagascar

The former trusteeship territory of French Togoland became the independent Togo Republic on April 27, 1960, but British Togoland joined Ghana. The French trusteeship territory of the Cameroons became the Cameroun Republic on January 1, 1960, and was joined in 1961 by the southern part of the former British trusteeship territory of the westen Cameroons (Figure 2.14).

Such fundamental changes in the French territories precipitated the anticipated independence of French-speaking Belgian Congo which took place on June 30, 1960, but there the departure of the Belgian administration, teachers, doctors, etc. on the day of independence left a vacuum which speedily turned to complete chaos, far from being resolved at the time of writing these words. Belgium remained in control of the trusteeship territory of Ruanda-Urundi,

Figure 2.14   Diagram showing the partition of the continent from 1875 to 1963.

The right-side timeline annotations:

- 1873 — Death of Livingstone.
- 1875
- 1876 — Brussels Conference. International African Association founded.
- 1877 — Stanley descended River Congo, thereby completing E-W crossing of Africa.
- 1880 — Events of 1876 & 77 initiated partition of Africa.
- 1884 — Germany secured first colony (S. W. Africa)
- 1885 — Congress of Berlin. Principles of effective occupancy and notification agreed. "Spheres of influence" decided upon. CONGO FREE STATE (Free trade throughout basin) formally established and recognized.
- 1890 — "SCRAMBLE FOR AFRICA" truly begun.
- 1895 — Spheres of influence and boundaries of colonial possessions defined by treaties between various European powers. Demarcation of boundaries begun. (Territories opened up)
- 1899 — ANGLO-EGYPTIAN SUDAN (condominium)
- 1900 — established. France recognized British influence in upper Nile.
- 1905
- 1908 — Belgian control of Congo Free State formally assumed.
- 1910 — UNION OF SOUTH AFRICA established.
- 1911 — (consequence of Boer War of 1899-1902)
- 1912 — GERMAN CAMEROONS extended to Ubangi and Congo. Italian conquest of TRIPOLI.
- 1914 — French Protectorate over MOROCCO.
- 1915 — WORLD WAR I. German colonies captured.
- 1918
- 1920
- 1921 — BRITAIN, FRANCE & BELGIUM received Mandates from League of Nations over former German colonies (shaded* for this year but hereafter not shown separately)
- 1925
- 1930
- 1935
- 1936 — Italian conquest of ABYSSINIA.
- 1939
- 1940 — WORLD WAR II. Italian colonies captured.
- 1945
- 1946
- 1950 — As result of World War II, ABYSSINIA regained independence and assumed control of ERITREA; LIBYA became independent (subject to U N supervision until 1952); SOMALILAND returned to Italian control.
- 1960 — Most former French territories independent republics within the Community. CONGO independent.
- By end of 1963 nearly all British territories had become independent within the Commonwealth.

which became independent in 1962 as the Kingdom of Burundi and the Republic of Rwanda.

In the meantime the political development of British territories proceeded according to plan. Reference has already been made to the Republic of the Sudan which on January 1, 1956 replaced the former Anglo-Egyptian Sudan. The Gold Coast became independent as Ghana in 1957 (Figure 2.15), Nigeria in 1960, and Sierra Leone in 1961, leaving only the small colony of Gambia in West Africa. In East Africa the trusteeship territory of Tanganyika became independent, very quietly, in 1961, Uganda in 1962, Zanzibar and Kenya in 1963. All these countries elected to remain members of the British Commonwealth. Northern and Southern Rhodesia and Nyasaland were joined in a federation in 1953 with what approximated to Dominion status, but Nyasaland withdrew in 1963 and the Federation came to an end. Nyasaland became independent in 1963, assuming the name Malawi.

The Union of South Africa insisted on following its policy of *apartheid,* so out of line with developments elsewhere and especially with the views of other members of the British Commonwealth. This led to the inevitable break, and in 1961 the Union became the Republic of South Africa and withdrew from the Commonwealth—the first major self-governing country to do so. The Republic defied the United Nations in ignoring the trusteeship status of South West Africa, which it insisted on incorporating.

The Italians allowed temporarily to return to Africa in charge of the trust territory of Somalia, formerly Italian Somaliland, withdrew when Somalia became an independent republic on July 1, 1960, when the Republic also incorporated the former protectorate of British Somaliland.

Figure 2.15 The Supreme Court at Accra, Ghana. Typical of the permanent work of the European powers, now a legacy to the independent states of Africa. (Official Photograph.)

Figure 2.16   Africa at the end of 1963. The dates are those at which the new states became independent.

The small Spanish colonial possessions remain, as do the large Portuguese colonies of Angola and Mozambique and the smaller Portuguese Guinea and S. Tomé-Principe Islands, but unrest suggests change is not far ahead.

Figure 2.16 has been drawn to show the position at the end of 1963—a remarkable contrast to the map for 1950.

BIBLIOGRAPHY

The partition of Africa as it took place in the crucial years 1880–1895 is well shown and well illustrated by maps in the *Partition of Africa,* by J. Scott Keltie (London, 1895).

Later changes are shown in *The Map of Africa by Treaty,* by Sir E. Hertslet (London, His Majesty's Stationery Office, 1909; 3 volumes and atlas).

Reference may also be made to articles in the *Encyclopaedia Britannica, Encyclopedia Americana,* and to *Philip's Historical Atlas,* by Ramsay Muir and George Philip (George Philip, London).

For the story of the white exploration of Africa, a standard work is Percy Syke's *A History of Exploration* (London, 1934). For the development of Africa up to 1960 G. H. T. Kimble's *Tropical Africa* covers the numerous different topics involved. It supplements and extends Lord Hailey's *African Survey* (Revised 1956, Oxford University Press).

The changing political scene may be followed from such standard sources as the *Statesman's Yearbook* (New York, Macmillan, annually about July) and Whitaker's Almanack (annual).

CHAPTER THREE

The Physical Background

Geography and man

Throughout much of Africa, especially tropical Africa, the course of man's life is still dictated in large measure by the physical environment. Even where the weapons of modern Western science have been introduced, the physical factors are so strong that their influence is everywhere clearly seen in the pattern of population distribution. The focal points of modern Africa's industrial development are clearly associated with sources of minerals and power and are thus related to the age-old geological structure of the continent. That population density in rural areas is primarily related to climatic conditions, especially rainfall, has long been clear, but the subtle and intimate relationships between the form of the land surface, drainage, soils, and land use are only now being slowly appreciated. It is because of the paramount influence which they exert that the various physical features of Africa will now be examined in detail.

Structure and earth history

Throughout the many millions of years of the earth's geological history there have always been areas of relative stability separated by belts of instability. Although at the present time the earth is enjoying in the geological sense one of its quiet periods, so that earthquakes disturb the surface but rarely and volcanic activity is at a minimum, it is still true that there are certain earthquake belts and certain lines of crustal weakness with which volcanoes are associated. In times past the belts or regions of orogenic, or mountain-building, movement have fluctuated in position, and so have the position and the shape of the stable blocks between. Those stable blocks are sometimes referred to as the great "unfolded" masses of the earth's surface —an entirely false concept, because they usually consist of rocks which have been most intensely folded, broken, recemented, and worn down by long ages of denudation and erosion. The important fact is that they are blocks which underwent their evolution in the early days of the earth's history; since then they have acted as rigid masses and have not been directly affected by later folding movements, except that they may have been rent by fissures.

Unique in so many other aspects, Africa is again unique in that the whole continent save the extreme north (Barbary States or Northwest Africa) and the extreme southwest (in the Cape Province of South Africa) consists of one great rigid block of ancient rocks which has remained little changed in its essential geology since the days—perhaps 200 million years ago—when the Karoo beds of South Africa were laid down.

The great Alpine storm, as it has been called, of middle Tertiary time which caused the rise of the Alps and most of the great present-day mountain chains of Europe to the north affected only the northwest of Africa, where the Atlas and associated ranges are of this age. The picturesque ranges of the Cape of Good Hope with their folded sedimentary rocks belong to an earlier period of mountain building.

We get thus a mental picture of the huge continental mass of Africa consisting essentially of an ancient rigid earth block. In its general characteristics and the nature and composition of its rocks, it closely resembles other ancient earth blocks, but notably those of Brazil to the west, peninsular India to the northeast, and the western half of Australia to the east. Indeed, the resemblances between these different areas are so strong that we are tempted to wonder whether they may not once have formed part of a single continental mass. The more closely they are studied, the more evidence is forthcoming of similarities. The question obviously arises, were these earth blocks, now widely separated, once part of a single continent? Associated with the masses of South Africa, peninsular India, and western Australia, there are beds roughly of the same age as the coal-bearing beds of Europe and North America. Resting on the ancient rocks are sediments, shales and sandstones, which must have been deposited in shallow basins on their surface. These rocks are often coal-bearing, and among the plants which contributed to the formation of the coal, remains of a remarkable genus *Glossopteris* are dominant. Although this *Glossopteris* flora is common to the basins of the ancient blocks mentioned, it is absent from the Coal Measure beds of Europe and North America. The argument is accordingly that the ancient blocks of Africa, India, and Australia, perhaps also of South America, were part of an ancient continent to which the name Gondwanaland has been given (Figure 3.1). *Glossopteris* and its allies flourished all over this continent, but a wide ocean separated Gondwanaland from northern land masses where an entirely different assemblage of plants was in existence.

There are many other pieces of evidence to support the existence of Gondwanaland. At a stage in its history it was subjected to one or more

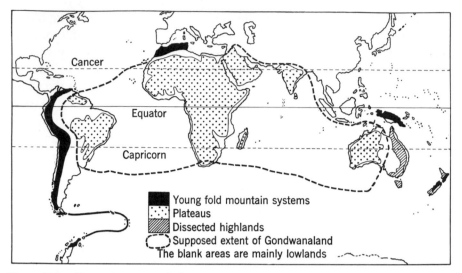

Figure 3.1   The main structural elements in the southern continents. The interrupted line encloses the fragments of former Gondwanaland.

glaciations so that ancient boulder clays or tills of glacial origin exist. But the *Glossopteris* flora of the swamp forests of Gondwanaland flourished over 200 million years ago. What has happened in the meantime? There are at least three possibilities:

1. The seas may have eroded away the former land connections.
2. The old continent of Gondwanaland may have been fractured by great rifts or faults, some sections remaining above sea level, others sinking so as to be covered by sea.
3. The present-day masses may represent fragments which have drifted away from one another.

Evidence has been adduced to show that the specific gravity of the rocks underlying the continents is lower than the specific gravity of rocks found beneath the great ocean basins. On this evidence it has been postulated that the continental masses may be regarded as blocks having the approximate composition of granite resting on a lower layer having the approximate composition of basalt. The lighter continental rock material has been given the name sial from the dominant elements silicon and aluminum, while the heavier layers have been given the name sima from the dominant elements silicon and magnesium. It is of course known that there is a rapid rise in temperature as the earth's crust is penetrated and that at no great distance from the surface extremely high temperatures occur, so that if it were not for extreme pressure the rocks would be molten. It is quite possible that these lower layers of the earth's crust are at least in a plastic condition. Having gone so far, we find that it is not difficult to go further and to believe that the continental masses of sial, floating, as it were, on a plastic layer of sima, are able to move, to split into sections, to drift apart or to be pushed closer together.

The general concept of the lateral movement of continental masses is by no means new, but worked out in detail it has become associated with the name of George Wegener, as Wegener's Hypothesis of Continental Drift. Thus the position may have been that the South American, African, Indian, and Australian sections of Gondwanaland formed one whole continent which has split up, and the constituent sections drifted apart. Gondwanalad, however, existed some 200 million years ago. There has been ample time for the drifting apart of the separate sections. Biologists who note the similarity between the present-day floras and faunas in the three southern continents, and especially between the existing land animals in these areas, are helped by the Wegener hypothesis only if the drifting apart of the continental masses has taken place within, say, the last million years or so.

In between these two extremes it would seem to be quite clear that the great continental mass of Africa drifted, or was pushed, northwards, for it is on this basis and almost on this basis alone that we can explain the intense folding of the Alps and associated Alpine ranges in Europe, including the Atlas ranges of North Africa. These movements were at their height in Miocene times, let us say 20 million years ago. Many attempts have been made in recent years to detect actual, present-day, lateral movements of the continental masses, but without very positive results. A new approach, however, is through the study of paleomagnetism. It would seem that igneous rocks are endowed with a permanent magnetism at the time of their solidification, and the study of its orientation suggests a confirmation of the drifting hypothesis.

The geologist on the available evidence would therefore be justified in saying that the northward movement of the continental mass of Africa took place in middle Tertiary times, and ceased when the Alpine earth movements ceased. There is no direct evidence of later movement, so the geologist is not in a position to help the biologist to explain the present distribution of the fauna and the flora of the southern continents. There is certainly no justification for attempting to fit the present details of the coastline of South America into the coastline of West Africa. In any case, it is the edges of the continental shelves which should fit into one another and not the existing coastlines.

In broad outline, both the geological structure and the geological history of the African continent are relatively simple, however much remains—and very much does remain—to be investigated in detail.

The ancient crystalline basal complex is exposed over very large areas. In some sections the dominant rocks are granites, or granitic rocks, which show varying degrees of alteration, and fall into the groups known as ortho-gneisses (metamorphosed granites) and para-gneisses (metamorphosed sediments). Elsewhere the dominant rocks are also very highly metamorphosed—not only gneisses but schists of varied character which may originally have been sediments and volcanic rocks.

In consisting of these two main groups the ancient African mass resembles in general the other ancient earth masses, such as the Canadian Shield or the Brazilian Plateau (Figure 3.2). Certain parts of the complex are highly mineralized, and Africa is of course a repository of a number of extremely valuable mineral deposits. For reasons which will appear later there are considerable possibilities of new discoveries. Resting on these very ancient metamorphosed rocks, often with basal conglomerates, are sedimentary rocks, for the most part comparatively little altered, some of which are also believed to be pre-Cambrian in age; others are early Paleozoic. These too may be economically very important, because of the association of gold and other metallic ores with them. The gold of the Rand comes from pre-Cambrian conglomerates; the copper of the Katanga from rocks of early Paleozoic age.

The ancient earth block, from its establishment in earliest times to the present day, has been subjected to vertical movements of elevation and depression, but only to relatively slight subsequent folding. Consequently there are considerable areas of its surface covered by older Paleozoic rocks of marine origin, little altered, for the most part nearly horizontal, though sometimes gently folded. Where these Paleozoic rocks are folded it is claimed that the folds can be termed broadly Hercynian, and in West Africa, for example, the gentle Hercynian folds trend from northeast to southwest. It should be noted that the older marine Paleozoic sediments are succeeded by rocks of Carboniferous and Permian ages, with which are associated the coal seams of Africa's one important coal field, in South Africa.

The post-Paleozoic sedimentary rocks in Africa were either deposited in shallow seas which locally invaded the continental mass and occupied extensive gulfs, as in parts of West Africa, or were laid down in broad, shallow basins on the surface under fresh or brackish water conditions. The large stretches of sandstone and other sediments, so important in North Africa, called broadly Nubian sandstones, are of later Mesozoic or early Tertiary age.

With the absence of folding and the long-continued exposure of huge tracts to atmospheric weathering, the surface of Africa was reduced to an almost level surface, referred to below as the Miocene Peneplain. This ancient surface has since been raised many thousand feet above sea level, and in the process three important things have happened.

In the first place, the great rigid block of Africa gave way under the

Figure 3.2   Provisional map of ancient mountain belts in South and Central Africa. This map is intended to show that the very ancient rocks of the African mass, like those of the Canadian Shield, were intensely folded and erected into great mountain chains which were later worn down to a common level. The figures are estimated ages in millions of years. (After Arthur Holmes, *Report of the 18th International Geological Congress of 1948*, Vol. XIV, 1951.)

strain, and great fractures developed from north to south on the eastern side of the continent and locally elsewhere. Thus from the Red Sea in the north, almost to the borders of the Transvaal in the south, were formed those gigantic troughs, or *graben,* the famous rift valleys of East Africa, since occupied in part by the East African lake system. The general position of the East African rift valley system is shown in Fig. 3.3.

Figure 3.3   The rift valleys of East Africa. A simplified version is shown in Chapter 18. This map is after Maurette.

In the second place, volcanic activity was also associated with this faulting or cracking of the rigid masses. There are enormous areas covered with flows of lava in Ethiopia; there are other lava-covered areas in East Africa, and a number of magnificent volcanic cones as reminders of this volcanic activity. Mount Kenya, Mount Kilimanjaro, and Mount Elgon are three outstanding examples. More localized fracturing in the west is associated with the great volcanic peak of Cameroon Mountain. Incidentally, it may be noted that the rift valley area of East Africa is still an area of relative instability and hence appears as one of the earthquake belts of the world of today. In both southern and eastern Africa, old volcanic necks or pipes became plugged with a consolidated lava of very basic composition which is the source rock of most of Africa's diamonds.

In the third place, broad, shallow basins in the uplifted surface gave rise to vast inland seas or lakes which have since disappeared or have left but small remnants. In them were deposited huge stretches of Quaternary and recent alluvium; hence the Quaternary lake basins of the Upper Niger, of the Lake Chad region, and of the Central Congo. The rivers of today meander across these old basins before tumbling over the edge of the plateau to reach the present sea coast. Lake Victoria affords an example of a large lake of this character on the plateau surface.

Elsewhere the older rocks are still hidden by a mantle of aeolian deposits, the wind-borne sands of the great Sahara and other wastes.

The plateau surfaces

From the foregoing description we see that the interest of the geographer lies often in the geomorphology rather than the geology of Africa.

One of the most striking features of the African landscape is the vast extent of level or gently undulating surfaces. At high levels on the plateau we have the illusion of traveling over a lowland plain, often monotonous in the extreme. Such plains occur at different levels and are erosion surfaces which may be found up to heights of 8600 feet (as in the Basuto Highlands) above the present sea level. They have been discussed briefly by Dr. F. Dixey,[1] who points out that, since the widespread movements of the late Karoo or post-Karoo times (Permo-Carboniferous), central and southern Africa have been a stable land mass subject to periodical uplift. The main periods of uplift have been separated by intervals long enough for possibly three important erosion cycles to have run their course and for resulting peneplains to have developed. There are also certain incompleted cycles, whereas the whole has been modified at a late stage by the rift faulting of East Africa, accompanied by volcanic activity, and the related gentle warping of regions to the south and southwest.

[1] "African Landscapes," *Geog. Rev.,* **XXXIV**, July 1944, pp. 457–467.

One well-marked, high-level erosion surface is found in a number of widely separated plateau remnants—at 7000 to 8000 feet on the Cape ranges, where it is quite independent of the folding of the rocks; at 8000 feet in southwest Africa, and rather higher in the Basuto Highlands; at 7000 to 7500 feet in the Nyika Plateau. This peneplanation is ascribed to the late Jurassic and indicates that the rise of the African continental mass has been of the order of 7000 to 8000 feet since that time.

At lower levels there are remnants of other surfaces. In early Cretaceous times troughs were opened and later filled with sediments (as in the Nyasa trough), but a really well-marked erosion surface is that at about 4500 feet, ascribed to the Miocene or mid-Tertiary. It may seem surprising that so much of this surface is preserved, but the major rivers such as the Congo, Zambezi (with the Luangwa, Shiré, and Lake Nyasa), Limpopo, and Orange have carved out for themselves great valleys in troughs floored by the Karoo sediments of low resistance (Figure 3.4). It is on the weaker sediments and on Cretaceous beds filling the Nyasa and Luangwa troughs that the Pliocene or late Tertiary erosion suface at 2500 to 4000 feet has been developed.

Dr. Dixey finds it unnecessary to postulate warping of the Miocene surface or block faulting to explain the higher plateau surfaces as others have done. He considers that the low divides between the great river basins, such as between the Congo and Zambezi, are features of the old Miocene peneplained surface—legacies from the past.

It is almost certain that vast areas of Africa have been exposed to atmospheric weathering for many millions of years. On the old Miocene peneplain surfaces, therefore, the solid rocks may have been disintegrated to a very considerable depth, but the soils which have been formed have been formed in situ, and their mineral particles consist of comminuted fragments of underlying rocks. Not infrequently it is possible to trace a vein of quartz from the underlying rock through into the subsoil and to find an abundance of fragments of the shattered quartz in the surface soil, a feature of the utmost significance in determining the nature and usability of African soils.

The geological map of Africa

We are now in a position to interpret the geological map of Africa. The continent is far from mapped in detail, but the broad lines of its rock formations are now known.

Rocks of the ancient pre-Cambrian mass, the whole comparable in character to the Canadian Shield except for the weathering of the surface, reach the surface and so are "exposed"—that is, they are not covered by later rocks—over approximately a third of the whole of Africa. It must be remembered that large parts have been subjected to the action of the atmospheric elements for many millions of years, so that the solid rocks themselves may be

Figure 3.4 The African plateau and the Zambezi gorge. Vast stretches of Africa are savanna-covered plateau. Here the Zambezi plunges over Victoria Falls into a zigzag gorge cut out of great cracks in the plateau surface. (Courtesy the late Major Cochran-Patrick.)

obscured by many feet of laterite and other products of weathering. This superficial mantle makes the search for ore bodies particularly difficult, and there is little wonder that spectacular finds are still being made and are almost certain to be made far into the future, especially as modern methods of prospecting, such as geophysical methods, are applied. Mineralization of the rocks and consequent occurrence of metallic ores are always irregular, but deposits are widely distributed in Africa. The present share of the continent in world production of certain mineral products is discussed in Chapter 10.

It must be borne in mind that the rocks of the ancient complex underlie nearly the whole of Africa and that metalliferous deposits may lie buried, but not too deeply for future exploitation, where sediments cover the old mass. The sands of the deserts, the alluvium of the old lake basins, perhaps some of the flows of lava, may one day be penetrated to reach ore bodies hidden below.

The older sedimentary rocks, especially the shales and sandstones of Karoo (Permo-Carboniferous) Age, are important in two ways. They have their seams of coal in South Africa, the Rhodesias, and Tanganyika. In the second place, the beds are usually almost horizontal, and weathering has given rise to those mountains of circumdenudation, the flat-topped mesas, which are such a characteristic feature of the landscape in so many parts of Africa. This is especially true in South Africa, where resistant volcanic rocks are interbedded with the sediments.

There are such huge areas as those of the Congo with its great stretches of soft sandstone (see Chapter 17) and the middle Niger and Chad basins (Chapter 14) with sediments of continental origin. There are also sediments of marine and brackish-water origin, representing incursions of the sea at times when the whole continental surface was lower than at present, and which are largely confined to basins along the seaward margins of the continent. In 1950 the American Geographical Society published a map of such basins where it was considered oil might occur (*World Geography of Petroleum*) but that was before the spectacular discoveries of oil and natural gas which have so transformed the economic geography of the Sahara (Chapter 13). Prior to the first major strike in Saharan Algeria in 1956 it could be said, as in the first edition of this book, that Africa had no oil apart from the small fields along the shores of the Gulf of Suez in Egypt, and seven tiny fields in Morocco and Algeria. The picture is now very different, in large measure owing to modern methods of geological prospecting which enable investigation of what exists beneath the superficial sands, gravels, and alluvia occupying vast areas. The discovery of underground sources of water has been scarcely less important in suggesting an agricultural utilization of previously useless desert areas.

The relief map of Africa

The common generalization that Africa consists of a gigantic plateau bordered, except on the northwest where the Atlas ranges occur, by narrow coastal plains may now be stated more exactly. In fact Africa consists of a succession of plateau surfaces at varying elevations, generally higher in the south and lower in the north, often with abrupt edges. On the surface of the plateaus are shallow depressions, some forming basins of inland drainage, others drained by rivers which pass over cataracts or through gorges as they leave the plateau surfaces to reach the coastal plains (Figure 3.5).

In the south of the continent the average elevation is over 3000 feet, and the magnificent scarp of the southeastern edge known as the Drakensberg usually exceeds 10,000 feet (Figure 3.6). Rising from the plateau surfaces, flat-topped mesas are common features; rocky hills with "tors" are features of the old rocks where granites occur. The divides between the broad, open

Figure 3.5 The relief of Africa. This map indicates the general plateau character of the continent. The ocean currents influencing climatic conditions are also indicated.

river basins are usually inconspicuous, and the ridges between tributary valleys are so little developed that the water partings can be detected only by careful leveling.

The lofty plateau of East Africa is complicated in several ways. The great north-south trenches of the rift valleys (Figure 3.3) are deeply incised in its surface, and the section between the two main rifts has collapsed in the center, which is occupied by the huge but shallow Lake Victoria, over 26,200 square miles in area and the world's third largest lake (after the Caspian Sea and Lake Superior). From the surface of the plateau rise the great volcanic piles of Kilimanjaro (19,340 feet) (Figure 3.7), Kenya (17,058), Elgon (14,172), and many others. Different in character is the lofty horst of Ruwenzori, rising to 16,794 feet. Northward a large part of the mountain complex of Ethiopia is over 4000 feet in elevation.

The great basin in the heart of equatorial Africa is that of the Congo and

Figure 3.6 The edge of the African Plateau—Drakensberg Mountains of Natal. This shows clearly the horizontal beds of sandstone here making up the plateau. (Copyright Aircraft Operating Company of Africa.)

its tributaries. From an average elevation of rather over 1000 feet in the center of the basin, the land rises gently to 3000 and 4000 feet around the rim. The whole is indeed like a shallow saucer.

The plateau surfaces and basins to the north of the Congo are at generally lower elevations, and parts of the Sahara actually sink below sea level. There are areas characterized by mesas; there are some rock-edged highlands, notably the Futa-Jallon-Liberian massif, and the Tibesti Mountains tower to snow-covered heights in the midst of the Sahara. The volcanic pile of Cameroon Mountain (13,350 feet) repeats in the west some of the features of East Africa, being associated with fault lines trending northeast to southwest.

Utterly in contrast are the Tertiary fold ranges of the Atlas and Anti-Atlas ranges, with the elevated plateaus of the Shotts which lie between.

The coastal plains between the edge of the main plateau and the sea vary in character, as well as in width. Sometimes there are steps up to the plateau, sometimes a belt of foothills between a coastal plain and the plateau edge. Only in parts of northern Africa does the plateau edge tend to disappear or become inconspicuous.

African rivers and river basins

It may be said that two-thirds of the surface of Africa is drained by seven or eight major rivers; much of the remainder is occupied by basins of inland drainage with no outlet to the sea (Figure 3.8).

The Orange River basin. In southern Africa the plateau slopes in general from the high eastern edge (the Drakensberg) to the west. Nearly all the surface is drained by the Orange River, the chief tributary of which is the Vaal. The southern half of the Kalahari Desert in Bechuanaland lies in the same basin, but the watercourses are nearly always dry. True to the African type, the Orange passes over the Great Falls on its way to the Atlantic Ocean, but its bed is usually dry before the ocean is reached through the coastal desert belt of the Namib. Even in the damper parts of the High Veld the streams are frequently nonperennial, so that the whole system has no use for navigation and but limited use (discussed under South Africa) for irrigation.

Yet the Orange in flood can be an impressive sight, and the same is true of the Cunene, a considerable stream marking for part of its course the boundary between Southwest Africa and Angola. Consequently, exaggerated

Figure 3.7 Flying over the highest point of the African continent. The snow-capped Kilimanjaro in Tanganyika reaches 19,340 feet and is an extinct volcano. This picture shows the view looking into the old crater. (Courtesy British Overseas Airways Corporation.)

0 250 500 750
Miles

0 400 800 1200
Kilometers

Figure 3.8   The rivers and river basins of the heart of Africa. This map shows that the great river basins have little relation to political units, the boundaries of which are indicated by fine dotted lines.

claims have been made for the value of this river as a potential source of irrigation water.

The Limpopo basin.   For much of its course the Limpopo forms the boundary between the Transvaal on the south, Bechuanaland on the west, and Southern Rhodesia on the north. It is one of Africa's lesser rivers, but it drains well-watered country eastward to the Indian Ocean, and its basin includes lands of much economic importance.

The Zambezi basin.   In many ways the Zambezi is a "typical" African river. Its upper course drains a huge shallow basin, floored with alluvial deposits, in the heart of the African plateau. Those headstreams which drain the drier western lands are nonperennial streams, but the main river is constant and navigable by native craft over much of its plateau course. Then the great river cascades over the world-famed Victoria Falls (343 feet high, compared with 165 feet of Niagara) and passes through a narrow zigzag gorge excavated in the crushed rock of successive fault lines (Figure 3.4). There are long navigable stretches in the lower courses before the river is joined by the Shiré, draining the waters of Lake Nyasa to the sea. Thus, in common with the greater African rivers, the headstreams of the Zambezi could be used for local irrigation, but little such use is made of them. The plateau courses are navigable over large stretches; the various falls and changes in level provide an enormous potential source of power; the lower reaches are valuable for navigation, though interrupted by gorges and rapids; but only a relatively minor port (Chinde) has grown up on the delta—not on the main stream. Immediately below the Victoria Falls the Zambezi gorge is spanned by a railway and road bridge completed in 1904 (see Figure 3.4). The 900 miles from this point to the sea forms a very serious obstacle to north-south communications, but the construction of the Kariba Dam and the conversion of the Kariba gorge into the largest man-made lake in the world have transformed the economy of a vast area. The Lower Zambezi Bridge was built where the river is 3775 yards wide and can claim on this basis to be the longest bridge in the world.

The Congo basin. Even more than the Zambezi, the Congo is the river of tropical Africa. It also has a great shallow basin on the surface of the plateau, but the whole is cut by the equator and so enjoys the higher and better-distributed rainfall characteristic of equatorial latitudes. As a result, all its mainstream and tributaries are perennial, most are navigable for long stretches by country boats, and the main river and major tributaries, except for rare interruptions, are navigable by river steamers. Although Stanley Falls interrupt navigation in the heart of the basin, the main drop from the plateau to the Atlantic Ocean occurs through a succession of rapids and falls below the lake, known as Stanley Pool (800 feet above sea level), only 250 miles in a direct line from the open sea. The deep, sheltered mouth of the Congo has proved more useful than those of other rivers. The port of Matadi has grown up at the head of ocean navigation (85 miles from the sea), Boma lower down on the opposite (northern) side, and Banana on a delta distributary.

The Niger basin. The Niger repeats some of the main features of the Zambezi. It has a long plateau course with many "tributaries" from the northern side which are normally dry watercourses. Its mainstream is valuable for navigation until the chief rapids and falls, a long way from the ocean, are reached. Below the falls there are again long navigable stretches; the important tributary, the Benue, invites comparison with the Shiré. The main headwaters of the Niger are in the very wet Futa-Jallon highlands of the Sierra Leone border, less than 200 miles from the Atlantic Ocean, but the river transports this water 2600 miles before discharging it into the ocean. In so doing, it swings in a great loop into the arid Sahara lands and so confers an immensely valuable gift of irrigation water on land well suited to receive it —in the neighborhood of the so-called inland Niger delta above Timbuktu.

The Nile basin. With a total length of about 4000 miles, the Nile rivals the Mississippi and Amazon for its sheer length, but in other ways it has features which are unique. The mainstream, the White Nile, is a relatively constant river, because it receives the well-distributed equatorial rainfall collected in the natural reservoir of Lake Victoria, from which it spills over in Owen Falls. Uniting with the Albert Nile draining Lake Albert, its main navigable course begins below the Fola Rapids when it enters the great Bahr-el-Ghazal basin. It may be said to pass out of that saucer-shaped hollow shortly before it is joined by the Blue Nile at Khartoum. Since the Blue Nile receives the monsoon rain of the Ethiopian mountains, it is a fluctuating stream and so responsible for the annual rise of the united Nile as it passes over its six cataracts and enters its amazing 10-mile-wide, cliff-bound trench through Egypt. Below Cairo the Nile delta is the prototype of all deltas, its triangular shape resembling the Greek capital letter Δ inverted, establishing the term for all time.

The Lake Chad basin. This may be noted as one, indeed the largest, of the inland drainage basins of the great Saharan region. The proved diminution in the size of the lake since it was first seen by Europeans is of major interest in the study of the supposed "desiccation" of Africa, which will be discussed later (Chapter 14).

The African coastline

One glance at a map of the continent shows that there are no deep bays or gulfs penetrating into the solid continental mass. There is literally nothing to compare with the Gulf of Mexico or Hudson Bay. Africa's rivers have deltas, not estuaries, and so there is nothing which compares with the mouth of the St. Lawrence or even with the Hudson, except perhaps the Congo. As far as shipping is concerned, both in sailing ship days and at the present, the word which is applicable to most of the African coastline is "inhospitable." Rocky headlands sheltering bays fit for anchorage are rare; the best examples are found in the ports of Dakar, Freetown, Cape Town, and Simonstown. An island may offer shelter—Zanzibar and Mombasa, for example. There are a few well-protected bays or inlets such as the land-locked bay of Port Natal, now converted into the port of Durban, or Lourenço Marques. River mouths may offer shelter, though they are usually obstructed by a sand bar—for instance, Calabar on the Cross River or Duala on the Cameroon River. In general the coasts of Africa present to the approaching vessel a line of breakers through which small craft such as surf boats may make a precarious passage. Beyond the breakers, the shore is often sandy, but the sand bars and spits are cut off from the mainland by extensive though shallow lagoons, often with mangrove swamp-forests. In places the lagoons may form a valuable natural harbor where the entrance is adequate or, like Lagos, can be deepened. Elsewhere the shoreline may be sandy and shelving with desert or forest right to the beach; cliffs are rare. Exceptions to the latter statement are naturally found in southwest Africa around the Cape of Good Hope and in northwest Africa (Barbary States), where the structure of the terrain itself differs so much from the rest of Africa.

The absence of natural harbors along vast stretches of Africa's coastline has necessitated the construction of expensive artificial harbors before any marked development of foreign seaborne trade became possible. A good example is in Ghana. There Takoradi is entirely artificial and has now supplanted Sekondi, and Tema has replaced Accra, where goods had to be landed by surf boats from ships anchored far offshore. Pointe Noire, built to serve the needs of French Equatorial Africa and now in the Congo (Brazzaville) Republic, is another example.

The continental shelf

Except for the Mediterranean and the Red Sea basins, the continental shelf around Africa is everywhere narrow. The shelving shores on which the oceanic rollers break extend but a short distance from the coastline before the gentle submarine slope gives place to the abrupt edge of the continental shelf and the drop to oceanic depths of 2000 to 3000 fathoms. In the Atlantic, Ascension, St. Helena, and Tristan da Cunha are true oceanic islands—the tops of volcanic piles rising from great ocean deeps—and the same is true of Mauritius and Réunion in the Indian Ocean.

This fact has several important results. Where winds are offshore, the main surface waters are replaced by cold oceanic waters welling up from those depths when temperatures remain about 34°F. The cold currents which lave the African shores—the Canaries and Benguela—not only flow from colder to warmer areas but also have their waters replenished in this way, with a correspondingly increased effect on the temperature of the air masses above them, and so on neighboring lands.

Because the shallow waters overlying the continental shelf around the Japanese and British islands are particularly favorable to breeding and growth of fish, these islands have great fishing industries. In Africa, where such favorable conditions are absent over long stretches, commercial fishing has been slow to develop. Off South Africa the fishing industry which has been developed is associated with certain offshore "banks," but both here and off Angola, the great possibilities of onshore fisheries are now being realized.

BIBLIOGRAPHY

A. Bernard, *Afrique septentrionale et occidentale,* Vol. XI, *Geographie Universelle,* Paris.

F. Maurette, *Afrique, equatoriale, orientale et australe,* Vol. XII, *Geographie Universelle,* Paris.

A. Wegener, *The Origin of Continents and Oceans* (translated by Skerl), London, 1922 (historical interest).

J. W. Gregory, *The Rift Valleys and Geology of East Africa,* London, 1921 (historical interest).

F. R. C. Reed, *The Geology of the British Empire,* London, 1921.

Bailey Willis, *East African Plateaus and Rift Valleys,* Washington (Carnegie Inst.), 1936.

E. B. and S. Worthington, *Inland Waters of Africa,* London, 1933.

F. Dixey, "African Landscape," *Geog. Rev.,* **34,** 1944, 457–465.

CHAPTER FOUR

African Climates and the Water Problem

Africa lies between 35°North and 35°South, with the result that, excluding the lands associated with the lofty Atlas ranges in the north, the high plateau in the south, and isolated mountainous areas elsewhere, the whole continent has average temperatures over the crucial figure for plant growth of 42°F. throughout the year. Despite the elevation of the plateau in East Africa, frost is practically unknown throughout humid intertropical Africa. Furthermore, violent fluctuations of temperature which are associated with the movements of fronts in the North American continent are absent. Thus plant life is assured of temperatures which permit growth throughout the year; the farmer is assured of a regular temperature regime which, though it may scorch, is unlikely to wither by unexpected cold. In Africa climatic interest centers on rainfall rather than on temperature. For rainfall the story is very different. Viewed over the averages of a span of years the rainfall regimes may appear regular enough, but few places enjoy an "average" rainfall. Instead there are violent fluctuations from year to year, serious differences in the dates when the rains come, violent spasmodic downpours rather than steady falls.

The key to the whole of Africa's development is control of water. Drainage and flood control are needed where rainfall is regularly or occasionally excessive; storage and irrigation are needed where rainfall is normally moderate, both to guard against bad years and to extend the growing period; irrigation is essential where rainfall is low, despite the fact that in a majority of years the rainfall may be sufficient for dry zone crops. Unless there is elaborate provision for the storage of food produced in excess in good years—which there is not in Africa—without irrigation the land can support only the population which it can support in the *bad* years.

Being situated in low latitudes and almost entirely surrounded by water, there is no immediate source of cold continental air to affect the continent.

South Africa is separated by 2000 miles of ocean from Antarctica and, unlike South America, has few invasions of cold polar air from that direction. Though northern parts of Africa are affected by conditions in Euro-Asia and are more "continental" in the wide range of temperature, there is an approximately symmetrical distribution of climatic types north and south of the equator. The greatest differences are between the northeastern and southeastern segments of the continent. In the northeast the great African hot desert area continues across the Red Sea into Arabia, and Ethiopia comes within the ambit of the great Asiatic monsoon. In the southeast, on the other hand, Africa is open to the influences from over the open south Indian Ocean.

Gradual transitions from one type of climate to another are the general rule over the whole of Africa. There are no great mountain chains such as act as climatic divides in America or Asia, though the Atlas mountains in the north restrict good winter rains associated with Mediterranean cyclones to the coastlands. The elevation of the great African plateau, especially since its higher parts are in the east towards the windward, modifies both temperature and rainfall. The July temperatures of the East African plateau actually on the equator are 20 degrees lower than they would be at sea level and actually 10 degrees lower than those of the coastlands of the southeast, outside the tropics, at the same season. The moderate rainfall of the East African plateau is due in part to the lifting of rain-bearing winds so that the heavy equatorial rainfall and equatorial climate do not extend across the continent. The East African plateau, right on the equator, is thus suited to European crops and farm animals, and the equatorial rain forest is absent.

Climatic conditions around the African coasts are considerably influenced by oceanic currents. Along the west coast of northern Africa the cold Canaries current flows southward. The low sea temperatures are due partly to the northern origin of the water, partly to the upwelling of cold bottom water to replace the surface waters constantly propelled towards the southwest by the dominant northeasterly winds. Coastal fogs are frequent, but hot seasonal temperatures are relatively low. With offshore winds, the coastlands are very arid. Similar effects are associated with the cold northward-flowing Benguela current off the shores of southwest Africa, where conditions resemble those of northern Chile. The Canaries and Benguela currents both swing westwards while between them the eastward-flowing equatorial countercurrent or Guinea current brings very warm water to the Guinea or West African coast. Because the air currents are onshore the coastlands are constantly bathed by very warm and moist air masses, with a resultant heavy rainfall almost from Dakar to Libreville.

The east coast of Africa with its onshore winds driving warm surface currents towards the land is entirely different. South of the equator the island of Madagascar splits the main South Equatorial current of the Indian Ocean, and the Mozambique current flows southward from off Mombasa to about Lourenço Marques, where it merges into the Agulhas current. The presence of these warm surface currents results in sea-surface temperatures 15 to 20°F. higher than on the west coast, and the warm moist air masses associated with them afford a moderate to good rainfall along the coastlands. In the north Indian Ocean, circulation of waters is reversed according to the Asiatic monsoon. In the season of the northeast monsoon (November to April), the drift of water is from northeast to southwest along the coast—a cool current flowing *towards* the equator; in the season of the southwest monsoon, the air movement is offshore, and the current is alongshore from southwest to northeast. Because neither condition favors precipitation, the coast is arid from the equator northward.

Turning now to the main features of the atmospheric circulation over Africa, we see that the continent is dominated by the world distribution of pressure—the two extra-tropical high-pressure belts and the equatorial low-pressure belt (Figure 4.1). These so-called permanent belts move northward in the northern summer, lagging behind the overhead sun, and southward in the southern summer. For the month of January (northern winter, southern summer) the position is shown in Figure 4.2. The Azores high-pressure system extends over the relatively cool Sahara, the south Atlantic high-pressure belt lies to the south of the continent, and the equatorial low is south of the equator.

Figure 4.1 Theoretical arrangement of world pressure belts and winds in relation to Africa in January. LP = Low Pressure; HP = High Pressure.

Pressure (millibars) – January

After Brooks and Mirrlees

Air Movements – January

········· Fronts

After Brooks and Mirrlees

Rainfall – January

< 1 inch
1–2 inches
2–4 inches
4–8 inches
8–12 inches
> 12 inches

Cancer

Equator

Capricorn

0   1000
Miles

0   1500
Kilometers

After Brooks and Mirrlees

Figure 4.2   Climatic conditions over Africa in January. (After Brooks and Mirrlees, "A Study of the Atmospheric Circulation over Tropical Africa," *Geophysical Memoirs,* **Vol. VI, No. 55, 1932, London, Meteorological Office.)**

In July, as shown in Figure 4.4, the January conditions are largely reversed. The Sahara, which has become extremely hot, gives rise to a huge low-pressure area, whereas South Africa comes under the influence of the extratropical high-pressure belt. At this season conditions over northeastern Africa are complicated by the great Asiatic monsoon.

These pressure systems give rise to the movements of air masses which are in turn responsible for the distribution of rainfall over the continent. Brooks and Mirrlees[1] distinguish seven air streams, as shown by arrows,

[1] C. E. P. Brooks and S. T. A. Mirrlees, "A Study of the Atmospheric Circulation over Tropical Africa," London, Meteorological Office, *Geophysical Memoirs,* Vol. VI, No. 55, 1932.

lettered *a, b, c, d, e, f,* and *g* in Figures 4.2, 4.3, and 4.4. They may be compared with the theoretical arrangement of winds shown in Figure 4.1. Two other air streams affect the extreme northwest and southeast of the continent. The air streams are:

(*a*) The Atlantic Northeast Trades, blowing toward the southwest from the Azores high-pressure system.

(*b*) The Harmattan, the air stream blowing from the Saharan high-pressure belt across the Sudan and toward West Africa.

(*c*) The Egyptian air stream, blowing up the Nile valley as a northerly wind and reaching as far south as Bechuanaland.

(*d*) The Atlantic Southeast Trades, blowing toward the equatorial low-pressure belt over the South Atlantic. On crossing the equator, which they do especially during the northern summer, these winds become southwesterly and produce a monsoon effect in West Africa, but penetrate in January only a short distance inland.

(*e*) The Arabian or Indian Northeast Trades, blowing from the high-pressure system of southwest Asia in the winter months only, being eliminated and reversed by the monsoon currents for the other half of the year.

Figure 4.3   Wind conditions in April. Showing variable position of the main intertropical front or convergence zone (ITCZ). (After Brooks and Mirrlees.)

Pressure (millibars) - July

Air movements - July

Rainfall - July

Figure 4.4 **Climatic conditions over Africa in July. (After Brooks and Mirrlees.)**

(*f*) The Indian Ocean Southeast Trades are the dominant influence over the southeast part of the continent.

(*g*) The Southeast Africa air is a dry mass.

(*h*) and (*i*) These air streams, also shown in Figures 4.2, 4.3, and 4.4, though not studied by Brooks and Mirrlees, are the westerly air streams of midlatitudes. That over the Mediterranean is a cyclonic belt of alternating depressions and wedges of high pressure, responsible for the winter rainfall from Morocco to Egypt. That over the southern ocean is associated with strong, more regular winds, the Roaring Forties (so-called from their prevalence in the forties of south latitude), and is responsible for the winter rainfall of the Cape.

Since Brooks and Mirrlees prepared this illuminating analysis of the air circulation over Africa, climatologists have become accustomed to thinking in terms of air masses. Thus Haurwitz and Austin[2] distinguish:

(a) *Tropical Maritime Air* (mT)—warm, moist air, originating over the ocean north and south of the equator.

(b) *Tropical Continental Air* (cT)—warm, dry air originating over the vast, dry Sahara and also over the Kalahari.

(c) *Polar Maritime Air* (mP)—invading the extreme northwest of the continent in the northern winter and a similar type invading the extreme southwest in the southern winter.

(d) *Polar Continental Air* (cP)—as already noted, such air does not reach Africa from the Antarctic, but during the southern winter the continental cooling tends toward the creation of a mild type of cP air over the highlands of South Africa.

The maps (Figures 4.2 and 4.4) leave no doubt of the close association between the main air streams and rainfall. In January the Northeast Trades (the Harmattan and Egyptian air streams, b and c) blow from colder to warmer latitudes and are dry winds. The air stream from the South Atlantic (d) brings a small rainfall to the Guinea coast, but farther south it blows from over the cold Benguela current to the heated land and no rainfall results. The effects of the Indian Ocean streams (a and f) are just what one would expect.

Similarly the position in July is easily explicable.

Of supreme importance to Africa is the intertropical front, shown in Figures 4.2, 4.3, and 4.4, where the two main masses of mT air meet and ascending air currents result, producing rain. Over the plateau surface of Africa there are no outstanding physical features, no ranges of mountains to act as climatic divides or to help fix the intertropical front (Figure 4.5). Consequently its position at all seasons is ill-defined and varies not only with the seasons but noticeably also from one year to another. In the month of April, for example, the intertropical front may lie almost as near the West African coast as in January, and all lands away from the coast remain under the influence of the dry Harmattan. Or it may lie 500 miles farther north, and the same lands have welcome rains from moist tropical air. It is, in a few words, the irregular behavior of the intertropical front which is responsible for Africa's greatest curse, irregularity of rainfall (Figure 4.6). Since it differs thus markedly from an ordinary front, it is now more usual to refer to the Intertropical Convergence Zone (ITCZ). The old seaman's term "the Doldrums" should also be noted.

Although continental Africa does not suffer from the destructive hurri-

[2] B. Haurwitz and J. M. Austin, *Climatology*, New York, 1944, pp. 332–336.

Figure 4.5　A pair of giraffes on the East African plateau. They are silhouetted against a heavy evening sky, which suggests the meeting of two air masses along a front. There are few natural climatic divides in Africa. (Courtesy British Overseas Airways Corporation.)

canes which are so serious in parts of tropical and subtropical America, the cyclonic storms associated with the intertropical front produce very heavy and sometimes destructive falls of rain.

Despite the several systems of climatic classification in common use, the general picture in Africa is clear. The scheme shown in Figure 4.7 is derived from Finch and Trewartha—familiar from its use in the *Atlas of World Maps* (Army Service Forces Manual, M 101, 1943). It distinguishes:

A	Tropical Rainy Climates	*A*
1	Tropical Rainforest Climate, better called the Equatorial Climate. This is limited to areas within 10° of the equator, but the similar 1t (Windward Coasts) characterizes the eastern coastlands of Madagascar.	*Af*
2	Tropical Savanna or Summer Rain Climate, covering more than a third of all Africa.	*Aw*
B	Dry Climates	*B*
3	Low Latitude Dry Climates	
	3a　Desert	*BW*
	3b　Steppe	*BS*
4	Middle Latitude Dry Climates	
	4b　Steppe	*BSk*

| C | Humid Mesothermal | C |

5 Mediterranean   *Ca*
6 Humid Subtropical   *Cfb*

The symbols on the right hand are those of the well-known classification of W. Köppen, where *f* indicates no dry season; *w* is winter
dry; *s* is summer dry; *k* is cold (mean annual temperature below
18°C. or 64.4°F.); *b* is mean temperature of warmest month below
22°C. or 71.6°F.

British geographers normally use simple climatic-vegetation regions modified but slightly from the scheme introduced by A. J. Herbertson in 1905.[3]

[3] "The Major Natural Regions," *Geog. Jour.*, **XXV**, 1905, 300–312.

Annual Rainfall

< 10 inches

10 – 20 inches

20 – 30 inches

30 – 40 inches

40 – 60 inches

60 – 80 inches

80 – 100 inches

> 100 inches

Figure 4.6   Average annual rainfall.

Figure 4.7   The climatic regions of Africa. (After Finch and Trewartha, *Atlas of World Maps*, Army Service Forces Manual, M 101, 1943.)

In the original paper Herbertson distinguished very simply in Africa:

3. The warm temperate regions:
   (*a*) The western margin with winter rains (Mediterranean type)
      [= 5 of Finch and Trewartha]
   (*b*) The eastern margin with summer rain
      [= 6 of Finch and Trewartha]
4. (*a*) The west tropical deserts (Sahara type)
      [= 3 of Finch and Trewartha]
   (*b*) Intertropical tablelands (Sudan type)
      [= 2 of Finch and Trewartha]
6. Equatorial lowlands (Amazon type)
      [= 1 of Finch and Trewartha]

It is interesting that the two schemes of classification, in view of the different starting points, should prove to be practically identical.

As already noted, Pierre Gourou, the well-known French authority on tropical climates, draws a distinction between *pays tropicaux,* lands within the tropics having an annual rainfall exceeding 800 millimeters or 16 inches, and *pays désertiques,* where the annual rainfall drops below 16 inches.

In recent years much attention has been paid to *effective* rainfall, and a "humid" month is defined as one in which precipitation exceeds the maximum possible evaporation for that month—which is between 3 and 4.5 inches. A suggested definition of the humid tropics is the area where mean monthly temperature is at least 68°F. (20°C.) for eight months of the year, vapor pressure is at least 20 millibars and relative humidity at least 65 for half the year, and mean annual rainfall is at least 40 inches (1000 mm) and for at least six months is over 3 inches per month. On this basis the climatic regions marked 1, 1t, most of 2, and H on Figure 4.7 would be included.[4]

The equatorial or tropical rainforest climate (1)

The keynote of the equatorial climate is monotony: constant heat, constant humidity, and constant rainfall. There is little or no seasonal rhythm, little relief at night from the heat of the day. Yet there are no great extremes: in lowland stations the thermometer remains around 80°F.; on the hottest day it rarely rises to much above 90°; in the coolest night it does not sink below 70°. With early morning mist there may be a feeling of chill, more apparent than real. As the sun climbs high at midday there is a sense of great heat, often dispelled by afternoon cloud and rain, giving place to clear starlit nights. Plant growth takes place throughout the year, so that luxuriant vegetation is the rule. It is the absence of seasonal rhythm which constitutes the "unhealthy" aspect of a climate which has been described as a good servant but a bad master. H. J. Fleure characterized equatorial lands as regions of "constant endeavor."

Some stations have two rainfall maxima during the year; others (especially towards the margins) have a season rainier than the rest of the year, but typically there is no dry season. It is this feature which distinguishes the truly "equatorial" climate from the wettest parts of the tropical savanna or windward coasts. In many parts of the region, lying in the belt of equatorial calms or doldrums, the rainfall is convectional, and regular winds are absent. The heat of the sun causes evaporation from water surfaces and damp land. The heated, saturated air rises and is cooled by convection so that rain falls on almost the same area from which the moisture originated.

With increasing elevation the daily and monthly temperatures are lowered, and, although there is some increase in the daily range, there is little in the annual. With lowered temperatures rainfall is also less.

On the margins of equatorial regions and notably along the wet part of the West African coasts, moisture-laden air masses moving in from the sea play a larger part.

In the tables which follow, the first two stations (Debundja and New

[4] F. R. Fosberg, B. J. Garnier and A. W. Küchler, Delimitation of the Humid Tropics, *Geog. Rev.,* **51,** 1961, 333–347.

Antwerp) may be called typical equatorial; the second two (Entebbe and Nairobi) show stations modified by elevation; the third two (Freetown and Lagos) show the wet margins.

Windward coasts (1t)

In Africa Finch and Trewartha show this type of climate on the eastern coastlands of Madagascar, from latitude 12° to 25°South. This is in the belt of the southeast trades, but in January the equatorial doldrums belt of rising air affects the northern end of the island, and this is the wettest season. But there is no dry season; the southeast winds rising to cross the mountains deposit at least 3 inches even in the driest months, September, October, and November. Only some of the tropical cyclones which originate over the south Indian Ocean and affect Mauritius and Réunion, especially from January to April, reach Madagascar. The constant onshore winds prevent any violent daily fluctuations of temperature, and the annual range is also small. The figures for Tamatave illustrate the conditions.

In many ways the wetter coastal regions of West Africa—Sierra Leone and Liberia—belong to the "windward coasts" rather than the equatorial.

The tropical savanna (2)

This is *par excellence* the climate of tropical Africa, just as the varied forms of savanna which result are the dominant natural vegetation of the vast intertropical plateaus. Since the savanna stretches from the equatorial rainforest on the one hand to the desert margins on the other, the savanna climate must clearly vary greatly also. In fact the variation is primarily in the total amount of precipitation, commonly from 80 inches on the equatorial margins (but greatly exceeding this on exposed slopes) to 16 inches where it merges into the "low latitude steppes" of Finch and Trewartha. There is a consequent effect on temperature, but what is constant throughout is the rhythm of the seasons. A cool or at least relatively cool dry season (November to February in the northern hemisphere) gives place to a hot dry season, so that in the northern hemisphere the hottest month is early in the year, commonly in April or May. The coming of the rains causes a lowering of the temperature, except where the falls are too small to have this effect, and the rainy season is thus equivalent to our midlatitude summer. For reasons already indicated as related to the movement of air masses and the associated fronts over a continent where there are few physical barriers to air movement, the break of the rainy season may be early in some years, greatly delayed in others. Annual totals show a wide variation from year to year, whereas in any given year the incidence may show remarkable irregularities (Figure 4.8), since the rain falls almost entirely as heavy showers or thundershowers. The

Figure 4.8   Some African temperature and rainfall graphs. Over the vast bulk of Africa a rainfall, whether heavy or light, well distributed throughout the year is unknown. The temperature graph showing a great range is characteristic of the heart of the Sahara.

irregularities between one month and another as well as from year to year increase as the average total fall decreases. Thus in one year a place with an "average" fall of 40 inches may have abundant moisture for a good harvest; the next year the fall may only total 20 inches, and famine conditions result. This is in addition to the so-called hungry season, which occurs after all the crops of one harvest have been consumed and before the first crops from the new harvest are ready for consumption (Figure 4.9). A good example of the climatic vagaries is afforded by a station in the Gambia, where the rainfall totals for 18 successive years were as follows:

1901	45 inches		1910	44 inches
1902	29		1911	28
1903	57		1912	34
1904	38		1913	24
1905	66		1914	49
1906	64		1915	48
1907	34		1916	38
1908	44		1917	38
1909	57		1918	54

Figure 4.9　The "hungry season" in northern Ghana. This village is typical of much of the overworked poor lands on the drier margins of the tropical lands. The soil is thin, and the yam heaps poor. The children show signs of malnutrition, notably the bulging stomach. (Official Photograph.)

Taking individual months in the same place, we find that June showed a range from 2.24 inches in one year to 12.32 in another. Over the same period May ranged from nil to 1.90 inches, and October from 0.24 to 9.08 inches.

The figures for temperature show that plant growth is normally possible throughout the year. Though the day temperatures, especially in drier regions, greatly exceed those in the equatorial belt, they do not reach the extremes found in the great deserts. There is everywhere close correlation between daily and annual temperature ranges and the situation relative to the sea and to moist air masses. Bathurst on the coast in Gambia (13°North) has a range from 74°F. in January to 80°F. in July (when rainfall is 12 inches), but October, when the rains have almost ceased (average 4 inches), is one degree hotter than July. Inland stations such as Kayes show a range from 77°F. in January to 96° in May.

Low-latitude deserts and low-latitude steppes (3a and 3b)

Essentially deserts result from low precipitation. On the margins towards the equator it is difficult to say where "desert" fades into what Finch and Trewartha record as "steppe," and where the steppe gives place to tropical "savanna." For the savanna limit many would follow Gourou, using the 16-inch isohyet. On the poleward margins a low rainfall limit may be taken to indicate where the steppelands fade into the Mediterranean. In the heart of the Sahara such rain as falls (as at Tamanrasset) comes in storms at irregular intervals; along the southern margins the "rainy season" is the hot season or summer; along the Mediterranean margins it is the winter—well exemplified by Alexandria.

Like all deserts, the African regions have great temperature extremes. The daily range in the heart of the desert is as much as 50° to 60°F.; the highest recorded temperatures on the surface of the earth are claimed by the Sahara. Shade recordings of 136°F. are said to have been made; the surface of the ground frequently exceeds 170°F. Most of the heart of the Sahara has a July mean exceeding 95°. The annual range is between 30° and 40°; in the north the coldest month has a mean of 50°F., so that frost is quite usual.

The mean annual cloudiness is normally less than 10 per cent, so that cloudless skies are the rule—bright sunshine by day, starlight by night. The atmosphere is so dry that the wet-bulb thermometer may be 40 degrees lower than the dry. The air may be so dry as to inhibit plant life, and it has been claimed that a man needs to drink a minimum of 10 pints of liquid a day to maintain health.

Conditions in the corresponding area in southern Africa are much less severe. There the most arid strip is along the coast (the Namib); the so-called Kalahari Desert has in fact sufficient vegetation to be classed at worst as semidesert only.

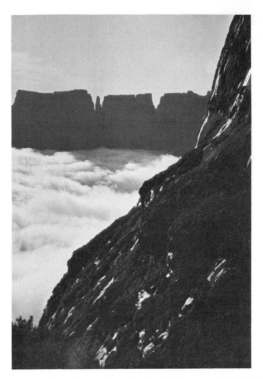

Figure 4.10   The Drakensberg above the clouds of the coastal plain. This picture shows dramatically the contrast often to be found on the African plateau heights from the plains below. (Copyright Geographical Publications Limited.)

Middle latitude steppe (4b)

In Africa this is the climate of the damper parts of the South African High Veld. It owes its character in large measure to elevation which results in a lower temperature throughout the year (Figure 4.10). Although snow is not unknown and winter frosts occur during 3 to 6 months, the area is too near the moderating influence of the ocean to suffer from the climatic extremes of northern steppelands and prairies. Graaff Reinet shows a spring or early summer rainfall maximum and also one in the fall. This station is only 2500 feet above sea level; places like Bloemfontein have characteristically lower winter averages.

Mediterranean climate (5)

The Mediterranean climate, deriving its name from the fact that it is characteristic of so many countries around the Mediterranean Sea, is one of the most distinctive of all climatic types. It shares its hot dry summers with the neighboring desert lands; its cool moist winters derive their rainfall from the westerly air streams which bring the rain through a succession of depressions or lows to lands nearer the poles. The rainfall may show a fall maximum (the "former rains" of the Bible) and a spring maximum ("latter rains") rather than a single winter maximum, but the fact that the supply of moisture coincides with the cool season results both in a slow formation of soil and a slow vegetative growth. In the long, hot summer plants need to conserve their moisture, and, unless they tap deep-seated supplies by very long roots, they have reduced leaf surfaces with such protective devices as hairs (for example, olive tree), waxed or leathery surfaces (laurels, evergreen oak, pines). The thick "cork" bark of the cork oak is another protection against loss of moisture. Cultivation of grain and herbaceous crops necessitates an early harvest before the scorching heat of late summer, or a dependence on irrigation.

The Mediterranean climate is found in the northwest and extreme southwest of the continent, where mountain ranges, deep valleys, and coastal strips of varying exposure give marked and rapid local variations in temperature and rainfall. Rainfall (see Figure 4.6) generally increases with elevation. Though rare at sea level, frost and even snow occur at comparatively low elevations and are usual at greater heights.

The examples given on page 81 include the island site of Funchal (Madeira), the coastal stations of Algiers and Tunis in the north, Cape Town in the south. Marrakesh, inland at a height of 1542 feet, though dry, shows a fall and a spring maximum.

Humid subtropical climate (6)

In Africa this is the climate of Natal and neighboring parts of the southeastern coasts of the continent at about latitude 30 degrees. Durban shows the small range of temperature near the coast, increasing slightly inland as indicated in Pietermaritzburg. In neither place is the range as great as in areas like the southeastern United States.

Undifferentiated highlands (H)

The whole of the African plateau exhibits climatic modifications due to elevation. In Nairobi, on the equator, the modification is profound and is shared by the large area of highland in East Africa. There remain, however, parts of the continent, notably the mountain knot of Ethiopia, where rugged or varied relief results in a vertical zonation of climatic types; the same is true of the great volcanoes of East Africa. This is the reason for the inclusion of "undifferentiated highlands" on the map—where parts rise to the snowline.

Climate and the African

No aspect of life in tropical Africa exceeds rain in importance. From north to south and from west to east innumerable ceremonies and customs have sprung from the vital necessity of an adequate fall of rain in an area

The Equatorial or Tropical Rainforest Climate

Station		Jan.	Feb.	Mar.	Apr.	May	June	July	Aug.	Sept.	Oct.	Nov.	Dec.	Range	Year
Debundja (Cameroons) (39 ft.)	°F.	79.3	79.9	79.2	78.8	78.3	76.8	74.7	74.5	75.6	75.9	77.9	78.6	5.4	
	Rainfall (in.)	8.0	10.9	17.1	17.3	24.8	59.7	64.4	57.7	65.2	45.2	26.6	15.1		412.0
New Antwerp, Congo (Leo.) (1230 ft.)	°F.	79.2	80.1	79.2	78.1	79.2	78.4	76.5	76.3	77.0	77.4	77.9	78.1	3.8	
	Rainfall (in.)	4.1	3.5	4.1	5.6	6.2	6.1	6.3	6.3	6.3	6.6	2.6	9.3		67.0
Entebbe, Uganda (3863 ft.)	°F.	71.1	71.1	71.3	70.3	69.8	69.4	68.6	68.6	69.4	70.1	70.1	70.2	2.7	
	Rainfall (in.)	2.6	3.6	5.8	9.7	8.5	5.1	2.9	3.1	3.1	3.5	5.0	5.1		58.0
Nairobi, Kenya (5450 ft.)	°F.	63.8	64.7	65.2	63.9	63.4	61.6	58.5	59.3	61.6	64.8	64.0	62.3	6.7	
	Rainfall (in.)	1.9	3.6	4.2	8.9	5.6	2.2	0.9	1.1	1.2	2.3	5.3	2.8		40.0
Freetown, Sierra Leone (223 ft.)	°F.	81.3	82.3	82.4	82.4	81.5	80.3	78.6	77.9	79.1	80.1	81.2	81.4	4.5	
	Rainfall (in.)	0.4	0.3	1.2	4.1	11.5	20.0	35.6	36.6	28.5	12.6	5.1	1.4		157.3
Lagos, Nigeria (25 ft.)	°F.	80.9	82.2	83.3	82.5	81.8	79.3	78.0	77.7	78.4	79.5	81.4	81.5	5.6	
	Rainfall (in.)	1.1	2.1	3.7	5.7	10.5	18.7	10.7	2.8	5.3	7.8	2.6	0.8		71.8

Windward Coast (1t)

Station		Jan.	Feb.	Mar.	Apr.	May	June	July	Aug.	Sept.	Oct.	Nov.	Dec.	Range	Year
Tamatave, Madagascar (16 ft.)	°F.	79.3	80.6	78.3	76.5	72.5	69.3	68.4	69.3	71.2	73.8	76.5	78.6	12.2	
	Rainfall (in.)	15.0	14.3	17.8	12.0	9.8	14.4	13.2	8.5	7.1	5.3	3.9	9.6		130.9

The Tropical Savanna

Station		Jan.	Feb.	Mar.	Apr.	May	June	July	Aug.	Sept.	Oct.	Nov.	Dec.	Range	Year
Gorée (Dakar), Senegal (20 ft.)	°F.	68.5	66.2	68.2	68.9	71.6	78.3	81.1	81.5	82.4	82.0	78.3	72.0	16.2	
	Rainfall (in.)	0	0	0	0	0	0.9	3.6	9.9	5.2	0.7	0.1	0		20.4
Kayes, Mali (197 ft.)	°F.	77.2	80.8	88.7	94.1	96.4	90.5	83.7	81.7	82.2	84.5	83.1	77.2	19.2	
	Rainfall (in.)	0	0	0	0	0.6	3.9	8.3	8.3	5.6	1.9	0.3	0.2		29.1
Mongalla, Sudan (1440 ft.)	°F.	80.4	81.7	82.6	81.0	79.0	77.4	75.9	75.7	77.2	78.1	79.0	79.2	6.9	
	Rainfall (in.)	0.1	0.7	1.5	4.2	5.4	4.6	5.2	5.8	4.9	4.3	1.8	0.3		38.8
Luluabourg, Congo (Leo.) (2034 ft.)	°F.	76.1	75.7	76.3	77.0	76.6	76.3	76.5	76.3	75.9	76.3	76.6	77.2	1.5	
	Rainfall (in.)	7.2	5.4	7.9	6.1	3.1	0.2	0.1	2.5	6.5	6.6	9.1	6.6		61.3
Salisbury, S. Rhodesia (4880 ft.)	°F.	69.7	68.8	68.2	65.7	60.6	56.9	56.1	60.2	66.4	70.7	70.7	69.6	14.6	
	Rainfall (in.)	7.5	7.4	4.5	1.0	0.5	0.1	0	0.1	0.3	1.1	3.7	5.8		32.0

Low Latitude Deserts and Low Latitude Steppes

Station		Jan.	Feb.	Mar.	Apr.	May	June	July	Aug.	Sept.	Oct.	Nov.	Dec.	Range	Year
Alexandria, Egypt (105 ft.)	°F.	56.1	57.2	60.1	63.7	68.5	73.4	77.0	78.1	76.3	73.0	66.4	59.4	22.0	
	Rainfall (in.)	2.1	0.9	0.5	0.2	0	0	0	0	0	0.3	1.3	2.6		7.9
Khartoum, Sudan (1280 ft.)	°F.	70.3	73.4	79.2	86.0	90.7	91.4	88.5	86.5	88.2	87.4	80.2	72.1	21.1	
	Rainfall (in.)	0	0	0	0	0.1	0.3	1.6	2.2	0.7	0.2	0	0		5.1
In-Salah, Sahara (Southern Algeria) (919 ft.)	°F.	54.7	59.4	67.8	76.1	85.6	94.3	99.3	97.0	91.6	80.1	68.2	57.7	44.6	
	Rainfall (in.)	0	0	0	0	0	0	0.1	0.4	0.3	0	0	0	0	0.8
Swakopmund, S. W. Africa (20 ft.)	°F.	62.6	63.1	63.3	59.9	60.6	58.5	56.5	54.9	56.1	58.1	58.6	61.5	8.4	
	Rainfall (in.)	0	0.1	0.2	0	0	0	0	0	0	0.1	0	0.2		0.6

Middle Latitude Steppe

Station		Jan.	Feb.	Mar.	Apr.	May	June	July	Aug.	Sept.	Oct.	Nov.	Dec.	Range	Year
Graaff Reinet, Cape Province, South Africa (2500 ft.)	°F.	71.8	72.3	68.2	61.8	56.5	53.0	51.0	53.8	59.0	63.8	68.5	71.5	21.3	
	Rainfall (in.)	1.7	1.4	2.7	0.9	1.2	0.4	0.2	0.7	1.3	0.9	2.5	1.4		15.3

The Mediterranean Climate

Station		Jan.	Feb.	Mar.	Apr.	May	June	July	Aug.	Sept.	Oct.	Nov.	Dec.	Range	Year
Funchal, Madeira (82 ft.)	°F.	59.4	59.2	59.7	61.2	63.5	67.1	70.2	72.1	71.4	68.4	64.4	61.2	12.9	
	Rainfall (in.)	3.4	3.6	3.4	1.9	1.1	0.4	0.1	0.1	1.2	4.0	4.7	3.2		27.1
Algiers, Algeria (72 ft.)	°F.	49.3	50.4	52.5	55.8	61.0	67.8	73.4	74.7	70.3	63.7	56.8	51.8	25.4	
	Rainfall (in.)	4.0	2.6	3.3	2.0	1.7	0.7	0.1	0.1	1.2	3.4	4.1	4.0		27.2
Tunis, Tunisia (141 ft.)	°F.	48.4	51.3	54.3	58.3	64.4	72.0	77.7	78.6	54.5	66.7	58.8	52.3	30.2	
	Rainfall (in.)	2.1	2.0	1.9	1.5	0.9	0.5	0.1	0.2	1.0	1.9	2.1	2.4		16.6
Cape Town, Cape Province, South Africa (40 ft.)	°F.	69.9	70.3	68.1	63.2	58.9	55.7	54.7	55.6	57.9	61.2	64.4	67.9	15.6	
	Rainfall (in.)	0.7	0.6	0.9	1.9	3.8	4.5	3.7	3.4	2.3	1.6	1.1	0.8		25.3

The Humid Subtropical Climate

Station		Jan.	Feb.	Mar.	Apr.	May	June	July	Aug.	Sept.	Oct.	Nov.	Dec.	Range	Year
Durban, Natal, South Africa (260 ft.)	°F.	76.3	76.8	74.9	71.8	67.8	64.8	64.3	65.8	67.6	69.5	72.0	74.6	12.5	
	Rainfall (in.)	4.6	4.9	5.4	3.4	1.9	1.2	1.2	1.7	3.2	5.1	5.0	5.1		42.7
Pietermaritzburg, Natal, South Africa (2225 ft.)	°F.	73.3	73.4	71.4	67.8	61.9	57.6	58.6	62.4	65.2	67.4	69.1	71.8	15.8	
	Rainfall (in.)	5.1	6.2	5.1	2.6	1.1	0.3	0.1	0.8	1.8	2.5	5.3	5.0		35.9

marked by violent fluctuations from year to year. In the heart of the Low Veld of the Northeastern Transvaal is found the rain cult of the Bantu Lovedu people, which is centered on the Rain Queen, the "transformer of the clouds."[5]

At the other end of Africa, as recently as 1943, white government officials attended the solemn ceremony of installation of the **Ret,** or rain-making chief, of the Shilluk of the Upper Nile Province of the Anglo-Egyptian Sudan.[6]

When the rains come, they may do so with alarming suddenness and ferocity. Kenneth Bradley, in his interesting *Diary of a District Officer,*[7] has recorded how in one year at Fort Jameson in Northern Rhodesia the thermometer stood at 103°F. in the shade on November the eleventh. That night 2 inches of rain fell. The next day it was still raining, and the thermometer had dropped to 65°. Within a couple of days burnt-over pastures or brown grass slopes are bright green again, but gulleys may have been formed on overgrazed land or unprotected soil, and a dangerous cycle of soil erosion started. Floods and washouts on roads and railways may happen overnight. It is equally true that the water may drain off before it can really be used.

It remains a curious fact, discussed below, page 85, that the African is not naturally "water-conscious"; he fails to make best use of his resources. Over vast areas with a marked wet and dry season, life during the rains is not difficult. Heat and moisture combine to encourage plant growth, and a varied assortment of vegetables becomes available for human food. This is the time for sowing. The months which follow are the months for harvesting the various grains—corn, millets, peanuts, and rice—but harvesting of all crops is over 2 months before the rains break. Thus the months of March and April north of the equator, September and October to the south, are slack months in the cultivation year. If the harvest has been poor, so that food does not last over this period, or later, until other food is available, this is the "hungry season," often one of great distress.

Where there are reliable river floods this "hunger period" is absent. This is clearly seen in the Central Barotse plain of Northern Rhodesia, where the Zambezi floods annually with a maximum in March and April. The people, the Lozi, live on mounds in the plain free from floods (the ownership of which is very important) and cultivate the soil as gardens, at the same time keeping cattle and fishing, so that they enjoy a varied diet.

---

[5] E. J. Krige and J. D. Krige, *The Realm of the Rain-Queen,* New York, 1943.
[6] *African World,* April 22, 1944.
[7] London and Toronto, Harrap, 1943.

Climate and the white man

The high death rate among Europeans serving in the tropics, and perhaps especially the disastrous mortality among British soldiers serving in India and compelled to march and fight in close-fitting cloth uniforms and small caps, gave rise to beliefs about the influence of climate on the white man which persisted, with very little foundation, for more than a century. The direct effects of climate have been confused with the serious effects of disease, especially insect-borne and water-borne. Among the myths was the danger of sunstroke, which was believed to affect particularly the spine (hence the wearing of spine pads) and through the head, which accordingly needed protection by a sun helmet or solar topee, without which no self-respecting Britisher would venture abroad in sunlight or even with the sun lurking behind clouds. Medical men had been denying the existence of "sunstroke" in the old accepted sense for a decade or more before the experience of troops in New Guinea, Burma, and Africa in World War II finally dispelled the myth. Heat-stroke apoplexy is real enough, and is best countered by all those measures which encourage the body to "breathe"—loose, light clothing and abundant water to encourage perspiration. Light rays received through the eyes may be dangerous; hence the wearing of dark glasses.

As exact evidence based on controlled experiments accumulates, the trend of the evidence indicates that there is nothing in the tropical climate to inhibit hard manual labor for white as well as colored men, though temperature and humidity conditions may be above the optimum for both physical and mental energy. Carrying out tests on myself during some years of residence in the tropics, I found a definite lowering of mental ability at 100°F. in dry air and obviously at much lower temperatures with high humidity. For my own part, a controlled temperature of 70° to 75° is most conducive to mental exertion—probably rather lower for physical—with a relative humidity of 60 to 65.

The absence of seasonal rhythm in the equatorial lands has already been cited as a deleterious climatic factor. In addition, high humidty as well as exceptionally high actual temperatures may be quoted as direct effects of climate. That high temperatures have a direct effect is instanced by the relatively harmless but very annoying condition known as "prickly heat," an intense irritation which may or may not show on the surface of the skin.

Tropical climates have of course many indirect effects on the white man. Since the intake of a large part of our food is required for the maintenance of bodily temperature in cold latitudes, it follows that there is less need for energy-giving carbohydrates or "fuel." Yet the white man is reluctant to change his habits, and an accumulation of fatty tissue is often to be noted. The need for a large intake of moisture often leads to excessive intake of alcohol. In short, the feeding and drinking habits among whites in many parts of the tropics are, or have been, such that the survival of the individual becomes a daily miracle.

The long-assumed superiority of the white man has given rise consciously or unconsciously to the concept that manual labor is not for him in a country where there are others to do such work; then to the idea that such work is physically impossible.

If we thus destroy some of the old shibboleths, we do not prove that white settlers can be at home anywhere in the tropics. The harmful effects of certain high temperatures have been admitted, but when the "white man's grave," as West Africa was once called, gained its notoriety it was not primarily the climate which was responsible. Disease is another matter.

Interest in the effects of tropical climates on the white man has shifted from the influence of heat and humidity to more subtle considerations. On the supposedly "healthy" highlands there seems to be some undue stimulation of the nervous system. There is often an increased irritability in the individual, and there is some evidence of decreasing mental stability, especially in the second or third generation of white settlers. Is it the influence of cosmic rays, the increased reception of radiation, the slowness of adjustment to lower atmospheric pressure, or are there other factors? The answers are still lacking.

In recent years the whole position has greatly changed with the widespread use of air-conditioning, rapidly becoming as common as central heating in cold lands. Not only can temperature and humidity—but not pressure —be adapted to human needs and varied at will, but similar controls make possible delicate manufacturing processes notably fine quality printing previously impossible in the humid tropics.

The African water problem

So much of Africa suffers from aridity—permanent, seasonal, or occasional—that some writers have gone so far as to say that no rain falling on the surface of the continent ought ever to be allowed to reach the sea. We may perhaps modify this by adding "until it has fulfilled some function of benefit to mankind." Primarily the water is needed to ensure food production, though Africa, because of its plateau character, has more potential water power than any other continent. In the south the Orange River, with the Tana, does not normally reach the sea, drying up before it disgorges into the Atlantic. But the aim that no river should reach the sea is scarcely compatible with the development of power at the falls which mark the main drop from the plateau and are usually near or relatively near the mouth.

In contrast to the peoples, for example, of southeast Asia, where wells, shadoof, water wheels, Persian wheels, flumes, "tanks" with irrigation ditches, terracing, and many other devices for reaching, storing, and using water are almost universal, the Africans of the tropics are not "water-minded." With certain exceptions their crops depend upon the rains when they come, and their domestic supplies are laboriously carried from stream or lake. They rarely dam a stream to maintain a supply either for domestic use or for watering crops. Wells are the exception rather than the rule, and there is rarely an attempt to prevent pollution by animals of other sources of supply such as a pond.

It is with this position in mind that we suggest that the solution of the African water problem should begin with the education of the African and the development of small schemes which he himself can construct and understand. The position will change, but in the early stages a pump is "white man's magic," to be discarded as soon as it fails to work, while anything which "belong him government" is something quite apart. The higher up a stream conservation takes place, the better, and the first need is instruction in building a dam or weir of any local material—soil, rubble, stone. Of course it is better still if laterite blocks or precast porous concrete is available. The next stage is to teach the advantages of keeping the supply as free as possible from contamination and of saving labor by conducting a gravity supply by pipe or flume to the villages. Since this is largely a saving of woman's work, it is unlikely to rank as first priority among African men.

There is little exact knowledge of the water cycle in tropical Africa. Run-off is probably between 2 and 12 per cent of rainfall, percolation between 2 and 40 per cent; evapotranspiration may be anything between 40 and 96 per cent. Provided it can again be made available, the best place for water storage is underground. Where there are natural water-holding beds, such as gravel or alluvium, in which underground water finds its level in the permanent water table and can be reached by shallow wells, the position is excellent. The African can be taught to dig and line wells, and such a primitive device as an endless porous rope of fibers absorbing water and passing through two wooden rollers to squeeze out the supply is within the power of any African to make and maintain. Unfortunately, over much of Africa's underlying complex of ancient rocks the water table behaves irregularly, and a well is both difficult to dig and uncertain of its supply. There is much to be said, in hilly or rolling country, for horizontal "wells" into the hillsides from which water would flow by gravity as an artificial spring. It should be noted that artesian conditions are rare in Africa.

Undoubtedly very much might be achieved in Africa by small schemes—dams and wells—made and understood by the people themselves. Big schemes of water control and power development, involving capital and experts for construction and maintenance, stand in a very different position. The success of the great Gezira scheme and the more recent Kariba dam (see page 426) are proof of what can be done, but much of tropical Africa is not yet ready for the big project. The Uganda (Nile) project, described in Chapter 11, illustrates the vital need to regard Africa as a series of basins. How rarely the basin, as a unit for water conservation, coincides with a political unit is clearly seen in the map on page 58.

Over the plateau surface of Africa there are many marshy areas. Some are natural hollows; others are due primarily to vegetation acting as a sponge. These marshes present a problem. Some can be drained and converted into agricultural land, but is this the right procedure? It has been argued that their presence has prevented the spread of desert conditions and that it is essential to maintain them as insurance against increasing aridity. This view is perhaps the one now generally held, and the problem is to make the marshes productive by use. Can parts be converted to rice fields? Can regular cutting of papyrus give a valuable source of paper-making material? Can marsh grasses palatable to cattle be established and provide an all-year supply? Can pastures be improved around lakes stocked with fish, giving a much-appreciated food supply?

Not unconnected with the marsh land is the puzzling problem of the fluctuations in level of Africa's great lakes. Sometimes this fluctuation is certainly due to accumulation of vegetation (with silt) at the outlets. An interesting case study is afforded by Lake Nyasa and its outlet, the Shiré River. The lake fluctuates in level as much as 20 feet, and the upper part of the Shiré River has such a shallow gradient that water may flow upstream after a heavy rainstorm. Lower down the river flows over a rocky ridge through a gorge with facilities for a power dam site before reaching a flood plain often invaded by water from the Zambezi.

It is, of course, impossible to separate the water problem from many of Africa's other major problems. Africa has little coal; therefore the chief source of domestic fuel is wood. This means constant cutting of woodland, and a depletion of timber reserves introduces the danger of soil erosion. If water power could be harnessed to provide electricity at a low cost to the peasant consumer, this danger would disappear and more land would be released for other purposes.

BIBLIOGRAPHY

Many basic data will be found collected in W. G. Kendrew's *The Climates of the Continents* (New York, Fourth Edition, 1953) now revised to include the modern concept of air masses. Reference should also be made to B. Haurwitz and J. M. Austin's *Climatology* (New York, 1944) and to the pioneer work of Brooks and Mirrlees mentioned in the text.

The excellent summary by J. H. Wellington in *Southern Africa,* Vol. I, pp. 191–272 covers most of the southern half of the continent. For additional data see F. L. Wernstedt, *World Climatic Data* (Africa), Penn. State Univ.

The complex question of the influence of climate on human beings has given rise to a large, if scattered and still incomplete, literature. Reference may be made to the writings of Clarence A. Mills, *Living with the Weather, Medical Climatology,* and the popular summary, *Climate Makes the Man* (London, 1944). A. Grenfell Price's *White Settlers in the Tropics* has limited reference to Africa. A valuable summary of all aspects will be found in C. E. P. Brooks' *Climate in Everyday Life* (New York, Philosophical Library, Inc., 1951). See also Karl J. Pelzer's "Geography and the Tropics" in *Geography in the Twentieth Century* (New York, Philosophical Library, Inc., 1951). The findings of an important committee are summarized by D. H. K. Lee in *Climate and Economic Development in the Tropics* (New York, Harper, 1957).

On the water problem, reference should be made to E. B. Worthington's *Inland Waters of Africa,* 1933, and to the official reports and other writings of Frank Debenham, especially *Report on the Water Resources of Central Africa* (His Majesty's Stationery Office, Colonial Research Publication No. 2, 1948) and *Journal of the Royal Society of Arts,* C, 1952, 147–158. G. H. T. Kimble's *Tropical Africa,* already quoted, has a particularly valuable chapter on the "waters of the land" (Vol. I, pp. 225–263).

CHAPTER FIVE

Soils

When C. F. Marbut wrote the section on soils for Shantz and Marbut's *Vegetation and Soils of Africa,* much less was known of soils than of vegetation. Vegetation had been described, it may be inadequately and unscientifically, by many travelers and could be studied in photographs, but soils had usually been recorded as "fertile" or "infertile" or described simply as "red" by those same travelers. Although the colored soil map by Marbut on the scale of 1:25,000,000 is thus impressive and shows sixteen soil groups, it is definitely stated that the differentiation of soils on the map is "based on: (1) studies of about a dozen samples collected in Africa by H. L. Shantz; (2) rather definite data in the literature for certain localities in Tanganyika Territory, Kenya Colony, Belgian Congo, and French Guinea; (3) deductions from the known relations of climate, native vegetation, and topography to soils as determined by studies made in the United States and Europe and from the relation of climates, vegetation, and topography to the soils of those localities in Africa whose soil character has been definitely determined" (see Figure 5.1). It is almost true to say that, in 1922–1923, when those words were written, knowledge of the soils of 11 million square miles rested on the examination of a dozen soil samples and a great deal of deduction which, however brilliant, was still based on hypotheses.

The failure of the great East African Groundnut Scheme in 1949–1950, described in Chapter 18, must be ascribed in large measure to a lack of accurate knowledge of soils and their behavior under new methods of cultivation. It is an index both of continued ignorance of tropical soils and of the costliness of that continued ignorance.

[1] For help with this chapter I am greatly indebted to Mr. G. V. Jacks, Director of the Commonwealth Bureau of Soil Science.

Figure 5.1   Simplified soil map of Africa. (After Marbut.)

Yet much progress has been made. There is a large and increasing mass of information on tropical soils in general. We owe a great debt to the late Dr. R. L. Pendleton not only for his long-continued field and laboratory work on tropical soils in many countries but also for his great labor of love in translating from Dutch into English the monumental work of E. C. J. Mohr, *The Soils of Equatorial Regions*.[2] Although this book refers primarily to the East Indies, the first part is devoted to general considerations in which Mohr defines soils in terms of soil-forming factors and introduces formulas for soils based on parent material, soil, climate, and age. In equatorial soils

[2] Published by J. W. Edwards, Ann Arbor, Mich., 1944.

there is little variation in temperature, so that once again attention is focused on the fluctuations of soil moisture through the seasons.

An outstanding contribution to the study of African soils was made by Geoffrey Milne,[3] whose tragically early death robbed soil science of a great pioneer. It was Milne who introduced the catena or catenary concept, which he mapped by vertical stripes of varying width to indicate dominance of each constituent type. He wrote:

> Throughout districts characterized by an undulating or hummocky topography, certain sequences of changing soil profiles are found repeated. An example, met with over a large part of the dissected peneplain of Uganda . . ., consists of the sequence of soils between the crest of a low hill and the floor of the adjacent swamp, the profile changing from point to point of this traverse in accordance with conditions of drainage and past history of the land surface . . . a sequence of this kind is termed a catena or catenary complex . . . which can be made specific by prefixing a locality name.

It is clear that this principle is of very wide application.

Milestones in the progress of the study of African soils were the International Conference held at Goma in 1948 and the First Commonwealth Conference on Tropical Soils held in the same year. The *Proceedings* of the latter conference include many papers of importance, and in the preceding years a firm foundation of knowledge had been laid by the work of Van der Merwe in South Africa, Trapnell and others in Rhodesia, and Tothill in Uganda and the Sudan. Workers in Africa were greatly stimulated by the extensive journeys undertaken by C. E. Kellogg, whose knowledge of American soils was unrivaled.

Many workers have been preoccupied with the importance of temperature and moisture on soil formation, and earlier work on the importance of mineralogic and microscopic examination of soils has tended to be overlooked. In 1950, however, the late Cecil F. Charter, then director of the Gold Coast Survey, demonstrated afresh the supreme importance of the character of the mineral particles examined under the microscope. His work has shown the danger of arguing from one continent to another and has demonstrated the significance of the study of geomorphology—the evolution of land forms. Had the implications of his work been understood earlier, many millions of dollars might have been saved in the East African Groundnut Scheme. More important, many millions will still be spent in vain unless the implications are appreciated by administrators. It is of course universally known that when soils are subjected to mechanical analysis the mineral particles of

---

[3] "A Provisional Soil Map of East Africa (Kenya, Uganda, Tanganyika, and Zanzibar) with Explanatory Memoir," *Amani Memoirs* (East African Agricultural Research Station), 1936. See *Geog. Rev.*, **XXVI**, 1936, 522–523. See also *Transactions of the Third International Congress Soil Science*, 1935, **I**, 345–347.

which they consist can be graded according to size into stones, coarse sand, fine sand, silt, and clay. An international classification has been drawn up which defines the size of particles as follows:

Diameter greater than 2 mm. stones
Diameter between 0.2 and 2 mm. coarse sand
Diameter between 0.02 and 0.2 mm. fine sand
Diameter between 0.002 and 0.02 mm. silt
Diameter less than 0.002 mm. clay

A "sandy" soil, for example, includes more than 60 per cent of coarse and fine sand but less than 10 per cent of clay. Loamy soils and loams contain a smaller percentage of coarse and fine sand but more of clay, and so on.

But what is the origin of these mineral particles? It is of course in general the underlying rocks, whether solid or "drift" deposits. Over the vast areas of Europe and North America the underlying rocks are of sedimentary origin—superficial deposits laid down or redeposited by wind, river water, ice and melt water from ice, sea water, or older, solid deposits of sandstone, shale, and clay. When examined under the microscope, the tiny mineral fragments, especially of the all-important, stable mineral quartz, are found to be more or less rounded—partly rounded if deposited under water, more fully rounded and polished if wind-borne. By comparison, we have seen that a very large part of the African continent has been land for many millions of years. The old Miocene peneplanation surface has been subjected to atmospheric weathering for 15 or 30 million years. The mineral particles of African soils are thus very frequently derived directly from the underlying solid rocks; the particles have *not* been transported. The underlying crystalline complex is commonly of varied metamorphic rocks seamed by quartz veins (Figure 5.2). The quartz veins, and the quartz of the various metamorphic rocks, have been shattered into tiny "sand" grains, but the grains are *sharply angular* and of different sizes. It was the Scottish road engineer, John Loudon

Figure 5.2   Diagram showing the formation of African sedentary soils from subsoil.

McAdam (1756–1836), who realized that angular rock fragments of different sizes could be compacted into a solid, durable road surface by simple pressure or rolling. This is the principle of the macadam road. The rock fragments of an African soil thus present the ideal conditions for the formation of a "macadam" surface. It would seem that even the pounding by the raindrops in a tropical downpour may sometimes be sufficient to consolidate the surface. Although the bare foot of the African cultivator may tread with impunity on the soil, a caterpillar tractor has the same effect as a road roller and consolidates the surface into a hard macadam layer. Immediately the majority of mechanical cultivators are ruled out. There are other consequential results of this soil structure. It was found in the East African experiments that disc plows lasted but a very short time. The angular quartz grains (harder than any steel) embedded in a clay matrix seem to have acted just like diamond dust in a circular iron wheel; they rasped the steel discs of a plow in an incredibly short time. If this was the cause of their failure at Kongwa, another weapon of large-scale agricultural science is rendered impotent. There is no real alternative yet, in many parts of Africa, to the African hand cultivator with his hoe, quite apart from the costs associated with mechanized cultivation and other aspects which are considered in Chapter 7.

Any student of elementary chemistry knows that a chemical reaction is normally hastened by the application of heat. That is why the test tube is heated in the Bunsen burner, why a hot solution of acid does its work more quickly than cold. Furthermore, a lump of sugar or salt dissolves more quickly in hot water than in cold. Although it is now recognized that some very interesting chemical reactions take place under cold conditions, it is still true to say that the majority of chemical reactions which can be observed in soils in midlatitudes are hastened in the tropics. With air and surface soil temperatures approximating 80°F. (27°C), it would seem that downward leaching—the solution by percolating rainwater of substances in the surface layers and their removal to lower layers—takes place with greater rapidity than in midlatitudes, though this is not agreed by all workers. In the dry season, where a dry season occurs, evaporation is rapid, and with it the deposition of salts in the soil. According to local conditions, a "hardpan" primarily of ferruginous oxides may be formed either at the surface or at a varying distance below it. Perhaps of even greater significance is the rapid oxidation of organic compounds when exposed to the atmosphere. In midlatitudes the turning of surface layers of the soil permits air to reach organic matter and encourages the work of aerobic (air-loving) bacteria which convert decaying organic matter into valuable humus and organic food directly available to plants. Plowing in the tropics, on the other hand, may expose organic matter, such as fibrous roots, which combines with the oxygen of the atmosphere so rapidly as to form the gas carbon dioxide, which disappears into the air.

A well-known feature of the humid tropics is the extraordinary depth to which rock weathering may take place. This is accentuated in the many parts of Africa where there is no definite water table. Another complicating factor is found in those regions which have a long dry season. The stunted tree or scrub vegetation secures its continued existence by the development of extremely long roots, so that moisture retained at great depths can be used. Incidentally, the clearing of such scrub may be extremely difficult—a bulldozer is almost useless.

It was proved by actual experiments in Ceylon long ago that frequent plowing can literally plow all the goodness out of a tropical soil. It becomes increasingly doubtful whether plowing is the right treatment for the soils of vast areas of tropical Africa. The luxuriant growth of an equatorial rain forest suggests a soil of great fertility, and the fallen leaves suggest a ready source of organic matter. But when the forest is cleared and the atmosphere reaches the soil directly, it is rapidly reduced to complete sterility. The relationship of air temperature to humus content has been demonstrated in Java, where at an elevation of 3000 feet and an average annual temperature of 68°F. (20°C) the humus content of surface soil was 14 per cent. It dropped to 5 per cent at lower levels and a temperature of 76°F. (24°C). In tropical lowland soils it is often below 2 per cent. The beneficial action of frost, which, because water expands when it freezes, breaks up clods of clay soil and prepares a natural seed bed in the colder parts of midlatitudes, is absent in the tropics. Instead, the mechanical action of heavy downpours of rain may further consolidate an already heavy soil.

Although the incidence of soil erosion has cast doubts on the virtues and the value of huge plowed areas in middle latitudes, it is still true to say that there the well-managed farm in the fall is likely to exhibit a succession of neatly plowed fields, with the air reaching the soil. It will be a farm kept clean, and the land will be free of weeds. In tropical Africa it is scarcely too much to say that such a farm would be all that is wrong. The exposure of the soil to the atmosphere would result in rapid deterioration in nutrient status; it would be inviting soil erosion. When working in West Africa the worst example of soil erosion I actually witnessed was on a government experimental farm which had been clean-plowed and was then unfortunately subjected to a fall of rain, 2.5 inches in one night. Every furrow was an incipient if not an actual gulley.

By our standards the African's farm is very dirty; his land is full of weeds. But the golden rule is to keep the soil covered with vegetation; the problem is to introduce a "cover crop" which will both keep the soil covered and add to its nutrient status. Various leguminous crops (with bacteria in the root nodules which convert atmospheric nitrogen to nitrogenous plant food) have been introduced for this purpose, and the African cultivator has been encouraged to hoe them into the soil. Because this hoeing is done by hand, the already heavy labor of cultivation is thereby doubled, and the hoeing-in of greencrops has not proved popular with African cultivators. The custom has long been to clear a tract of land by burning, cultivate by hoeing in the ashes, and abandon after a few years. The tract cleared is too small for serious erosion to take place. The tree roots are left and bind the soil, while weeds spring up unhindered to protect the soil. In regions of heavy rainfall the land may be ridged by hoes into a succession of little basins as shown in Figure 5.3.

The practice of clearing land by burning as well as the practice of burning off pasture annually is almost universal in tropical Africa. Is this process injurious to the soil? No one needs to be reminded of the effect of burning clay—it becomes a brick. It is well known too that peat bogs and soils very rich in organic matter may, in middle latitudes, actually catch fire and burn for long periods. Thus burning off the vegetation in tropical Africa may both bake the surface soil to a bricklike form and fire the organic matter in the soil. As a matter of fact this does not happen unless the fire is very fierce; the secret is to burn off early in the dry season before the vegetation is too dry.

Figure 5.3   Basin cultivation in Southern Nigeria. This is a most effective means of preventing soil erosion. (Copyright L. Dudley Stamp.)

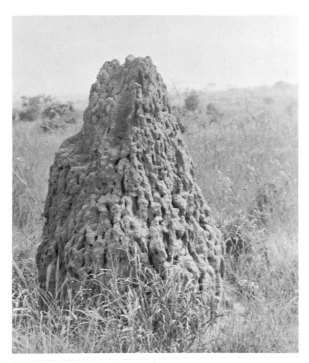

Figure 5.4   A termitarium, or ant-hill, near Accra, Ghana. (Copyright L. Dudley Stamp.)

In that case the soil benefits from the dressing of ash. Some experiments seem to show that the results of burning off a cover crop are as good as hoeing it in—with an immense saving of labor—but other recent work throws doubt on this conclusion. Until mechanized cultivation becomes the rule, burning will doubtless continue because it is simple and saves labor.

Very little is yet known of the part played by organisms and microorganisms in tropical soils. The microbiology of submerged riceland soils must obviously be very different from that of normally drained soils. Another interesting case of conditions peculiar to the tropics is afforded by those lands where termites (the so-called white ants) are abundant. Their termitaria, reaching many feet in height and believed in some cases to be centuries old, are familiar sights over much of drier tropical Africa (Figure 5.4). In land suffering from leaching and with soils and subsoils almost free of lime, the material of the termitaria has been found so rich in calcium carbonate as to supply fertilizer for a considerable patch of surrounding land. There are parts of the tropics where these afford the only fertile patches. Yet there does not seem to be any accumulation of phosphates which might have been expected from termite excreta. Termites break down organic matter such as twigs and leaves falling on the surface, but it is not clear that they help to build up humus; they may merely aid rapid oxidation.

Figure 5.5   Geological erosion in the Udi plateau of Nigeria. Although hastened by bush clearing, cultivation, and grazing, this is natural land erosion—more than just soil erosion—and cannot be wholly prevented. (Copyright L. Dudley Stamp.)

The mention of soil erosion introduces a subject of the utmost importance to all Africa. It is sometimes forgotten that erosion is a natural geological process; there is submarine erosion and, as soon as a tract of the earth's surface is raised up above the level of the sea, it is attacked by all the many forces of atmospheric weathering and subaerial erosion. High mountains are shattered by frost; bare rocks are split by the heating of the sun's rays, gulleys are cut in hillsides, the wind blows loose particles as surely as rain separates them from their parent source. The sum total effect is gradually to reduce all land surfaces to peneplains—almost planes or plains—and many examples of subaerial peneplanation can be found in the geological past. Since the greater part of Africa is a plateau high above sea level, these forces of nature are powerful and active. There are some plateau masses—the flat-topped hills of the Karoo; perhaps the sandy Udi plateau of Nigeria —where rapid erosion of the hillsides is inevitable (Figure 5.5). Wherever, however, slopes are relatively gentle, nature herself slows down the process by providing a mantle of soil, itself protected by a mantle of vegetation in the form of forest, woodland, scrub, or grass. Over vast areas, the surface is kept stable long enough for a complete soil profile to develop, for a soil of good depth to form. There is little loss of soil from a forest, little from grassland.

Soil erosion may be looked upon as a disease which is a malignant form of a natural phenomenon. It has rightly been described as a disease of civilization, but one so serious that it threatens the very extinction of mankind. A soil which has taken hundreds of years to form may be lost in a single night.[4] The cause is, primarily, the exposure of the naked soil by the removal of the vegetation cover which both protects it and, by the development of root systems, binds it together. The soil may be exposed by clearing the land of its natural vegetation for purposes of plowing and cultivation. While doubts have been expressed as to whether plowing is the right treatment for many soils of tropical Africa, the ever-present danger is that a furrow may become a gulley after a typical downpour of rain. If plowing *is* practiced it must be plowing which follows the contours (contour plowing) so that rainwater will not run *down* a furrow. Though strip cropping is another preventive device, the tiny fields separated by uncleared bush so typical of African cultivation are even better (Figure 5.6). On grazing land, soil erosion results

[4] Recent work in Australia, especially that of P. A. Yeomans described in *The Challenge of Landscape* (London: Faber, 1958), has shown that, given the right conditions, both soil and a soil biota may develop very rapidly.

Figure 5.6 An attempt to stop gullying shown in the last picture. Banks were thrown across the gully, grass and quick-growing trees were planted, but the work was not successful. It was all swept away by flood waters after heavy rain. (Copyright L. Dudley Stamp.)

naturally and speedily from overstocking. The animals eat the grass and herbs close down to the ground, preventing recovery and regrowth and so leaving the soil between exposed. Furthermore, they cut up the exposed soil with their hooves.

With increasing pressure on the land by man and animal, soil erosion in Africa has increased in intensity at an alarming rate. As land is lost or rendered unusable by erosion, the pressure on what remains becomes greater.

The muddy waters of rivers in spate are ample evidence of soil erosion. But this transport of river mud is a natural phenomenon and not necessarily harmful. If caught and spread over the flat flood plain, it may build up fertile land at the expense of hill country of little value from whence it came. That this has been known of the Nile for centuries is seen from Shakespeare's words:

> ... The higher Nilus swells,
> The more it promises: as it ebbs, the seedsman
> Upon the slime and ooze scatters his grain
> And shortly comes to harvest.

The drainage and economic use of alluvial plains and deltas are thus important aspects of development for Africa. The material removed by soil erosion may sometimes be "trapped" only a short distance away and valuable new land gained. Such methods, effectively followed in the Punjab, need to be adopted in Africa. Wind erosion and the so-called march of the deserts present more difficult problems.

It is extremely difficult to judge how far the observed spread of arid conditions in Africa is due to the climatic desiccation described elsewhere and how far it is due simply to misuse of land. The formation of "dongas" or gulleys in South Africa resulted in the appointment of a commission as early as the 'twenties. Yet when Dr. I. B. Pole Evans, familiar through many years of experience with the problem in South Africa, visited Kenya in 1938, he found some of the native reserves "a shambles—the result of land mismanagement and misuse." He criticized breaking the grass cover for cropping; the drainage of swamps, which he calls "precious assets," for cultivation; and the confining of pastoral tribes like the Kikuyu to reserves without control of the number of cattle. About the same time a commission enquiring into the conservation of natural resources in Southern Rhodesia found the African population had trebled between 1902 and 1938 and the number of plows had increased from 3400 to 94,000. As a result 1½ million acres were badly eroded, and some 16 per cent of former arable land had been completely destroyed. Incidentally, the erosion was worst on European-owned lands, especially when worked by Africans who, not being owners, had lost interest in conservation of the land.

Remedial measures to check existing erosion are one thing; more important than cure is prevention. It would seem that the twin lines of progress are control of grazing to prevent overstocking and the replacement of native grasses of little nutritive value by new strains capable of supporting a large number of head. Both these objectives have been achieved in New Zealand, but the problem in the tropics is relatively new. Not of least importance is the development of suitable strains of grass, though Guinea grass (*Panicum maximum*), a native of Africa widespread from Senegal to Natal, has already proved its value in many parts of the world and is certainly the best native forage grass of Africa.

Modern pedologists quite rightly study soils as soils. The description of the soil profile, the determination of the soil series, chemical, mechanical, and biotic analyses, and the genesis of the soil are all studied without, necessarily, reference to the natural vegetation which the soil supports or its use, actual or potential, by man. The emergence of pedology as a distinct branch of knowledge has resulted in a certain loss, a divorce of the study of soil from cognate studies. Yet, looking back to the early days of soil science, we see that it was Dokuchaev, viewing the problem over the wide homogeneous plains of Russia, who showed that each major climatic type produced its own peculiar soil or range of soils. His pioneer studies were followed by the well-known work of his pupil Glinka. By contrast, in a country of relatively homogeneous climate but great variety of terrain and underlying rocks, it was the British who considered soils in relation to geological formation. A great advance was marked by the work of F. E. Clements and his collaborators, and few scientists today would doubt the validity of his general thesis that the living plant, or assemblage of plants, forms an index of the sum total of environmental conditions, notably climate and soil. It seems clear, therefore, that there ought to be a close relationship between climate, soil, and vegetation. There ought, therefore, to be a distribution of great soil belts over Africa similar to that known in North America or Eurasia. Yet Marbut in his pioneer essay of 1922–1923 could say: "No book, paper, paragraph, or sentence dealing with this matter as a whole has been encountered, nor has any reference to the possibility or the probability of the existence of a series of soil belts covering the continent been found." The foundation which he then proceeded to lay and his tentative map have proved their worth. Milne and his coworkers in East Africa found it possible to develop a classification of soils applicable to their field studies based essentially on Marbut's scheme.

A marked advance was the publication of a colored soil map of Africa on the scale of 1:20,000,000, with explanation in Russian, by Z. J. Shokalskaia. Mr. V. P. Sokoloff of the School of Geography of The Johns Hopkins University has translated the text and made it available in mimeographed form. The map (with key in English) distinguishes twenty-two soil types in addition to seven more in mountainous regions. A greatly simplified version of part of the map is included here (Figure 5.7) to show the comparison with Marbut.

A few years later, at the Commonwealth Conference of 1948, C. E. Kellogg made "preliminary suggestions for the classification and nomenclature of great soil groups in tropical and equatorial regions" and F. D. Davol published an important paper on the soil groups of the Belgian Congo. They got over the difficulties created by the word "laterite" by introducing the general term "latosol."

Since we have described the main climatic types of Africa in a previous chapter we will now attempt to relate the main soil groups to them.

Soils of the equatorial and tropical regions

Marbut showed practically the whole of the equatorial regions of Africa and the moister parts of the tropical regions (except on the high plateaus of East Africa, where climate is modified by elevation) occupied by different types of red soils. The heart of the Congo Basin is covered by his "lateritic red loams," the wettest parts of West Africa by "laterites." The huge areas with a good but seasonal rainfall have "red loams" with areas of "ferruginous red loams" and strips of "immature red loams." The dominant soils of equatorial Africa are thus Marbut's "lateritic red loams" and "laterites."

The term "laterite" has given rise to much controversy and confusion. It is derived from the Latin word *later*, a brick, and was first used in 1807 by Francis Buchanan to describe a surface material widespread in the wetter parts of southern India. This material, the result of chemical alteration of many different rocks, may be formed to a depth of many feet, sometimes scores of feet, from the surface. When freshly exposed, the whole mass is relatively soft and can be cut with a spade; it is a mottled gray and yellowish rock with red streaks. On exposure to the atmosphere—deliberate exposure is carried out by cutting blocks and stacking them in the open air—the yellowish parts become dark red or brown-red and hard; the grayish parts remain soft and may be washed out by rain, leaving a mass which is not unlike a solidified sponge or a coarse brick. It is hard enough to be used for building and even for road metal. Indeed, the blocks form a cheap, convenient, and widely used building material in many parts of the tropics. This undoubtedly is the material to which Buchanan originally applied the name laterite, and it is still widely used in the country where he first described it.

Is laterite a rock in the geological sense, or is it a soil? Certainly the use of the term spread, and it became general for the word laterite to be used by travelers as synonymous with the red soils which occur over so much of the tropics. Then came the various attempts, through chemical analysis and microscopical examination, to define laterite precisely. One author at least found that the essential constituent was aluminum hydroxide and that the

Figure 5.7   Soil map of Africa. (Simplified from Z. J. Shokalskaia.)

iron oxides, likewise any quartz grains, were incidental. Other investigations showed that some rocks previously accepted as laterites had no aluminum hydroxide at all, and later came the attempt at a classification based on chemical composition, which proved to be highly artificial.

Reference has already been made to the high soil temperatures (approximating to 80° F.) in equatorial lands. Water at or above this temperature is an active solvent and permits many chemical reactions to take place. It would seem that within the zone of permanent saturation, that is, below the permanent water table, the solid rocks, whatever they may be, are steeped in this warm water, and various minerals such as the feldspars of gneisses and schists are converted into a bleached mass of hydrous silicate of alumina, from which iron salts are eliminated. *Above* this is the zone which is alternately saturated and dried according to the season. It is in this zone that laterite is formed. Any quartz grains in the original parent rocks remain unaltered, and a quartz vein from an underlying crystalline mass may be traced upwards into the laterite. But most other minerals undergo a complete change. In the dry season waters with iron and other salts in solution pass up by capillary action, and compounds are left when the water evaporates. In the wet season this zone resembles the lower one, and hydrous silicate of alumina is formed, to be washed or leached downwards. The lateritic layer thus comes to have an accumulation of iron salts—which on exposure to the atmosphere form one or another of the hard red or yellow-red hydrated oxides which make up the "brick" structure—and also, generally, aluminum hydroxide. It is not difficult to see that under certain circumstances a hard layer or hardpan may form not far below the surface. It may reasonably be said that laterite is thus a rock formed by chemical action from other rocks rather than a soil.

But clearly a surface soil developed from the underlying laterized rock is very little different except for possible additions of vegetable matter. Thus true laterite soil would be expected where rainfall is abundant (to provide the permanently saturated layer) but where there is a seasonal rhythm which leaves the overlying layer alternately wet and dry. These are the natural conditions in the wetter parts of the tropical belt or along the margins of the equatorial belt where there is a relatively dry season. The distribution of laterites on Marbut's map agrees with this hypothesis.

Workers in India and elsewhere have agreed that whereas laterite is formed in situ, the laterite may be weathered and the material transported. "On rolling areas," says Marbut, "where erosion is in progress and is somewhat active, thoroughly weathered products are never allowed to accumulate, and the soil belongs in some intermediate stage of development between freshly disintegrated rock and the completely weathered product." There are, accordingly, "red loams" (including immature red loams and ferruginous red loams) and "lateritic red loams" where 25 to 90 per cent of the constituents are those of true laterite.

All these equatorial and tropical red soils agree in being reddish and in being leached to a greater or lesser extent, but always to the extent of having lost their lime. The minerals of the parent rock have been almost completely changed so that the soils consist of quartz fragments (sand, often angular), hydrous aluminum silicates and aluminum hydroxides (clay or clay-like substances), and hydrated iron oxides (giving red or red-brown colors). The organic content is low except where decomposition of vegetation accumulated in swamps and hollows has been slowed down. The downward washing by rain of the finer particles in the soil has often left a sandy surface layer—a hungry sand which easily dries out—over a heavier impervious or "clay pan" layer. Milne and his coworkers in East Africa have distinguished two simple groups: red earths, laterized and red earths, nonlaterized. Each of these groups comprises a number of subgroups, depending upon the rocks of the subsoil—gneisses of the basement complex, granite, volcanic rocks, shales, sandstones.

The laterized red earths are described as ". . . very freely drained, leached, acid soils of various colors in the range pink, red, red-brown, orange-brown, brown. Uniform open structure and friable 'light' texture independently of clay content. Molecular ratio SiO_2/Al_2O_3, in clay fraction usually less than 2.0; less than 1.0 in soils of advanced laterization. Concretionary horizons are absent except in the nontypical case of a seasonally high water table. This group contains chiefly the soils of the evergreen forests and mountain grasslands."

The nonlaterized red earths are described as ". . . well-drained, moderately leached soils of the same range of colors. Free from calcium carbonate, profile neutral or acid. Clod-structured, with heaviness proportional to clay content. Molecular ratio SiO_2/Al_2O_3 in clay fraction usually 2.0 or above. When developed on basic rocks the soil may contain scattered pisolitic concretions, but concretionary horizons are typically absent from the profile, only appearing where there is seasonally a high water table, when the soil approaches the plateau soils in character."

Shokalskaia emphasizes that the end product of lateritic weathering is a rock which may form an "armour plate" (the *carapace latéritique* of French writers), which often forms a protective covering to the tops of hills or surfaces of terraces but cannot serve as a soil-forming material. Thus Kellogg and Davol use the word latosol as "a collective term for those zonal soils formerly called lateritic." They distinguish (1) Red, (2) Earthy Red, (3) Yellow, (4) Reddish-yellow, (5) Reddish-brown, and (6) Black-red Latosols.

The *plateau soils* are a group distinguished by Milne in Tanganyika and described as . . . "light-colored soils (gray, yellow, yellow-brown) of sluggish drainage or receiving excess subsoil water seasonally. Usually formed on locally transported material lying at slight slopes in maturely eroded topography, or where rock tables check percolation. Free from calcium carbonate, but often with concretionary ironstone ('murram') in the subsoil (Figure 5.8). The vegetation over large areas on this soil is open deciduous woodland." The concretionary ironstone often forms the resistant capping of flat-topped hills or the higher levels of a catena. Shokalskaia claims large areas as "slightly leached soils," whereas Kellogg recognized a podzolic group.

In tropical Africa there are small areas of *mottled clays*, derived from clay beds (for example, in Zanzibar and Pemba) which result from impeded drainage. They thus resemble the lower levels of laterites discussed above, and there may be a thin red surface layer. More important are the *black* or *gray clays*, which may be calcareous or noncalcareous. These "black cotton

Figure 5.8   A typical soil catena in East Africa. (After G. Milne.)

soils," sticky when wet and cracking deeply when dry, are dark colored and ill drained. Some occur on bottom lands, others are associated with shaley subsoils.

On the drier margins of the tropical lands Marbut maps some *"tropical prairie soils"* in West Africa (Figure 5.9). Towards the desert these pass into dark-colored soils of chernozem type, then into chestnut-brown soils before fading into the deserts proper. Shokalskaia confirms this arrangement.

Soils of the Mediterranean regions

Although the soils of those parts of North Africa which enjoy a Mediterranean type of climate are far from being fully investigated, there is no reason to suspect that they differ fundamentally from the soils developed in other Mediterranean regions of the world. The summer or hot season coincides with the dry season when surface layers are likely to be dried out and chemical action is accordingly greatly reduced. When moisture is present in the soil, air temperatures are low, yet not sufficiently low for frost action to be a dominant factor. Consequently soil forms slowly; soils tend to be both thin and immature. Both the coastal ranges of North Africa and the fine ranges of the Cape of Good Hope exhibit the familiar feature of bare rock with pockets of soil in the crevices, and it is on land of this type that the maquis or chaparral type of drought resisting vegetation flourishes—land of little economic value. Together with other parts of South Africa, the soils of the Mediterranean area have been studied in detail by Van der Merwe. Marbut had mapped most of the Cape areas as "brown soils" with a small strip inland of "chestnut-brown" soils. In North Africa he showed the better-watered parts as "brown soils," the open plains of Morocco and elsewhere as "chestnut-brown." In South Africa the valuable agricultural areas are where the valleys are floored by material washed down from surrounding ridges. Here soil-forming material may be present to a good depth and affords loams or sandy loams where the surface layers are partially leached by downward movement of water but where the rainfall is sufficiently high to prevent any accumulation of carbonates in the soil. Both the relief and climate are sufficiently like those of the Coast Range regions of California to produce very similar soils and agricultural conditions. Like the Californian soils, they have moderate to low percentages of lime, potash, phosphoric acid, and nitrogen and so require fertilizers and careful management to render them really productive.

Somewhere on the margins of these soil belts one might expect to find a belt or at least patches of black earth or chernozem where there is a nice balance between downward leaching and upward movement of water and an accumulation of organic matter. Where such soils have been observed, the extent is small.

Inland, in both North and South Africa, the Mediterranean soils give place to brown desert soils, shown by Marbut as a strip in North Africa but covering the whole of the great Kalahari area in the south.

Soils of the warm temperate coastal strip

Marbut has a special group, his Natal loams, for the soils of the well-watered coastlands of Natal between the Drakensberg and the Indian Ocean.

Figure 5.9   Degraded land near Dakar in West Africa. Exhausted by overcultivation—with millets and peanuts. (Copyright R. J. Harrison-Church.)

It is a belt of irregular, rolling country where soil-forming material is largely due to disintegration of rocks in place and to erosion by numerous small streams and consequent limited transportation of material. The soils are typical humid soils, developed under a higher rainfall than the Cape soils and with a summer maximum. The rainfall, however, varies both in total amount and seasonal distribution, though it is, for Africa, relatively constant. In some areas the balance is that needed for the development of chernozem; elsewhere downward leaching predominates, and reddish soils allied to those of the great tropical belt develop. Though varying greatly in texture, these soils have depth and exist in a climatically favored region, so that with the addition of appropriate mineral fertilizers they can be and are extremely productive.

Soils of the plateau grasslands

The gently undulating surface of the High Veld in the Orange Free State and southern Transvaal, lying west of the great scarp edge, has generally between 20 and 30 inches of rainfall. Under the natural grass cover a mature soil profile has developed; the rainfall is high enough to prevent accumulation of carbonates and other soluble salts in the surface layers but not high enough to leach the soil seriously. These are conditions normal for the development of black earth. It may be that average temperatures are too high and the soils tend to be reddish, but they are fertile, and it is on them that the famous "maize triangle" has been developed.

Passing northward on the highlands of the African plateaus, Marbut maps huge areas as "chernozem soils" and "light-colored soils of the chernozem group." Some of these, placed in the former group, have a black surface layer with a proportion of calcium carbonate high enough to effervesce with acid, passing down into a bluish gray subsoil with again high carbonate content. The subsoil consists of rocks with little or no carbonate. The dark color of the soil is not permanent; it disappears with the removal of carbonate, and it is doubtful whether these soils are in fact comparable with the black earths of North America or European Russia. Both where they are characteristically dark and where they merge into Milne's "plateau soils," it seems certain that these soils are special to Africa, have their own special behavior, and present yet another of the African "unknowns."

BIBLIOGRAPHY

Proceedings of the First Commonwealth Conference on Tropical and Sub-Tropical Soils, 1948, Commonwealth Bureau of Soil Science, Harpenden, England.
Includes papers on South Africa, Madagascar, Uganda, Zanzibar, Congo, Sudan, Nigeria, West Africa, and Algeria, as well as general papers.
H. L. Shantz and C. F. Marbut, *Vegetation and Soils of Africa,* American Geographical Society, 1923.

C. R. Van der Merwe, *Soil Groups and Sub-groups of South Africa,* Pretoria, Government Printer, 1941.

G. Milne, "A Soil Reconnaissance Journey . . . December 1935–February 1936," *Jour. Ecol.,* **XXXV,** 1947, 192–265.

C. G. Trapnell et al., "Vegetation-Soil Map of Northern Rhodesia," North Rhodesia Department of Agriculture, 1947.

J. D. Tothill (Editor), *Agriculture in Uganda,* New York, 1940. *Agriculture in the Sudan,* New York, 1948.

C. E. Kellogg and F. D. Davol, *An Explanatory Study of Soil Groups in the Belgian Congo,* Publication of I.N.E.A.C., 1949 Ser. Sci., **46,** 73.

S. Ju. Schokalskaja, *Die Boden Afrikas,* Akademie-Verlag, Berlin, 1953.

R. C. Haw, *The Conservation of Natural Resources,* London, Faber, 1959. Written from the point of view of South Africa.

CHAPTER SIX

Forest, Grassland, and Desert: Wildlife in Africa

It is a safe assertion that at least 80 per cent of all Africans derive their sustenance directly from the land and its products. There are still those groups, now few and rare, so close to nature that they fall into the category of "gatherers," gathering wild fruits and roots and maintaining life on what nature provides and they can find. There are others, more numerous, who depend upon the spoils of the chase, coupled with a little vegetable food raised in small clearings. There are still larger groups of cattlemen and herders who rely on the natural grasslands for pasture. Finally those peoples, so often the hereditary foes of the last, who have come to rely on food raised in their small clearings in the bush usually practice a form of land rotation, or shifting cultivation, and raise a series of crops dictated by the natural factors of climate, soil, and vegetation cover.

It follows logically that to all Africa the existing vegetation is of paramount importance. One is tempted to say the natural vegetation, for so it appears, but there is little doubt that the bulk of the vegetation which seems "natural" has been profoundly modified by man's long-continued activity. It is not uncommon to find evidence of former settlements in the heart of what seem to be primeval rainforests; it is still uncertain how much of the savanna or bush veld of Africa is "natural," how much the result of periodic firing by the human inhabitants and grazing by their animals. This is the same problem as that of the campos of Brazil.

But whether it is truly "natural" or only "seminatural," the study of the existing vegetation of Africa assumes a very great importance. The trees, shrubs, herbs, and grasses are plant indicators affording an index of the total effect of the environment and so pointing the way to potential or agricultural use of the land. The taxonomic botanist and the systematist are interested in collecting and describing species, and some magnificent books have been published on the flora of different parts of Africa. An outstanding example of such is the *Flora Capensis*. This, as its title implies, deals with the flora of the Cape Province of South Africa. It has been argued by some that even such floras covering large areas are "local" in the sense that they do not give a continent-wide picture of the distribution of what may be widespread species described under other names elsewhere.

The careful description of vegetation—primary vegetation survey and descriptive ecology—is newer, and by no means the whole of Africa has been adequately covered. Still newer are attempts to trace the evolution of Africa's plant cover, a study still in its infancy.

A great debt of gratitude is owed H. L. Shantz, at that time of the United States Department of Agriculture, and C. F. Marbut, then of the Bureau of Soils of the same Department, for their pioneer but still standard work, *The Vegetation and Soils of Africa*, published by the American Geographical Society in 1923. The first part, on the vegetation, is by Shantz. It is based on the study of over 500 references, which are listed, followed by an account of a special journey through the entire length of the continent. The provisional map of the continent which had been prepared was revised in the light of the first-hand experience gained. We may regard Shantz's book as summarizing all important work which had been done prior to 1920. Since that time there have been some important studies, notably by I. B. Pole Evans and R. S. Adamson in South Africa; by Trapnell and Clothier in northwestern Rhodesia; and, perhaps most noteworthy of all, by Gillman in East Africa. The last work is singled out because it introduces the dynamic viewpoint, the evolution of African vegetation. Thirty years after his pioneer journeys and only shortly before his death, Shantz revisited the localities he had previously studied. He took photographs from the exact spots he had chosen before and published the two series side by side. The general result was to show much less change than had been expected.

Although Africa did not directly suffer the glaciation which the Great Ice Age brought to North America, Europe, and Asia, the climate of the continent must have undergone wide fluctuations. It is one of the great scientific problems for the future to trace the effects of these climatic pulsations on the African vegetation and fauna. The ice ages in Europe seem to have been paralleled in Africa by relatively wet and dry periods—"pluvial" and "interpluvial" periods marked by fluctuating lake levels as well as alternating advance and retreat of ice on such mountains as Mt. Kenya. The dominant African vegetation must have waxed and waned between evergreen rain forest over huge areas and grassland or desert scrub. The present vegetation shows relics of former vegetation. On the whole, the evidence suggests that the present is a period of increasing desiccation, as in South Africa, where rooigras veld has been replaced by desert scrub,[1] though a great part of the supposed encroachment of the desert is the result of man's activity.[2]

In 1961 UNESCO, from Paris, published in both French and English an extremely valuable series of regional studies, under my general editorship, entitled *A History of Land Use in Arid Regions*. In it is shown that there must always have been arid belts in Africa, but that their position and intensity must have fluctuated.

Area Occupied by Each Type of Vegetation in Africa
(After H. L. Shantz)

	Area in Square Miles	Percentage
Forest	*2,056,700*	*18.4*
Equatorial (tropical) rain forest	875,000	7.8
Temperate rain forest	52,300	0.5
Oak-conifer forest	19,500	0.2
Dry forest	885,000	7.9
Thorn forest	77,600	0.7
Temperate brush	128,400	1.1
Oases	9,200	0.1
Mangrove forest	9,700	0.1
Grassland	*4,736,400*	*42.3*
High-grass–low-tree savanna	1,297,000	11.6
Acacia–tall-grass savanna	1,785,000	15.9
Tall grass	99,400	0.9
Acacia–desert-grass savanna and desert grass	1,074,000	9.6
Mountain grassland and alpine meadow	363,000	3.2
Dwarf palm–temperate grass	76,000	0.7
Marsh grass	42,000	0.4
Desert	*4,406,900*	*39.3*
Desert shrub–desert grass	1,220,000	10.9
Desert shrub	2,300,000	20.5
Salt desert shrub	4,900	0.0
Desert	882,000	7.9
Total land surface (without lakes)	*11,200,000*	*100.0*

These figures do not include Madagascar, which was not considered by Shantz and not shown on his map

For the purpose of his general description Shantz divided the vegetation into forest, grassland, and desert. Forests cover rather less than a fifth of the whole, grassland rather over two-fifths, and desert the remaining two-fifths. The bulk of the forest was described as "timberland"; the bulk of the grass-

[1] C. E. Tidmarsh, *Farming in South Africa*, **XXIII**, 1948, pp. 519–530.
[2] See the summary of evidence by L. D. Stamp, *Geog. Rev.*, **XXX**, 1940, and compare with the later work of Shantz and the UNESCO volume cited above.

land has scattered trees and is thus savanna. Different types of savanna, covering in all more than 37 per cent of the whole continent, may be regarded as the really characteristic African vegetation, just as the "tropical" climate is the characteristic climate. Though later work may have modified his figures to some extent, it is worthwhile to quote Shantz's table of vegetation types.

The large colored map on the scale of 1:10,000,000 published by Shantz has been simplified for the purpose of showing the main vegetation zones of the continent in Figure 6.1.

Although the simple classification of African vegetation used by Shantz is convenient for descriptive purposes, it fails to emphasize the essential unity and continuity of the vegetation of tropical Africa. In fact, even the threefold grouping into forest, grassland, and desert is artificial. Provided there is suffi-

Mountain forests and grass
Equatorial rainforest
Savanna
Dry forest
Acacia savanna and thorn forest
Desert shrub and grass
Desert
Temperate rainforest
Tall grass prairie (veld)
Mediterranean forest and brush

0   1000 miles

Figure 6.1   The main vegetation belts of Africa. (In the main after Shantz and Marbut.)

cient moisture, the climax vegetation in tropical Africa is high evergreen forest. This is naturally found along the equator wherever rainfall is high (60 inches or over), where the dry season or seasons, if present at all, are very short, and where temperature range is small. But it also extends into the wettest parts of the bordering tropical regions, notably near the coast of much of West Africa as far as Sierra Leone, where the dry season, though marked, is not long enough to counteract availability of underground moisture reached by plant root systems, and the temperature is not high enough nor the air dry enough in the dry season to induce excessive transpiration. Similarly, forest of comparable type may line river banks, where abundant moisture is available from the alluvial soils throughout the year and evaporation from water and soil surfaces keeps the air humid.

On the margins of equatorial lands where a dry season becomes marked and the overall rainfall less, leaf shedding as a protection against excessive transpiration during the hot dry season becomes general, growth becomes seasonal, and there is less of a struggle upwards to reach light and air. So the equatorial forest passes into what in India would be called "monsoon forest," which is deciduous, lower, and more open. With decreasing rainfall and an increasing length of dry season, the trees become smaller and more widely spaced and have adopted various protective devices. Some of these devices are designed to lower water loss by transpiration, seen in reduced leaf surface, umbrella-shaped form of the crown, and ability to wilt; others to store water by development of fleshy stems and leaves; others to make a permanent underground water supply available by very long roots. Still other devices are designed to avoid destruction by discouraging browsing animals; hence the numerous forms of spines and hooks.

With still lower rainfall, such thorn woodland passes through thorn thicket into thorn scrub, widely spaced thorny bushes on the desert margin. There are some species of tree which can exist through a wide range of environmental conditions and may be found from the margins of the rainforest almost to the desert. A very good example is *Acacia arabica* (behaving in much the same way in India also and like its near relative *Acacia catechu* in Indo China), which forms well grown trees 50 or 75 foot high in the wetter situations, but appears as stunted, spiny bushes only a few feet high in its most arid habitats.

There would thus seem to be no place at all for grassland in this scheme. Undoubtedly, in the more open woodland and scrub, grass and herbs form an important element in the ground vegetation which springs into life with the coming of the rains, but it is becoming increasingly certain that much, if not most, of Africa's grasslands are primarily the results of man's interference. Fires are difficult to start in the rainforests, but elsewhere they start and spread very easily in the dry season. Some may be started by lightning; the majority are the result of deliberate firing of dried grass or undergrowth. They have the effect of burning off the dry grass (but not harming the roots), nourishing the surface with ash, and so stimulating growth when the rains come. On the other hand, they destroy tree seedlings and even young trees and so favor the extension of grass at the expense of trees. In this they reinforce the action of grazing animals, both wild and domesticated, which eat off the grass and herbs without harm (unless to excess, because of overstocking) but destroy tree seedlings.

Thus, parallel to the sequence of woodland vegetation from rainforest to desert scrub is another of grassland with varying proportions of trees which have managed to survive. Another complication results from the very widespread practice of shifting cultivation, or bush fallowing. When a cleared patch is cultivated for a few years and then abandoned or left to recover, it is colonized in the first instance by a temporary assemblage of plants, replaced in due course by another; but it is often a long period of years before these "seral communities" are finally replaced by the "climatic climax vegetation." Some seres or seral communities become so firmly established that they show signs of permanence; a good example is afforded by thickets of bamboo.

A further complication in tropical Africa results from elevation. Parts of East Africa are sufficiently high and sufficiently wet for temperate rainforest to replace tropical vegetation, and mountain grasses or alpine meadows occupy considerable tracts.

All that has been said above applies to tropical Africa. In extratropical North Africa, north of the great desert barrier, are found those types of vegetation common to countries around the Mediterranean basin. Where rainfall permits, on well-watered hill slopes oak-conifer forest is the climax. Far larger areas are covered by the Mediterranean brush or scrub, resembling the chaparral of California, which in turn passes into desert scrub. On the high-level basins among the Atlas Mountains there are stretches of what may be called steppe.

Extratropical South Africa differs in that it is not cut off completely by a desert barrier from tropical Africa, and there is a merging of Mediterranean and tropical types of vegetation. The best-watered parts of Natal and the Cape, with the rainfall well distributed through the year, are clothed with a subtropical or temperate rainforest, but the natural vegetation covering those parts of the Cape with a winter rainfall is again a Mediterranean scrub, also merging with decreasing moisture into desert scrub. On the plateau of South Africa, over much of the Orange Free State and southern Transvaal, is the tall-grass–short-grass "prairie" of the High Veld.

Quite clearly, Shantz's colored map and still more the simplified version shown in Figure 6.1 involve much generalization. In making generalizations, both in the field and in the drawing office, it is difficult to avoid a subjective judgment. It has been pointed out that the impressions which are gained of much African vegetation depend very largely on the time of year at which the traveler sees the country. The grassland with scattered trees, after the grass has been burnt off and where the majority of the trees are leafless, may appear but little removed from a semidesert waste. If, however, it is seen after the coming of the early rains, with tall, lush grass and herbs, perhaps high enough to hide a man, and trees in full leaf, it appears comparable with an open forest having a very rich undergrowth.

Again, a very important advance was made by Gillman in his recognition of complexes and catenas. As he rightly says, distinct vegetation types, often widely different, occur nearly everywhere in close conjunction or juxtaposition, and the cartographical representation of such complexes is difficult. In his "Vegetation Map of Tanganyika," on the scale of 1:2,000,000, he uses a background color for the dominant vegetation, with dots indicating the relative frequency of associations of minor importance. Further refinement is possible by close or wide spacing of the dots. Much more important, however, is the recognition of a catenary complex. As described in the last chapter, the soil scientist, following particularly the work of G. Milne in East Africa, recognizes that the same sequence of soil types may be repeated over and over again throughout a large area. For example, where a plateau is intersected by broad valleys there will be certain types of soil associated with the valley floor, other types with the valley slopes, and still other types with the plateau surfaces or interfleuves. This sequence of soils is matched by a sequence of vegetation. Bearing this repetition in mind, both Milne for soils and Gillman for vegetation have used a system of coloring by vertical stripes (which quickly became known as pajama striping) to indicate those areas dominated by catenary complexes.

Bearing these refinements in mind, we may follow in general the broad classification of African vegetation given by Shantz, noticing, however, names which are commonly given to some of his vegetation types. Gillman, for example, objects to the use of such terms as "savanna," "steppe," and "veld" on the ground, he says, that "legitimate doubt may rise as to whether such importations from the languages of lands harboring their prototypes are correctly used out of their appropriate setting." Similarly, Gillman objects to the use of African vernacular words and claims that it is possible to use simple English descriptive names. Here, however, he immediately encounters a difficulty in that he succeeds in drawing a distinction between forests and woodland, whereas these two words are often used in English interchangeably.

FOREST

Equatorial rainforest

Shantz uses the term "tropical rainforest," and this well-known type of vegetation has also been known by the descriptive title, "evergreen rainforest." It is the dominant type of forest in those areas having more than 60 or 80 inches (1500–2000 mm.) of rainfall annually and a consistently high temperature throughout the year. As a rule there is little variation in the mean temperature between one month and another, the mean annual range rarely exceeding 5° or 6°F., and averaging about 80°F. (27°C). Night temperatures rarely drop below 70°(21°C.) or certainly 65°F. (18°C.); the day temperatures rarely rise above 90°F. (33°C.) or, still more rarely, above 95°F. (35°C.). This is the constantly hot, humid climate found on either side of the equator. As soon as there is a marked dry season, forest type tends to change.

A typical equatorial forest consists of large trees, approximately 125 feet high, with a relatively dense and interlocking canopy. The equatorial forests of the Amazon are often described as gloomy in the extreme, with little or no undergrowth. This is not typical of Africa, since there is often an understory of small trees, and the undergrowth is usually dense enough to prevent a distant view. Certainly in the more open parts there is a thick growth of herbs on the forest floor. Woody climbers, or lianes, are usually abundant, and many of the trees are supported by flanking (plank) buttresses. The thick undergrowth and the woody climbers make these forests extremely difficult to penetrate except along defined paths.

As a rule numerous species of trees are present, and it is rarely that one finds a single dominant or even a number of codominants. Although some of the trees yield excellent and much-valued timber, usually hardwood of the mahogany type, and though softwood timbers do occur, the difficulty of extricating examples of the trees desired is so great that there has been no commercial exploitation over very large areas of this type of forest (Figure 6.2). It may be regarded as one of the great untouched reservoirs of timber in the world.

The equatorial type of forest is not as extensive in Africa as was once supposed. It is broadly restricted to parts only of the Congo Basin and adjoining Equatorial Africa and to relatively small areas lying in the wetter parts of West Africa. It was long supposed that the African equatorial forests could be described as true primeval forests unaffected by man. It has been found, however, that under certain conditions revegetation is very rapid when the original forest is destroyed, and what appears today is in fact only second growth.

Where these forests occur bordering the great river courses, the underlying

Figure 6.2 Timber working in the equatorial rainforest of Spanish Guinea. This picture illustrates the heavy task of felling a hardwood tree—some with wood hard enough to turn an axe—by African hand labor. (Copyright R. J. Harrison-Church.)

soil is alluvial and may be described as a rich, deep loam of natural fertility. The myth, however, that all equatorial forest soils are naturally of high fertility has long since been exploded. When the forests are cleared, there are often sandy or lateritic areas which need dressings of ash and organic matter before they will produce crops, and in the high rainfall areas there are immediate dangers both of physical soil erosion and of the leaching of plant food by exposure to atmosphere.

These equatorial forests in Africa, because of their relatively open character, have an abundant animal and bird life, especially rich along the water courses where hippopotami and crocodiles are found. The nomadic pygmies of the heart of the Congo forests afford examples of groups of human beings still largely dominated by their physical environment, and just as animals and birds seek light and air by living in the treetops away from swampy conditions or ground likely to flood, so these primitive peoples have in certain cases built their homes high up in the trees. But these are generally temporary dwellings for people who are essentially nomadic. Elsewhere the African inhabitants have destroyed portions of the forest, particularly along the great waterways or where a short, relatively dry season makes burning possible.

Among the principal plants which are of economic value, pride of place goes to the Guinea oil palm. It furnishes the oil prized for food and for a variety of other uses, including the making of soap. Rubber is obtained from certain of the native trees and lianes, and is still exploited in some of the remoter areas. To an earlier stage belongs the importance of the forests for the ivory obtained from the enormous elephant herds. At the time when slave trading was widespread, it can be said that equatorial Africa yielded two main products to the outside world, ivory and black ivory.

African settlements in the equatorial forests are usually small clearings where a variety of crops can be and are grown: food plants such as yams, sweet potatoes, rice, manioc, and sugar cane; fruits such as bananas, mango, and guava; tobacco and beans; and of course the oil palm. Over vast areas of the equatorial forests little development has yet taken place under modern conditions, more, it may be said, because of scarcity of labor than because of climatic difficulties.

Temperate rainforest

Shantz described this as one of the most varied and interesting forests on the continent of Africa. It is that which occurs on the high mountains of Central and East Africa and on mountain ranges with a high rainfall at lower levels towards the south. It may occur also in the Ethiopian plateau area. Rainfall is high, probably 60 to 100 inches, and there is no long period of drought. Owing to elevation, temperatures are lower than those in the equatorial forests, but again the range both daily and annual is small. Typically the trees are tall, with smooth white or light-colored bark and often with buttressed bases. Species are less numerous than in the equatorial forest and are often dominated by the genus *Podocarpus*.

Oak-conifer forest

This is scarcely an African forest. It is, in fact, the ordinary Mediterranean forest so well known in countries surrounding the Mediterranean Sea; it is accordingly found in those parts of Morocco, Algeria, and Tunis where physical conditions are suitable. Forests are usually relatively open, with a sparse undergrowth of shrubs, grasses, and herbs.

Dry forest

According to Shantz, the dry forest varies in density from an open, park-like growth of trees to a relatively dense stand. "At no time are the grasses entirely replaced in the substratum. As a rule there are a few shrubs or young trees. The diameter of tree trunks is seldom over a foot and foliage is supported only on the upper part. It is a forest made up largely of flat-topped trees, and one can generally see through it from 100 yards to half-a-mile."

Gillman protests that forest is a misnomer for this type of vegetation, which he prefers to call simply "woodland," that is, land with an open cover of trees, the crowns of which do not form a thickly interlaced canopy.

The trees are usually leafless for a part of the year. This resting period, due entirely to drought, covers a relatively long period of the cool and hot dry season. This is the period when forest fires, either deliberately or accidentally started, sweep through the grass cover, and only trees large enough to stand the grass fires are able to maintain themselves. The rainfall is generally between 30 and 40 inches. It is during the rainy season that the main tree growth takes place.

These dry woodlands cover a larger extent than the equatorial rainforests, and certainly form a very characteristic African vegetation. From one region to another different genera of trees are dominant and form a basis for subdivision. In some areas trees are replaced by a thick growth of bamboo, which can be regarded as a tree in its reaction to climatic conditions rather than as a grass.

Thorn forest

This is the type of vegetation which Gillman prefers to call "bushland and thicket," which has been described also as thorn bushland. It is land carrying a more than 50 per cent cover of shrubs and small trees, which may be evergreen or deciduous, and frequently are spiny though not necessarily so. Herbs and low grass form part of the ground cover. It is on land of this type that the baobab tree (*Adansonia digitata*), with its great thick stems, forms an interesting feature (Figure 6.3).

Except for the scattered baobabs, the trees do not usually exceed 10 or 20 feet in height, and during the short growing season are a mass of foliage and flowers; but the growth period is short. Ofter various species of *Acacia* are dominant, including the *Acacia arabica*, which occurs under almost exactly similar conditions in India. In the drier parts *Euphorbia*, especially the candelabra euphorbia, is often conspicuous. This is obviously the vegetation of the rather drier parts of the tropical climatic region. The thickets are difficult to penetrate, and they hide game more effectively than the dry forests, where it can be so easily seen. The vegetation covers large, sparsely populated areas. It would seem that, except for some areas with good soil, much of such land is unsuitable for agriculture.

The remarkable unity of tropical Africa, exemplified by the widespread repetition of types of soil, vegetation, and human activities, is well illustrated

Figure 6.3   A large baobab tree near Livingstone, Northern Rhodesia. (Copyright L. Dudley Stamp.)

by Africa's most fascinating tree, the baobab. With its monstrous trunk, up to 30 feet in diameter; bushy, rather low crown; huge, white, solitary, drooping flowers giving place to large fruits (monkey bread) with seeds embedded in a slightly acid, mucilaginous pulp, it is a conspicuous tree as distinctive of Dakar as it is of the East African scrub or Victoria Falls. It may be that it was the fresh green leaves which were first seen by the Portuguese who coined the name Cape Verde. The tree seems to owe its widespread distribution in large measure to its power to survive grass fires; the trunks are often blackened. Its very long roots and water-holding tissue permit it to survive serious drought. The bark yields a strong fiber; the soft, white timber, though readily attacked by fungi, is a useful building material. The pounded leaves are used in food and seem also to have considerable medicinal value.

Temperate brush

This is a type of vegetation which is well known in lands with a Mediterranean type of climate in most parts of the world. It is the *maquis* of North Africa, closely comparable with the *maquis* of other lands around the Mediterranean Sea, and it is also the vegetation of the Cape region in South Africa, closely resembling the *chaparral* of California. It is of course characterized by a relatively luxuriant growth of bushes, sometimes with small trees, producing a great wealth of flowers, so that this type of vegetation boasts the richest display of flowering plants to be found anywhere in Africa. The drought which coincides with the hot season precludes many grasses and herbs from flourishing, but there are numerous bulbous plants.

Oases

Although the word "oasis" can properly be applied to all those areas within the desert tracts where underground water is sufficiently near the surface for vegetation to flourish, the oases of North Africa have usually a thicket of trees, of which the most typical is the date palm. But other palms may be found in oases also, and in addition thorny trees and bushes, such as *Acacia* and *Zizyphus*. Wherever oases have been occupied by man it is natural that the date palm has been encouraged at the expense of other vegetation, and the oases may become almost forests of date palms.

Mangrove swamps

Swamp forests are found along many of the coasts of Africa. They consist primarily of trees 25 to 75 feet high, either standing on large stilt roots which lift the main stem of the trees above high tide, or having rhizophores, that is, respiratory roots sticking up out of the tidal mud in which the forests grow. The trees grow essentially between the tide marks on extensive stretches of mud (Figure 6.4). The forests are often richer and the trees larger in those areas where they are only occasionally invaded by salt water at high tide and may merge into freshwater swamp forests.

GRASSLAND[3]
High-grass–low-tree savanna

In very large measure the distinction between forest and grassland in Africa is artificial. This is certainly true of the high-grass–low-tree savanna, which is composed of coarse, rank grasses reaching 5 to 12 feet in height, with small trees scattered throughout. The grasses do not form a turf, each plant being distinct at the base. The dominant grasses are commonly species of *Andropogon* and *Pennisetum*.

Growth is rapid, but in the dry season the grasses dry out and are burnt to the ground. At the beginning of the rainy season a dense fresh green cover quickly forms, and when the grass is fully grown it reaches almost to the level of the scattered trees. Except where there are paths it is extremely difficult to penetrate this grassland, since everywhere the grass grows higher than a man (Figure 6.5). A belt of such country frequently occurs in the re-

[3] See also the results of recent work in J. M. Rattray, *The Grass Cover of Africa*, Rome: FAO, 1960, with separate map.

Figure 6.4 Clearing mangrove swamps in Sierra Leone. The mangroves provide firewood, the clearance helps to control mosquito breeding and the land can be enclosed and prepared for rice. (British Official Photograph.)

gion of relatively heavy rainfall, 35 to 60 inches, bordering the tropical rain-forests.

The natural fodder afforded is of little value, and wild game are not as numerous as in the lower, drier grasslands, though this is the haunt of such large creatures as the elephant, the buffalo, and the rhinoceros. In the drier margins the shea tree occurs.

Acacia–tall-grass savanna

This type covers nearly 16 per cent of the surface of Africa; considering its wide distribution, it is remarkably uniform. The trees are scattered, often thorny and flat-topped, averaging 10 to 50 feet in height, and include many species of *Acacia*. The grass, when fully grown, reaches 3 to 5 feet in height. When the grass is green and the trees are in full leaf, the country resembles in appearance a great orchard or a park (Figure 6.6).

The natural grasses are not, however, very palatable, so that in parts of South Africa this grassland is known as the *sourveld*. In the dry season the abundant wild game and the cattle rely largely on the grasses which they can find along the water courses. This is the great hunting country of Africa, with

Figure 6.5   A coarse type of African grassland, Nigeria. Grassland of this sort is as impenetrable as forest. There is little value in the grass as fodder. (Copyright L. Dudley Stamp.)

a wide variety of antelope, giraffe, zebra, and lions. It is the country where corn (maize) and various millets can be grown, peanuts, manioc, beans, and peas, but it is country which suffers seriously from vagaries of rainfall.

Tall grass

This is the High Veld of South Africa, pure grassland with no trees. The grass when fully grown reaches about 3 feet in height. Although there is a rich flora, the most important plant is the rooi grass. On these grasslands there are winter frosts, and the rainfall of 30 to 40 inches comes mainly in the summer.

Acacia–desert-grass savanna and desert grass

The grass flora in this type of savanna varies from a relatively even, short-grass cover to a sparse growth of desert grasses in tussocks. Scattered through the whole are many small, thorny trees and bushes. This is natural grazing country, but overgrazing results in the disappearance of grasses, leaving only the trees. Most of the trees and bushes belong to the genus *Acacia,* many of the grasses to the genus *Aristida.*

Soils tend to be shallow, owing to the development of a hardpan about a foot or so below the surface. It is this type of country which yields the various gums still so widely collected in Africa.

Mountain grassland and alpine meadow

The grasslands which occur at high elevations in Central Africa and the Ethiopian plateau, the mountains of Kenya and elsewhere resemble in certain ways the Alps of midlatitudes, though often coarser in growth and less valuable as pasture. Climate conditions are such that this is land suitable for European-type settlement.

Dwarf palm–temperate grass

This is the vegetation of the valleys and low hills of the Atlas region.

Figure 6.6 A savanna with *Borassus* palms. One of the many types of African savanna, near Monga on the northern border of the Congo.

Figure 6.7   The Nile near Malakal, Sudan, showing floating masses of sudd. (Courtesy British Overseas Airways Corporation.)

Marsh grass

In many parts of Central and East Africa there are vast swamps where by far the most important plant is *Cyperus papyrus.* Papyrus swamps cover vast areas in the upper basin of the White Nile (Figures 6.7 and 6.8).

DESERT
Desert shrub–desert grass

This type is an arid variation of the acacia–desert-grass savanna, occurring notably in South Africa, where the chief grasses belong to the genus *Aristida,* owing to a rainfall of 5 to 15 inches.

In the drier parts of the South African veld it affords excellent grazing land, but of low carrying capacity. It is interesting that the grazing is almost as good during the dry season as the wet, since the dry grass remains palatable throughout the year.

Desert shrub

The desert shrub is characterized by scattered, evenly spaced plants which are either woody or fleshy. It is like the sagebrush desert of the Great Basin in the United States, and is represented in South Africa by the Karoo.

Salt desert shrub

This type occurs where evaporating water has left soluble salts in the surface soil, notably sodium chloride and sodium sulphates, or as "black alkali," otherwise sodium carbonate. The last is particularly harmful to vegetation. Most of the plants are fleshy-leafed, and the soil surface is often white with the accumulated salts.

Desert

True desert, a waste of sand, rock, or silt, devoid or apparently devoid of vegetation throughout the year, occupies a smaller area in Africa than is commonly believed: in all less than 8 per cent.

Vegetation and human life

In the preceding chapter a plea was made for a more intensive study of soils. The need is certainly just as great for a detailed survey of vegetation— plant indicators which do, in fact, afford a measure of the sum total of environmental factors. It is surely a case for an objective survey, of recording what is actually present, and then of seeking to interpret; but any such survey must show the very close relationship between African ways of life and the vegetation cover. The broad correlation is noted in the next chapter. All detailed studies in tropical Africa have tended to show the inseparable relationship of climate, soil, vegetation, and agricultural systems. At times other factors, notably disease, cut across what otherwise is an almost perfect correlation. The need for botanical studies relates also to individual species. How can man hope to establish plants of his own choosing unless it is clear how existing species survive or flourish? Africa needs, and needs badly, nutritious fodder grasses to replace indifferent or useless indigenous species. What precise conditions will they have to face? Or take the specific problem

Figure 6.8 A large herd of elephants crossing swamps in the Sudd Region of the Nile. (Copyright Aerofilms Limited.)

of Africa's swamps, the *dambos* of the south. They are held up by accumulations of vegetation rather than rock structures. Should they be drained and converted to arable land or rice fields, or do they form natural reservoirs of water which would otherwise run off and do incalculable damage by soil erosion? Does swamp vegetation give rise to special types of microclimate? These and so many other considerations point the need for ecological studies before the underdeveloped lands can be safely developed.

WILDLIFE IN AFRICA

Tropical Africa can probably claim to be richer in wildlife than any other major region on earth. For this there are several reasons. The varied environments—from dense equatorial forests through savanna, with abundant grass growth and with both swamp and gallery forests, to sparse scrub and desert—provide ideal conditions for many different forms of animal adaptation. The nimble monkeys and baboons swinging from tree to tree, the long-necked giraffe reaching to the tender shoots of savanna trees, the striped zebra invisible against the shimmering white and black of waving tall grass, the lion preying on the innumerable herbivores, the hippopotamus in its mud hole, and the log-like crocodile with just a snout above the waters of the sluggish stream are simple examples that spring to mind. The sparseness of the human population has, at least to the present day, left vast areas to the mammalian and bird fauna.

But conditions are changing rapidly. The time is not far in the past when Africa was of interest to the outside world mainly as the source of ivory, black and white. White ivory is still in demand, but the future of all the larger animals, as well as the elephant, is threatened for other reasons. Most governments in Africa are now alive to the need for the conservation of their native fauna; most countries have established national parks which are primarily nature reserves and have staffs, albeit too scanty, of wardens and naturalists. One great world industry seems at present to have no limits to its expansion: tourism. The wildlife of Africa is a major tourist attraction. It is readily seen in such great "parks" as the Kruger National Park of South Africa, the Murchison Falls and Queen Elizabeth Parks of Uganda, or the park on the very outskirts of Nairobi and within reach of an evening drive from the center of the city. These are but a few examples of the facilities for tourists to see the wildlife, facilities which bring in millions of dollars and can bring in far more. Neither the intrinsic scientific interest nor the solid commercial value of nature conservation is yet appreciated by the rank and file. Big-game hunting by safari parties can be easily controlled by license, but poaching by small bands of Africans is difficult to prevent. Elephants are slaughtered indiscriminately for the sake of their ivory, some rare birds for their plumage. Worse still is the slaying of the fast-disappearing rhinoceros for the sake only of the horn, believed to have medicinal qualities when powdered, or of lions for a few teeth and a skin of little value. But preservationists are also under fire from farmers and herdsmen who see in the wild cattle and other herbivores the carriers of dread diseases affecting their flocks and herds or even, in the case of the monkeys, of diseases affecting the human species.

One of the amazing aspects of conservation in Africa is the rapidity with which the wild animals get to know the sanctuaries where they are safe. Once national parks are established, the problem is often to stem the flow of animal immigrants and to deal with the overcrowding problem. A two-ton hippopotamus eats a lot of grass and is sorely tempted to go raiding into neighboring cultivated land. If an animal so large can ever be described as harmless, the hippo is one—so long as numbers are limited. Many of the wild animals become, in their parks, indifferent to humans, especially in cars, though remaining dangerous. This is true of wild buffalo. The extraordinary and fascinating story of Elsa, the lioness who, till her death from natural causes at the age of four, developed a deep affection for her human friends and, after mating with a wild lion, brought back her cubs to share the delights of civilization, has become a classic in the study of animal behavior.[4] The worldwide concern for the fate of wildlife trapped on islands in the rising waters of the Kariba Lake led to the widely publicized "Operation Noah."

There are other aspects of nature conservation far from fully studied, but of great importance in Africa. It may well be that the best form of economic land management will prove to be the maintenance of wild herds, the most economical method of augmenting protein supplies. The encouragement of fish breeding throughout African waters has already had an appreciable effect on health conditions.

[4] *Born Free* and *Living Free,* by Joy Adamson, London: Collins, 1958, 1960.

CHAPTER SEVEN

African Peoples and Ways of Life[1]

The population of the continent

From the point of view of its human population Africa has three main divisions:

1. Arab Africa, coinciding roughly with extratropical North Africa.
2. Negro Africa, coinciding broadly with tropical Africa.
3. White Africa, if one may use that term for extratropical South Africa, where whites of European stocks form a dominating minority.

Arab or Moorish Africa, including also Egypt, has been in contact with the successive civilizations of the Mediterranean basin from earliest times. Its history is written large in ancient monuments as well as in actual records, and it has never been out of touch with the peoples of Europe and western Asia. North Africa absorbed Mohammedanism, and Moslem-Arab traders carried their religion across the great desert wastes to the northern fringes of Negro Africa.

Negro Africa—the *Afrique noire* of the French—is the real Dark Continent, the unknown land, which remained so long isolated from the outside world. Because there are so few outstanding monuments from the past and virtually no written history, it seems to have been tacitly assumed that Negro Africa had little history and that its peoples had long been much as they were when first seen by Europeans. In reality much of Negro Africa had for ages been in a state of constant change. There was the continuing antagonism between the warlike hunting tribes and the cattle keepers and cultivators; there were the establishment, expansion, and fluctuating fortunes of the Moslem emirates or empires in the broad Sudan belt from the Gambia to the

---

[1] I am greatly indebted to my colleague Professor I. Schapera, formerly Professor of Anthropology in the University of Cape Town, for reviewing this chapter.

Nile; there was the great drift southwards of the Bantu. It is not always realized that the white settlers in the Cape Province of South Africa did not dispossess the Bantu of their lands; the Bantu had not yet arrived. Gradually some of the complex history of Negro Africa is being unraveled, but more important is what has happened in the past century. The partition of Africa resulted in the stabilization—almost the crystallization—of what had long been a very fluid and changing position. It was almost as if a snapshot had been taken of a football game and then every player had been compelled to remain almost as he then appeared in the photograph. Most of the political divisions of Africa are purely artificial in relation to the African peoples.

White Africa of the south embraces essentially the Republic of South Africa and Southern Rhodesia, with "islands" of white settlement on the Eastern Highlands farther north. Throughout, unless we regard the southwest of the Cape of Good Hope as a separate unit, the whites are a numerical minority, and for the most part economy of town and country alike is dependent upon African labor.

Demographically, less is known of Africa, especially Negro Africa, than of any other continent. When the United Nations published the *Demographic Yearbook,* 1948, only Egypt, Morocco, Tunisia, the Portuguese possessions, Sierra Leone, Nyasaland, and white South Africa with its enclaves can be said to have had a proper census, an actual enumeration of heads. Details of age composition were available for Egypt (date 1937) and Portuguese possessions (1940) only. Figures for marital status were available for Egypt and Mozambique only, and for no country were figures over a period of years available. In short, the Egyptian census of 1937 and figures for the white population of the Union of South Africa were almost the only reasonably complete records.

Since the publication of the first edition of this book the position has greatly improved. The *Demographic Yearbook* of 1957 showed only Ethiopia (with Eritrea) and Liberia as completely without figures, though what were then the Belgian Congo, French Equatorial Africa, and French West Africa had figures only for the nonindigenous population.

In nearly all cases where a first census on modern lines has been taken, earlier estimates have been shown to be seriously below the true figures. Thus the estimated population of 4,063,000 for Uganda in 1947 was replaced by 4,993,965 in the census of August 1948—an underestimate of 20 per cent. Similarly, the 1947 estimate of 4,200,000 for Kenya may be compared with the 1948 census figure of 5,373,078. The *Demographic Yearbook* of 1961 shows a further advance, with most of the new African states having now taken a census, many in 1960.

Against this background of proved unreliability of earlier estimates, it is difficult to generalize regarding the rate of growth of the African population.

Whatever may have been the position in the past, all indications are now that the rate of increase is very rapid. The reliable figures for Egypt are worth studying in this regard. Kimble in 1960 concluded that the current rate of increase in tropical Africa as a whole was between 1.0 per cent and 1.6 per cent, giving an annual increase of between 1.7 and 2.7 million. As the world rate now almost certainly exceeds 2.0 per cent per annum, these estimates would seem to be low. The *Demographic Yearbook* of 1961 gives a total population for the continent increasing from 206 million in 1950 to 254 million in 1960, or 2.2 per cent per annum. In tropical and southern Africa the figure was 2.1 per cent.

Population density

Detailed mapping of population density has long been carried out for South Africa and Egypt. Since the publication of the first edition of this book, Glenn T. Trewartha and W. Zelinsky have assembled all the available information for tropical Africa including Ethiopia, and a composite map based on their findings has been published by Kimble. It is a density map using administrative divisions and does not seriously invalidate the generalized map given here on the next page (Figure 7.1). The overall population density of the continent is of the order of 21 to 22 persons per square mile, compared with about 57 for the land surface of the world as a whole, excluding Antarctica. Looked at in another way, every inhabitant of the African continent has a share of land of all types of about 29 acres. The corresponding figure for the people of the continental United States is about 12 acres. If we eliminate one-third of Africa as being desert or mountain incapable of supporting a permanent settled population, the share of potentially habitable land is still over 20 acres per head. By comparison with densely peopled Europe, the African continent appears almost uninhabited. The people of Great Britain have a little over one acre of land of all types per head of population (or taking England and Wales alone, about 0.75 acre). In France the figure is about 3.5 acres per head; in Italy, with its large mountainous areas, only 1.8 acres.

It would be wrong, however, to visualize Africa as a continent of vast open spaces and no people. In the first place there are great contrasts. In the Nile valley, which forms the cultivable heart of Egypt, population density averages about 1200 persons per square mile; each person, therefore, is supported by the produce of about half an acre of land and a surplus of some agricultural produce is available for export! Nor is there any doubt that, given the existing forms of cultivation, there is overpopulation in parts of Nigeria, where the density exceeds 300 persons per square mile. Elsewhere there are both dry deserts and "forest deserts" virtually devoid of people. Broadly speaking, if one judges by densities in any other part of the world, most of Africa is underpopulated.

Figure 7.1   The density of population in Africa about 1960.

What population could the continent support? Calculations of potential population are likely to lead us into dangerous paths whether we are considering Australia, the United States, Canada, or Africa. I have dealt with this question at some length elsewhere.[2] It may be demonstrated that in the climatically favored lands of northwest Europe, using present systems of cultivation, one acre of cultivated land will support one person at a northwest Euro-

[2] *Land for Tomorrow,* Pattern Foundation Lectures, University of Indiana, American Geographical Society, 1952; rewritten and revised as *Our Developing World,* London, Faber, 1961. By using a Standard Nutrition Unit (SNU) of 1 million calories of farm production per annum —a good average standard to support one human being—it can be shown how much land is needed under given types of diet and methods of production to support one person. The world average is just over 1 acre.

Within the map legend:
Over 500 persons per square mile
250-500 persons per square mile
100-250 persons per square mile
50-100 persons per square mile
5- 50 persons per square mile
Under 5 persons per square mile

0   1000 miles

pean standard of living—measured in calories, 2500 to 3000 per day. Reasons are given in that work for believing that the most "underdeveloped" countries of the world are those lands in mid-latitudes which practice large-scale mechanized farming rather than intensive mixed farming. Far too little is yet known of the possible output of tropical lands. It is certain that a rice economy in favored conditions will support over one person per acre; Egyptian experience suggests two, albeit at a low standard.

We have already seen how tropical Africa is hampered by vagaries of climate, by inadequate control of water, by soils difficult to handle, by numerous and serious plagues of man, beast and plant. Western science has not by any means reached the point when those difficulties can be overcome, and at the moment much of Africa is supporting a maximum population, given the existing form of cultivation and land management and the present incidence of pests and diseases.

The peoples of Africa

If we exclude the European immigrants who have settled in certain parts of Africa in the past three hundred years, the peoples of Africa fall into five main groups (Figure 7.2).

1. Certain isolated and relatively unimportant negroid groups. These "aboriginals" include the Hottentots, who formerly inhabited the southwest, the Bushmen of the Kalahari scrublands, and the Pygmy Negrillos of the Congo forests.
2. The "true" Negroes, or the Guinea and Sudanese Negroes, who live in West Africa and the savanna belt eastward to the Sudan.
3. The Bantu, or Bantu Negroes, who occupy the greater part of the continent south of the equator.
4. The mixed Hamite-Negro peoples of the eastern-central parts of the continent, including the Nilotes of the Sudan.
5. The non-negroid peoples of northern Africa and the Sahara, including the Hamites and Semites (or Arabs).

The primitive negroid peoples. The *Bushmen* are nomadic hunters who wander about over hunting grounds using bows and poisoned arrows. Their only homes are temporary shelters of branches. Their skin is yellowish-brown, the hair of their heads is in small separate tufts, and in stature they scarcely exceed 5 feet. Their interesting and artistic rock paintings suggest that they were once widespread over the East African plateau but were pressed southward by more powerful Bantu tribes. When the Dutch reached south Africa, they were already confined to the plateaus of what is now Cape Province and the scrublands of the northern and eastern Kalahari. They have

Figure 7.2   Simplified ethnic map of Africa.

never benefited by contact with other cultures, though they seem slowly but surely to be blending with other peoples.

The *Hottentots* similarly retreated to the southwest under pressure from the north. They are believed by some to result from the crossing of Bushmen with primitive Hamitic stock and are a little taller than the Bushmen. They had adopted nomadic pastoralism, with their wealth in cattle and sheep, and had semipermanent settlements of beehive huts within a thorn fence. These were the "natives" encountered by the Dutch in the Cape, who caused wonder by the curious development, especially among the women, of fatty tissue on the buttocks (steatopygia). Their tribal organization disorganized by the Dutch invasion, used as servants by the settlers, they have largely disappeared as a separate race, but there is a strong Hottentot strain in the "Cape Colored" people (see page 438).

The *Pygmy Negrillos,* in stature only about 4 feet, 6 inches, were formerly widespread but now live in small communities, especially in the equatorial forest regions, obtaining their food from fruits, nuts, roots, and animals killed by poisoned arrows. They are noted for their marked negroid features of very broad nose and prognathous jaws. Though in friendly contact with surrounding Negroes, they have remained distinct. In some of the wetter regions they construct shelters in the trees.

The Guinea and Sudanese negroes. Whatever may be the focus of differentiation of the human race, it would seem that Africa was populated by successive waves of people from the northeast. What is regarded as the "purest" Negro type, the West African Negro, has gradually been pushed into the coastal belt of West Africa and there, in strongholds amid the rain forest, has remained unmixed with alien blood. Northward and eastward, in the more open savanna country, there is evidence of decreasing purity, or rather of increasing admixture with Hamitic blood, and the peoples profess forms of Mohammedanism.

The true Negroes are tall or of average height (males 5 feet, 8 inches), with somewhat long, narrow heads (moderately dolichocephalic: index 75), intensely dark skin color—really black in most cases, woolly hair, broad nostrils, thick lips, and prognathous jaws. They are essentially small cultivators, *not* pastoralists, using different types of hoe and living on yams, beans, millets, and bananas. They were formerly grouped into kingdoms, some of great extent and widespread influence. Good examples are afforded by the old kingdom of the Wolof (roughly now the Republic of Senegal), the former great kingdom of Mandenga stretching from Sierra Leone eastwards and antedating the Moslem era, the Ashanti kingdom centered on Kumasi, and the progressive Yoruba kingdom with its large towns of Ibadan and Abeokuta. Other groups include the Krue of Liberia—well known because they have long provided crews for merchant vessels along the coast—and the Fanti of Ghana.

Passing northward, the Songhai, who destroyed the Mandengan Empire about A.D. 1500 and established their capital at Timbuktu, show Hamitic mixture, were converts to Islam, and retained a strong military tradition. On the other hand, the Mossi farther south resisted Islam.

Farther east there are "islands" or small groups of primitive character, such as the so-called pagans of the heart of Nigeria. More conspicuous are the large Islamic kingdoms or emirates linked together by language (Hausa) with a Hamitic-Negro ruling class (the Fulani) and a more markedly Negro populace. Good examples are the Emirates of Kano, Katsina, Zaria, and Sokoto; culturally and economically they are advanced peoples famed for their skill in the preparation and working of leather and textiles.

Still farther east the Negroes are represented by the tribes of the Republic of the Sudan, but everywhere the Hamitic influence is considerable.

The Bantu. The Negroes who inhabit the greater part of central and southern Africa, though in excess of 50 million in total, exhibit a number of common physical characteristics. They also speak variations of a common language. In fact Bantu (properly Aba-ntu, or human beings) refers primarily to language. The peoples were split culturally into the contrasted groups of warlike hunter-pastoralists (Figure 7.3) and the settled agriculturalists. The former acknowledged the paramount authority of a chief who lived in a village or kraal built for defense and protection of the all-important cattle. Being aggressive, they seized the best lands, though despising agriculture, which might have been highly productive. A good example of these peoples is the Zulu. The agriculturalists were thus relegated to the poorer lands, and apart from suffering the vagaries of the climate, their unfenced lands were open to depredations from the cattle peoples. In social organization they were more democratic. The council of elders designated an "heir apparent" among the

Figure 7.3 Baholo performing a hunters' dance. These people are Bantu from the Angola-Congo border. The dancer's mask represents an antelope's head. Notice the characteristic drums and grass-thatched round hut.

eligible sons of a chief by his several wives, and acts were not by the chief so much as by the elders. The operation of this system among the pastoral-agriculturalists of Basutoland and Bechuanaland under conditions prevailing in 1950–1951 is described elsewhere (pages 476 and 478).

A broad grouping of the Bantu into Eastern, Southern, and Central groups has been generally adopted. Among the Eastern Bantu the Baganda, or people of Buganda, now part of Uganda, form one of the most progressive peoples of Africa. Before coming under British influence they had already evolved a political organization resembling a constitutional monarchy. They have latterly devoted themselves to the commercial cultivation of cotton, and are rapidly adopting European standards of education, housing, and dress. On the Kenya plateau, the Kikuyu are excellent cultivators, though like other Bantu they recognize cattle as symbols of wealth. The Akamba are likewise agriculturalists, though they too keep cattle, sheep, and goats. Both are traditionally at enmity with the pastoral, nomadic Masai (Hamite-Negro). Along the East African coasts are Bantu peoples speaking Swahili, a language which has become a *lingua franca* of East Africa, so that it is difficult to distinguish the "Swahili" peoples from others who have adopted their tongue.

The Southern Bantu include the groups which, over the past three centuries, have been most influenced by the European penetration from South Africa northward (Figure 7.4). In their territories the Bechuana, Basuto, and Swazi have preserved their tribal organization. They live mostly in villages, with a larger village or town as a capital and residence of a paramount chief, and are pastoralist-agriculturalists. Over the Republic of South Africa and the Rhodesias tribal organization has been greatly disturbed; the people have become integrated to a greater or lesser extent into the European economy as workers on the farms, in the mines, or in the towns. "Zululand" is now an integral part of the province of Natal; Matabeleland and Mashonaland are parts of Southern Rhodesia; with this territorial assimilation has gone much of the tribal identity.

The Central Bantu include the peoples of the Congo and equatorial Africa, organized at the time of European exploration into loosely defined Negro empires. The various groups, such as the Fang, are mostly agriculturalists, practicing shifting cultivation and making clearings in the forest, but are still seminomadic rather than settled, moving their whole sphere of operations after a few years.

The mixed Hamite-Negro peoples. Although the Bantu are believed to have a varying admixture of Hamite blood, there are peoples, mainly north of the equator in Central and East Africa, who are quite definitely of mixed blood (Figure 7.5). They include many of the people of the upper Nile basin, hence the general term Nilotes. The Dinka, a typical group, live in the Sudd

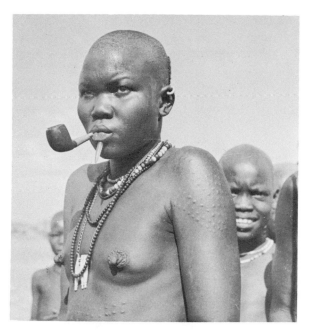

Figure 7.4 A typical Bari village matron from the Southern Sudan. Notice the shaved head, tattoo marks, bead necklaces and charm, chin and ear ornaments, and the good fat European pipe. A Negro type, with probably small Hamitic mixture. (Courtesy Sudan government.)

region. They are tall, cattle-rearing people having, by marked contrast to the Bantu, milk as a staple article of diet. The Masai, who are warlike in character and have penetrated southward into the East African plateau, form another well-known group. Broadly, the southern penetration of the Hamites and their intermarriage with the Negroes produced virile peoples. They introduced many arts, such as the working of iron, previously unknown to the Negroes, and probably the arts of cattle keeping and sheep rearing.

The non-negroid peoples. If North Africa were not isolated from the rest of the continent by the great Sahara, its people would still mark it off clearly and distinctively. The Hamites and Semites are absolutely distinct from the Negro, though, as we have already seen, there have been numerous intermixtures.

The Hamites are typically tall or fairly tall, light brown in color, with wavy or fuzzy dark brown to black hair, thin, straight noses, marked nonreceding chins, and thin rather than full lips.

The pre-Dynastic Egyptians were Hamites, and the modern Egyptians are still primarily of Hamitic stock, though in the north mixed with Arab; in the south, the Nubians show a Negro admixture. The Ethiopians, farther south, are also basically Hamitic, though Semitic influence is strong in culture and

Figure 7.5 A Mangbettu man from Niangara, northern Congo. Among these people deformation of the skull by tight binding is still practiced. They were formerly inveterate cannibals. The aquiline nose and beard indicate a Hamitic mixture with Negro stock.

language. Though at a different cultural level, the Galla and Somali of the eastern horn of Africa are also Hamites.

The typical Saharan nomads of the central desert tracts, the Tuareg and Ahaggar, are likewise Hamites. There seems to be a general tendency for the ruling class to be relatively pure, whereas there is a Negro admixture in the lower classes, below whom are Sudanese Negro slaves. Farther south, the Fulani of northern Nigeria are definitely a Negro mixture.

The third or western group of Hamites are those who inhabit the Atlas lands, the Berbers who have given their name to the Barbary States (Figure 7.6). The position is complicated throughout North Africa by the infiltration of Arabs who are typical Semites. In northwest Africa the so-called Arabs or Moors are rather Hamites who have absorbed the Moslem faith and perhaps some of the Semitic blood of the Arab invaders of the Middle Ages, especially of the eleventh century. Sometimes a distinction is drawn between the Berbers as sedentary agriculturalists organized into small village communities and the tent-dwelling Arab nomad acknowledging the autocratic leadership of a sheikh, often regarded as deriving his authority from Allah.

It would seem that true Semitic Arab blood, if weak in the Barbary States, increases eastwards, and that the nomadic "camel men" of the Libyan desert and the seminomadic cattle men farther south are mainly Semites.

There is no doubt that the distinction between Semites and Hamites owes much to their traditional origin from Shem and Ham, who, with Japheth, were the sons of Noah and so saved from the deluge. The record is in the tenth chapter of Genesis. The typical Semites are the Jews; the sons of Ham were dwellers in tents.

Language in Africa

In common with other parts of the world, in Africa the spread and consequent present distribution of languages tend to obscure race relationships. The map of languages given here (Figure 7.7) is simplified from one prepared by Joseph H. Greenberg and published in the *Southwestern Journal of*

Figure 7.6 Morning tea in a Moroccan village. The men are typical Berbers. The charcoal fire, bellows, brass tray, teapot, and glasses are practically the same throughout northern Africa. The tea is often flavored with mint and is made very sweet. (Copyright Geographical Publications Limited.)

Figure 7.7   The languages of Africa. In some ways this is a revolutionary classification of African languages and departs in several respects from the older, orthodox views. (Simplified from Greenberg.)

Anthropology, 1949–1950. He distinguishes sixteen families of languages, but some of these are spoken by very small and restricted groups only. Broadly, the whole of Negro-Bantu Africa is shown as speaking languages of one family, the "Niger-Congo," and almost the whole of Bantu Africa, the "central branch" of this group. Greenberg's map shows a large enclave in southern Africa as the click family, so called because there are click sounds incorporated in the languages. The Bushmen and Hottentots speak such languages, and there are clicks in the Bantu tongue of the Matebele. In reading Greenberg's map, we must remember that the more numerous Mashona and Bechuana of the Kalahari speak Bantu languages.

Over the whole of North Africa are the Afroasian (Hamite-Semitic) languages. The other smaller families of languages are those of the Hamite-Negro borderlands—mixed blood, specialized linguistic developments.

African ways of life

In general it is the environment, especially the climate and resulting vegetation, which determines the varying modes of life in Africa, and to a considerable extent the degree of civilization. Racial influences are obscure, geographical factors clear. In broad terms, the dense forests correspond with the distribution of the more primitive peoples, the savannas to settled agriculturalists, the more open grasslands to pastoral and hunting, often warlike, tribes. Peoples very distinct in their modes of life may nevertheless be closely allied in their physique and language; social organization tends to be a function of geographical environment.

Along the Mediterranean borders we find an agriculture established from very early times, with cattle, the plow, cereals, and Mediterranean fruits— especially barley, wheat, olives, figs, and the grape. Southward towards the desert margins, nomadic pastoralism based on sheep replaces cultivation; in the deserts cultivation is limited to oases, and human life depends on date palms and camels.

South of the deserts, in the semiarid open lands of the Sudan, are again pastoralists depending for their livelihood on cattle and sheep. Southward, with increasing rainfall and a modest rainy season, there is again some cultivation, precarious, and dependent mainly on sorghum and millet. Cultivation is by the hoe; use of the plow remains unknown.

The area of intermediate rainfall of the savanna between the steppes of the desert margins which are too dry and the forests of the equatorial margins which are too wet is favorable to cultivation. Large villages are the rule; there have been in the past empires of considerable size. Dependence for food is on millet and corn (maize), latterly on peanuts on the uplands and rice along the rivers. Tobacco is grown, sometimes cotton; kola nuts are gathered. Often cattle are bred, sometimes sheep and horses, and among the cultivators or mixed farming communities are tribes almost exclusively pastoral.

Unfortunately, where the rainfall becomes more reliable and where mixed farming should reach its maximum intensity, we encounter the "fly belts" where the tsetse fly virtually eliminates domestic animals. Here the basis of life becomes the yam, manioc, banana, and palm oil (Figures 7.8 and 7.9), with cocoa as a "cash crop" now developed to a great extent in Ghana and elsewhere.

As the closer forest is reached, villages are smaller, population sparser and patches of cultivation (shifting cultivation) more scattered.

On the plateaus of East Africa, and formerly in South Africa, the balance is somewhat different. The settled cultivators tend to be less numerous than and subordinate to the aggressive, often warlike, pastoral tribes. It is here that wealth has come to be measured in head of cattle, independently of

Figure 7.8 The Guinea oil palm. When wild, the palm grows very tall, so that men must climb the tree to obtain the fruit.

quality; indeed the cattle have little more practical value than the gold bars we civilized peoples bury in our vaults. Madagascar differs somewhat from the continental mainland in that cattle breeding is there associated with rice cultivation.

Africa is peculiarly poor in native food plants. Of those widely cultivated, one certain type of millet (Guinea corn) and perhaps some strains of rice are native. Despite its wide use, corn (maize) was introduced from America, and so were tobacco, peanuts, yams, and manioc. Actually it was the Portuguese, to feed their slaves before and during shipment, who introduced into West Africa the many new food plants which later became such a blessing to the people—manioc, sweet potatoes, yams, corn, peanuts, coconuts, and bananas coming straight from America, oranges from Portugal.

The barley and wheat of the north were introduced from Europe at an early date, as was the date palm from Arabia. Coffee seems to be native to southern Ethiopia as the kola nut is to West Africa, but most other fruits have been introduced. Cloves were introduced by the Arabs into Zanzibar because they could there use slaves for picking the buds.

The ass may be native to East Africa, and the camel to Egypt, but cattle and horses have been introduced, as well as European strains of sheep. West Africa gave us the guinea fowl.

Shifting cultivation

The system of agriculture commonly though somewhat misleadingly known as "shifting cultivation" is practiced through a very large part of tropical Africa. As a system it is better described as "land rotation" or "bush fallowing." In those areas inhabited by sedentary farming peoples, each village or settlement has proper to it a tract of surrounding land. The tract is probably only loosely defined except where settlements are close together and population dense. In a given year the villagers working together as a community clear a part of this village land, cutting and burning the woodland or scrub and then planting the crops appropriate to the climate and soil of the area. In due course the crops are harvested communally and the land used for a second and perhaps a third year. It is then abandoned, and a fresh tract of the village land is cleared. The abandoned land quickly becomes covered with a second-growth woodland or scrub. In due course the clearings reach a full cycle, and if a given tract has been allowed to lie fallow for about fifteen years it may be regarded as fully rested. Bush clearing is largely man's

Figure 7.9   The Guinea oil palm in a Nigerian plantation. When cultivated, the palms are kept low so that the fruit, to which the Agricultural Officer is pointing, can be reached easily. (Copyright L. Dudley Stamp.)

work. There is also surrounding the village itself, often as a series of enclosed gardens or "compounds" attached to individual huts, the "women's land," cultivated regularly to afford a supply of vegetables for the pot. Often the kokoyams, peppers, beans, melons, bananas, etc., are scarcely grown at all in the open farmland. The women's land is enriched by house sweepings, ashes, refuse, and manure afforded by chickens, goats, and human beings.

The system has often been condemned as wasteful of natural forest, of land, and of labor. But it has many good points. The natural forest is probably second growth of little value anyway. The land cleared in small patches protected by surrounding woodland escapes the evils of soil erosion, and its nutrient status temporarily enhanced by the ashes of the burnt bush is maintained by the fallowing, the soil not being exposed to the atmosphere long enough for serious oxidation. Expenditure of labor is minimized by burning, and no attempt is made to remove large stumps. The cultivation is by hand —by hoeing—so the stumps do not constitute the obstacles they would be if the plow were used. We may accordingly agree with Lord Hailey when he says that shifting cultivation is "less a device of barbarism than a concession to the character of a soil which needs long periods for recovery and regeneration."

Dr. E. B. Worthington, as a scientist, goes farther and claims that "shifting cultivation is admirably adapted to the needs of primitive peoples, provided there is sufficient land available." This last proviso leads us to enquire how much land is needed under this system. I see no reason to revise the calculations which I made some years ago in Southern Nigeria.[3] I worked on the basis that the average family was 3.6 persons and that each family required the produce from two acres of cultivation annually. If the land is allowed to rest 7 years after one year of cultivation each family would actually require 16 acres of village land. This gives a population density of 144 per square mile as the maximum which can be supported. Where the population density exceeds this figure, the fallow period must be cut down, and the land is likely to deteriorate seriously. In Northern Nigeria, with a lower and more precarious rainfall, I calculated that an average family of 3.3 would require 3 acres or 24 acres in all—a density of 88 per square mile, above which the land would be overpopulated. There are indeed some parts of West Africa so crowded that a year of cultivation is followed by only two years of bush fallowing. On the other hand, where villages are widely scattered, only a part of the "village tract" is ever used, or alternately there are stretches of "no man's land" between village tracts.

If we accept these calculations it is interesting to return to the population density map and note those parts of tropical Africa which appear to be over-

[3] L. D. Stamp, "Land Utilization and Soil Erosion in Nigeria," *Geog. Rev.,* **XXVIII,** 1938, 32–45.

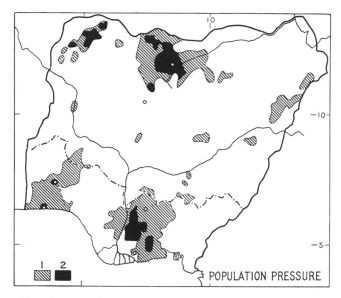

Figure 7.10   Map showing relative pressure of the population on the land in Nigeria. (1) Density over 100 to the square mile in the Northern Provinces or over 144 in the Southern Provinces. (2) Density over 200 in the north, 300 in the south. (From L. D. Stamp, *Geog. Rev.* 1938. Courtesy of the *Geographical Review,* American Geographical Society.)

populated. Figure 7.10, reproduced from a map in my article, shows the position as it was in Nigeria in the thirties. Since that time there has been a large population increase, but agriculture has become more efficient. The position is thus relatively similar.

Agricultural mechanization

Does the solution to the pressure of population on land lie in mechanization? In 1948 the British government sent a mission of three experts to enquire into the problems involved in the mechanization of native agriculture in tropical Africa. Their lengthy report[4] contains much material of great interest, and they point out that natural, economic, and social forces have combined to cause a low productivity of land and labor with little or no accumulation of capital, but that pressure of population on natural resources is so great in many areas that mechanization of agriculture would only be worthwhile if there are new and substantial demands for labor in nonfarm work. Furthermore, the substitution of tractors and other equipment demanding fuel and expert handling "for ordinary native farm labor would be the substitution of costly for cheap factors of pro-

[4] Colonial Office, Colonial Advisory Council of Agriculture, *Animal Health and Forestry,* Publication 1, London, His Majesty's Stationery Office, 1950 (by J. W. Y. Higgs, R. K. Kerkham, and J. R. Raeburn.)

duction." They argue that cheaper means than mechanical cultivation of raising productivity should be used wherever possible—especially the saving of labor by provision of proper water supply (to obviate the great expenditure of energy in carrying water from the river, pond, spring, or well to the home) and small water-driven grain mills (to save the endless labor of grinding by hand). It is argued that mechanical aids in the clearing of forest, breaking fallows, leveling for rice, and perhaps in farm transport might be advantageous but that "further use of tractors in weeding, harvesting, and threshing would usually cost too much as compared with any net increase in production it might bring." It is further argued that costs of tractor cultivation tend to be inflexible from year to year, whereas crop yields and prices are highly variable. Provided high overheads can be avoided, there is much to be said for "share" rather than cash charges for mechanical services. The authors also believed that mechanization will accentuate rather than relieve the social consequences of a transition from subsistence to commercial economies.

It is clear that effective use of mechanical implements would involve many changes in farm layout, land tenure, and systems of cultivation, perhaps only answered by the collective farm or some form of communal ownership and operation. Despite the arduous labor associated with cultivation by the hoe, as I have already said, there is some doubt whether even the plow should be used widely in tropical Africa. In Southern Rhodesia plows increased in number from 3400 in 1902 to 94,000 in 1938, and in that period 16 per cent of all the arable lands had become badly eroded. In one territory of Uganda plows increased in number from 282 in 1923 to 15,388 in 1937, and the fields had been increased in size but there was no improvement in crop yields.[5] If it does not promote erosion, the clearing of the soil by plowing compared with hoeing means that when the land is left fallow natural vegetation re-establishes itself much more slowly, and the period of fallowing needed to restore fertility is much longer.

The political development of tropical Africa

In the midnineteenth century, when the heart of Africa was being explored for the first time by white men, the people were organized broadly into what may be called tribes. Essentially the members of a tribe enjoyed a common language and a common economic motivation; they might be hunters, herdsmen, or cultivators. Those of the first two groups were nomadic or seminomadic, roaming within a recognized but loosely defined range. A tribe would have its own social and cultural organization, its own rituals, ceremonies, and laws, above all its own methods of electing its leaders or

[5] Frank Stockdale, *Report on Visit to East Africa, January–March 1937,* His Majesty's Stationery Office (Colonial Office), 1937.

chiefs. Tribes were often grouped and recognized the authority of a paramount chief or king. Less frequently, "empires" existed where a ruling race demanded recognition by subject peoples of different language, race, and customs.

Aims and objects of African tribes were often in conflict, and standing feuds were common. It was this factor which encouraged the slave trade—slavery had long been traditional among Africans themselves; the traders needed only to help one warring party against another. Where settlements were established, notably by the Dutch in South Africa, some African peoples (such as the Kaffirs and Zulus) defended their lands against the invading settlers, but others, the Hottentots, for instance, took the easier course of accepting service with the white man, with resulting breakdown of tribal organization.

With the partition of Africa there was often a conflict of interests among the Europeans concerned. Missionary pioneers like Livingstone were fired with the great urge to bring the benefits of Christianity—coupled with Western medicine to heal some of their suffering—to the "heathen"; it was they who stirred their governments at home to take steps against the evils of the slave trade. Many were the early administrators who devoted their whole working lives to improving the lot of the hapless African by stamping out this evil. There were others who sought to develop legitimate trade and a fair *quid pro quo* for the products of the country. Other traders preferred sheer exploitation—a handful of beads for a much-desired ivory—and whose methods of securing carriers and servants differed but in degree from slavery.

As the European administrations became stronger, these abuses were steadily mitigated, but two developments followed. One was based on the assumption that the European concepts of justice, law, and order as well as standards of values were unquestionably right and proper and should replace whatever existed before—if anything existed at all, which it was no one's business in particular to bother about. The other resulted from the large-scale development of resources, especially of minerals, and the encouragement of African production of cash crops. Mineral exploitation and other European developments made large demands on "labor," resulting inevitably in a disruption of tribal life, while the demand for crops such as cacao, palm oil, and peanuts meant a new emphasis and reorganization of economic life. Yet on the social side there was no tangible substitute for the old tribal organization, threatened with complete extinction.

Then there appeared on the scene the anthropologists and Lord Lugard. The social anthropologists set out to study objectively and scientifically the tribes of Africa, their modes of life, their laws and customs. Without this basic knowledge it would have been impossible to develop the system of indirect rule which has become so closely associated with the name of Lugard.

This remarkable man, Frederick John Dealtry Lugard, born in 1858, entered the British army and, at the age of thirty, came into prominence in command of an expedition of Nyasaland settlers against Arab slave traders. Administrator of Uganda on behalf of the East Africa Company, he later effectively prevented the British government from abandoning Uganda in 1892. Later sent to West Africa, Lugard rallied chiefs to support the British Royal Niger Company against French and German rivalry and raised the West African Frontier Force (1897). Appointed Commissioner of Northern Nigeria, he unified that territory before he left in 1906. Returning to Nigeria as governor of both Northern and Southern Nigeria in 1912, he secured their amalgamation as Nigeria on January 1, 1914, and ruled with great wisdom till 1919. It was in 1922 that he published *The Dual Mandate,* in which he deals with the duties of European powers in tropical Africa. His great principle, which he put into practice in Nigeria and which was later followed elsewhere in Africa, was to encourage and strengthen the traditional authority of the chiefs, to secure the progress of their people through them. This system of indirect rule was in sharp contrast to other systems of government, for example, the French, which encouraged African chiefs to become good administrators deriving their authority from the central administration rather than from their own people.

In these days neither approach is the right one. Although Lugard's principles may be said to have been applied with success over more than half a century in the three British protectorates in southern Africa (Basutoland, Swaziland, and Bechuanaland) as well as in many parts of Africa, the old tribal concept, as well as organization, is doomed to disappear. As more and more Africans receive their education in Britain or France or America, they return more truly "Westernized" than those Africans who have just drifted into towns to seek employment. They have concepts of democracy, of state and of nation quite foreign to their compatriots; they no longer fit into the old life any more than do their European clothes. A very interesting example of the clash of ideas was afforded by Seretse Khama, chief-designate of the Bamangwato tribe in Bechuanaland. While studying law in Britain at Oxford University, he married a white girl; he returned in 1950 with her to Serowe, the tribal capital. Although the rank and file of the people accepted her as their "white queen," the elders were divided. The British authorities realized that to permit the couple to remain meant at least a deep cleavage among the Bechuanas, at worst riots and bloodshed. Temporary banishment was decreed. This action was not based on racial discrimination, though sections of both blacks and whites disapproved strongly of the mixed marriage. Other sections disapproved of the "banishment" of one who had done no more than absorb modern Western standards and was admitted by all to be of the highest intellectual caliber. In due course, Seretse Khama and his wife returned as ordinary citizens and gained wide respect for their dignified bearing, while the chieftainship remained in abeyance.

Another example may be of interest. When my wife and I were working in Northern Nigeria in 1938, we were received in audience together with the Resident, the British Commander-in-Chief, and his wife, by the Emir of Kano. He received us seated on his throne, his cabinet on his right, the three white men on state chairs to his left facing the cabinet. As a compromise of Moslem and Christian views of the status of women, the two white women were permitted a small chair each a short distance away. The audience, the subsequent friendly chat, the tour of the palace with its purely African rooms and its Western type of dining room (with large refrigerator), and the entertainment to afternoon tea left an indelible impression of a great man and a dignified ruler. He spoke no English, but his son, a fine, stalwart man over six feet tall, educated in Britain, spoke English perfectly and entertained in Western style. He was acting as a district commissioner, as training. In due course he succeeded his father as Emir of Kano, then became a minister in the government of the northern region of an independent Nigeria.

In 1950 growing national consciousness—not, it should be noted, a strengthening of tribal organization—in the Gold Coast had led to various disturbances and to the imprisonment of certain "agitators." But the British Colonial Office, realizing the pace of political progress, granted a new constitution with an Assembly of seventy-five Africans and nine Europeans. An electoral roll of some 500,000 electors (broadly, all males and females over twenty-one) had to be prepared. The urban electors voted directly for their representatives; the rural electors in 2000 subdistricts chose their member of the electoral college to elect 33 members. Voting started on February 5, 1951, and it was recorded that between a quarter and a third of the rural electors came to vote. A candidate had to be proposed and seconded, and often the local voters had had a preliminary "palaver" and the candidate was unopposed (Figure 7.11). At other times a man was put forward with the words: "The chief and the elders have spoken. Is not that enough?" It was not enough, and so once again tribal organization bowed before Western democracy; the gorgeously robed chiefs (Figure 7.12) deferred to the Western uniform of the returning officers. Six years later, in 1957, the country became independent and assumed the name Ghana (see Fig. 7.13). In 1960 it was declared a republic within the Commonwealth. The country had been prepared for democratic self-government; under the new constitution it has a Parliament consisting of the President and a National Assembly of 114 directly elected members (ten women) but has been moving towards a one-party dictatorship.

It is perhaps not too much to say that any form of "development" on Western lines seems destined to destroy the old tribal organization. The construction of railways, roads, and other public works means recruitment of

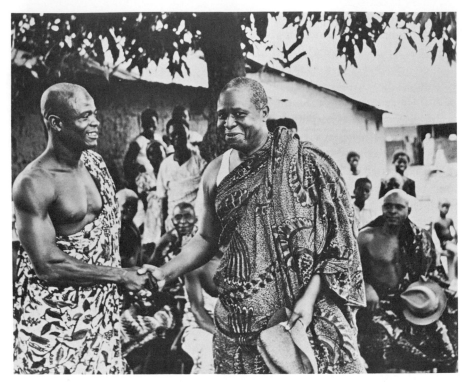

Figure 7.11   A successful candidate chosen to represent his party on the electoral college, Gold Coast Elections, 1951. (British Official Photograph.)

large labor gangs, and so do large-scale agricultural developments (see page 188). The Rand gold mines need 100,000 African workers; other mining enterprises have similar large labor demands.

The weakness of the British concept of indirect rule was that it tied modern development to a tribal system which many—European and African alike—regarded as outworn and in any case doomed to extinction. As Professor W. M. Macmillan observed: "Anthropological studies give more evidence than one had feared of the cruelty and sometimes the essential injustice of tribal institutions. I would deny that there is evidence that any African people wants to be left as it is." He suggested that the African's desire was to acquire "not only our mechanical and material efficiency but that spiritual freedom, unknown to tribal society, which comes of respect for the dignity of personality and for the rights of the individual, and is nourished by free play of critical opinion."[6] This has indeed been proven by events.

In Northern Nigeria, with its firmly established emirates, indirect rule had an excellent foundation on which to work. The position was very different

<hr>

[6] W. M. Macmillan, *Africa Emergent* (1938, revised 1949), Penguin Books, London.

elsewhere. The African in general has a profound respect for age; tribal leaders are likely to be advanced in years and correspondingly fixed in outlook. Not appreciating that authority came from age, the British officials naturally encouraged younger energetic Africans to take leading roles in tribal affairs. In so doing they unwittingly destroyed the very authority they sought to strengthen. If not dead, indirect rule is dying.

The French are essentially realists. Their plan was, broadly, to extend to Africa the system of administration tried and proved in France and to train Africans to take their places as administrators who derive their authority by appointment from above, not by election or nomination by chiefs. When the French Empire was replaced by a Union, "colonies" gave place to Overseas France (France d'Outre-mer), and the African was offered the prospect of becoming a citizen of Greater France. But this did not last for long. When de Gaulle was recalled to power in 1958 the French African territories were offered an immediate choice of independence either within or outside the French Community (La Communauté). Only Guinea chose to leave; by the end of 1960 independence had been achieved. The French are believers

Figure 7.12   The paramount chief of the Ashanti holds a Grand Durbar, 1951. The Golden Stool, symbol of the nation, is displayed. (British Official Photograph.)

Figure 7.13   Delegates from the new countries of Africa now play an important part in the work of the United Nations. (United Nations photo.)

in individualism and private enterprise. Frenchmen had been encouraged to settle in Africa, even tropical West Africa, to make their way as traders or professional men just as Africans had been shown how the way is open to them to succeed along the same lines. The French have never bothered much about color bars. Intermarriage and concubinage are regarded as matters for individual decision.

Both the British and French systems had resulted in a body of trained Africans ready for self government. The tragedy of the Congo in 1960 is due in large measure to the fact that the Belgian administration had not.

It is difficult to generalize regarding the Portuguese areas, because Portuguese Guinea, Angola, and Portuguese East Africa, the three chief territories, offer such marked contrasts. The relative stagnation in the first and large parts of the third may reflect natural conditions as much as Portuguese apathy. In Angola and Portuguese East Africa much of the development which has taken place—railways, roads, and ports—has been by foreign capital. If the African population is to be regarded as having been left very much to itself, the one conspicuous result has been the marked outward migration.

Christian missions

In recent years there has been a distinct tendency to overlook, perhaps to forget, the dominant part played by Christian missions in the material as well as the cultural development of Africa. The early navigator-explorers were followed shortly by missionary priests, but thenceforth the growth of the slave trade obviously rendered untenable any permanent stationment of missionaries drawn from the same peoples as the slavers. Nevertheless, as inland Africa came to be known, all the great Christian churches were early in the African field and vociferous in their condemnation of the evils they found. Livingstone's base was the mission in Bechuanaland. His reports and the reports of other missionaries roused public opinion in America and Europe against slavery to such a stage that governments, however unwilling, had to take action, sometimes to the extent of expending millions of dollars with little prospect of return, as in the case of the East Africa railway from Mombasa.

Christian teaching has always included the education of the young and the care of the sick. Almost everywhere in Africa the missionaries, supported entirely by voluntary contributions from home and often tolerated rather than helped, occasionally even obstructed, by administrators on the spot, have been the pioneers in establishing schools and hospitals. Usually, when the missions had successfully built up the framework of education and of medical services, governments stepped in and took over both management and credit (Figure 7.14).

Missions have always realized that to reach the people their workers must know the local language. In the study of African languages missionaries have been pioneers. Since they came to convert the "heathen" and to teach them

Figure 7.14   The University of East Africa, Makerere College. The universities of tropical Africa are a lasting memorial to European concern for the higher education of Africans. After World War II the University of London guided the establishment of autonomous university colleges at Accra, Ibadan, Makerere (Kampala), Khartoum, and Salisbury—all to become, in due course, independent universities. (Copyright L. Dudley Stamp.)

what they believed to be right and true, missionaries as a whole may lack the interest, which is basic to the anthropologists, in the study of all that is now denoted by indigenous cultures. Certain tenets of dogma and ritual may have been stressed in ways inappropriate to African circumstances; Western ideas of behavior may have been pressed with little realization of the effect. For example, it is often said that by their insistence on the Western attitude toward nudity, that it is of itself an evil, missionaries are responsible for the spread of an undesirable attitude towards sex. Certainly in education, curricula and methods of teaching have often been transplanted bodily from the home country. In the British areas I have often heard African children being taught the irrelevant details of English history and geography. The boy or girl educated in the mission school learns, it is said by some critics, to despise his fellows and to seek only to copy his teachers, with the disastrous result that he becomes an outcast from his own people rather than a leader. Despite all this, the Africa of tomorrow will be even more an essential part of a world which has been largely framed for good or ill according to Western ideas. In familiarizing the Africans with the background of our culture the missions have done a great and pioneer work.

Some statistics of leading Christian denominations are published annually, but certain matters are not revealed by figures. One is the growth of indigenous African churches, notably in West Africa, where aspects of old pagan beliefs and customs may have been absorbed in forms of Christianity, thus differing from the American or European churches which first brought the faith to the people. Somewhat different is the Dutch Reformed Church of the Afrikaans-speaking South African, sometimes described as the strongest national church in the world. Of ancient origin is the Coptic Church of Ethiopia, to be considered later (see Chapters 11 and 16).

BIBLIOGRAPHY

C. G. Seligman, *Races of Africa,* Second Edition, London, 1939.
R. L. Buell, *The Native Problem in Africa,* New York, 1928.
Lord Hailey, *An African Survey,* Second Edition, Oxford, 1945.
L. P. Mair, *Native Policies in Africa,* London, 1936.
Lord Lugard, *The Dual Mandate in British Tropical Africa,* Third Edition, London, 1926.
W. D. Hambly, *Ethnology of Africa,* Chicago, 1930.
W. M. Macmillan, *Africa Emergent,* Second Edition, Penguin, 1949.
M. Fortes and E. E. Evans-Prichard, Editors, *African Political Systems,* London, 1940.
I. Schapera, *Migrant Labour and Tribal Life,* London, 1947.
G. H. T. Kimble, *Tropical Africa,* New York, 1960. Professor Kimble's great work is oriented toward the understanding of the African peoples and their ways of life and is an indispensible work of reference.

CHAPTER EIGHT

The Plagues of Africa— Pests and Diseases[1]

The evil reputation which Africa, especially tropical Africa, so long held as an unhealthy continent was linked essentially with climate. It was the "unhealthy climate" which caused West Africa to be known as the "White Man's Grave," and different parts of the continent are still referred to as unhealthy or contrasted with such areas as the healthy Kenya highlands. That climate has a direct effect upon the healthy, normal functioning of human beings is, of course, undeniable—but not to the extent, or anything like the extent, formerly believed. The dangers of life in most parts of tropical Africa are not due directly to climate but to the many diseases which flourish under those climatic or other physical conditions prevalent in the continent. Diseases to which man and animals are subject are numerous and severe, often fatal, and although their causes are now generally known, their elimination is another matter. It has been said with good reason that the tsetse fly, carrier of the germs of sleeping sickness in human beings and nagana in domestic animals, is still the real ruler of Africa. In the tsetse-fly belts both animal husbandry and mixed farming are impossible, so that agricultural progress is virtually eliminated. Though the locust does no direct harm to man, a countryside devastated by locusts is a countryside of starvation. Pests and diseases thus constitute a very important factor in African development, past, present, and future.

Mosquitoes

We are accustomed to summer plagues of mosquitoes in many parts of the world, and many a fishing or hunting vacation in the far north has been ruined by the unwelcome attention of mosquitoes. Annoying and even painful, mosquito bites are not in themselves serious, but when the mosquitoes are carriers of serious disease it is another matter. Malaria, the most wide-

[1] I am indebted to the late Professor P. A. Buxton for the final revision of this chapter.

spread of all diseases in tropical Africa, and yellow fever, one of the most dreaded, are both carried by mosquitoes. Directly or indirectly, malaria is the chief threat to health and life in most parts of tropical Africa. It can be fatal, but its indirect effects in undermining health and so rendering its victims more susceptible to other infections are even more important. It is a debilitating disease, and so the greatest contributor to inefficiency in the whole range of human activities. Malaria is caused by a minute animal parasite transferred by mosquitoes of the genus *Anopheles* from man to man. The female parasite is fertilized in the stomach of the mosquito. The resulting offspring pass into the saliva of the mosquito; when it bites a man they are transferred to his blood, and fever develops after a period of a few days. There are four types of malarial parasite of the genus *Plasmodium* which cause fevers of somewhat different types. The commonest is subtertian. Several species of *Anopheles* are known to be carriers, but it is *Anopheles gambiae*, widely distributed in Africa, which is the chief villain. It was formerly restricted to Africa but was accidentally introduced into Brazil. Incidentally, this is one of the great dangers of the speed of modern air travel—the accidental transportation of noxious pests—and explains the elaborate precautions now insisted upon by the health authorities of many countries. Blackwater fever, a consequence of malarial infection, has been a most serious disease.

The control or elimination of malaria depends upon the destruction of the mosquito by preventing it from breeding. Unfortunately *Anopheles gambiae* breeds very easily and does not bother greatly about the character of the water where it deposits its eggs; small rain pools, stagnant water left in riverbeds in the dry season, even marshes with up to 66 per cent of sea water will all serve. Not unexpectedly, the incidence of malaria is greatest at the end of the rains and while there is still stagnant water not dried up. A thin film of oil over the stagnant waters prevents the larvae from breathing and so eliminates the mosquito. Although the spraying of pools and other water surfaces around a town may be possible and there are areas which have been rendered malaria-free, such control would seem to be virtually impossible for a whole continent. It is probable that over large areas of tropical Africa all children who survive to adolescence have been infected with malaria and have developed an immunity. Although apparently healthy, they have probably lost both stamina and efficiency. In such populations adults may develop an acute attack of fever which runs its course and after a few days terminates naturally just as in temperate latitudes a cold disappears after it has run its course. To the stranger, especially the European, coming into these malarial areas the diseases strikes with devastating effect. Quinine has long been used as a prophylactic lessening the severity rather than preventing the disease, but more effective is a small daily dose of atebrin (or mepacrine). A course of atebrin to a sufferer seems to produce immunity. The American Geographical Society has devoted Plate 3 of its great *Atlas of Diseases* (*Geographical Review,* **XLI,** 1951, pages 638–639) to the chief species of malaria vectors. It shows the distribution in Africa of the chief species of *Anopheles* widely distributed in the world and also of other species important in Africa (Figure 8.1).

Yellow fever is a terrible infectious disease caused by an ultramicroscopic virus transmitted from man to man by the mosquito *Aëdes aegypti.* An attack of yellow fever confers immunity, that is, if a victim recovers from his first attack he is safe for life. It seems certain that immunity is earned by many

Figure 8.1   Malarial mosquitoes in Africa. Species of mosquito carrying malaria exist in all parts of Africa shown in solid black on this map. (Adapted from the world map published by the American Geographical Society, 1951.)

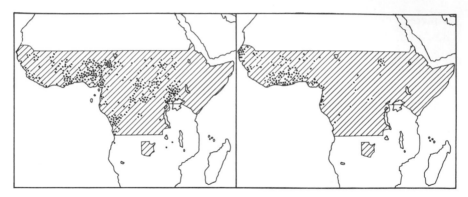

Figure 8.2 Yellow fever in Africa. The hatched area is that recognized officially by health authorities for international purposes as liable to yellow fever. Tanganyika was added 1952. (Delineated by the Expert Commission on Quarantine.) The map on the left shows by dots where positive results have been obtained in immunity tests. The map on the right shows by dots yellow fever cases recorded 1924–1941. In 1941–1961 very few cases were recorded. (In part after Findlay.)

Africans in early life by mild attacks, but if the disease strikes severely it is fatal in 90 per cent of cases. The unfortunate victim starts vomiting and goes on vomiting until the strain causes death by heart failure. There is nothing that the attendant can do but watch the patient die this horrible death. Every now and then there are epidemics, and, although the numbers involved are in ordinary years small, there is this constant fear of a serious outbreak. Fortunately there is a safe and effective inoculation against yellow fever, and for all travelers to and from tropical Africa it is an essential requirement. The mosquito *Aëdes aegypti* is very widely distributed (Figure 8.2), far more widely than the disease, and it breeds freely in anything which will hold water, especially, it would seem, in villages and towns. The provision of piped water supplies and efficient drainage would make towns safe provided other water surfaces were controlled. In parts of West Africa efforts have been made to make illegal the growing of certain palms which hold stagnant water, but unfortunately even the banana holds water between its great leaves and the stem. The same mosquito in Africa is responsible for transmitting dengue, or "break bone," fever. Though rarely fatal, this fever throws the victims out of action for two or three weeks. New arrivals are particularly liable; they have high temperatures and a skin eruption while the pain in joints and muscles is acute. They feel as if every bone in their bodies were literally breaking.

There are other diseases transmitted by mosquitoes. The condition known as elephantiasis, the enormous swelling of the legs and sometimes of other parts of the body, is caused by a minute worm transmitted by mosquitoes.

Tsetse flies

The name tsetse fly is given to the twenty odd species of African blood-sucking flies of the genus *Glossina* (Figure 8.3). They are rather larger than houseflies and can be recognized by their prominent proboscis projecting horizontally in front of the head and by their habit of resting with the wings lying one upon the other. They are found in "fly belts," especially on the margins of bush or forest near rivers or lakes, and are particularly active and troublesome during the hotter parts of the day. Certain species carry the single-celled organisms known as trypanosomes, which are the cause of fatal diseases both in man and animals. When the tsetse fly sucks blood from an infected subject it draws up some of these organisms, which undergo a developmental phase within the fly and are then passed into the blood of the man or animal on which the fly may next feed. The fly *Glossina palpalis* transmits *Trypanosoma gambiense,* causing sleeping sickness in man, and the fly *Glossina morsitans* transmits *T. rhodesiense,* causing the Rhodesian form of sleeping sickness in man, and also several other trypanosomes causing nagana disease among domestic animals. It is possible that monkeys can act as "carriers" of sleeping sickness, and many wild antelopes, though unaffected themselves, are carriers of the diseases of cattle. Sleeping sickness spread from West Africa, where the population has acquired a certain immu-

Figure 8.3   A tsetse fly (*Glossina*). Notice the position of the wings when at rest and the characteristic proboscis projecting horizontally forward. (Courtesy of the late Professor P. A. Buxton.)

nity, to Uganda and East Africa generally, and caused severe mortality in the early years of the century. Not only are the insects difficult to control—clearing of vegetation round villages and elimination of scrub are important—but the pupae lie buried in shady ground difficult to attack by insecticides. The toll taken of cattle has led to a demand for the wholesale destruction of African wild animals, believed to be carriers. The accompanying map, for the material of which I am greatly indebted to the late Professor P. A. Buxton and Mr. H. S. Leeson, shows the distribution of tsetse flies (*Glossina*) in general and within that the areas (shown in black on Figure 8.4) where sleeping sickness in man occurs. The huge area is obvious.

In the early years of this century, sleeping sickness produced an immense

Figure 8.4 Sleeping sickness and tsetse fly areas. (Compiled from information supplied by the late P. A. Buxton and H. S. Leeson.)

epidemic in Uganda, where it appears to have killed two-thirds of the local population within a very few years, perhaps the greatest epidemic that has ever been recorded. Elsewhere in Africa it was a killing disease, especially when associated with insufficient food and consequent poor physique. The French in West Africa found that the annual mortality of patients treated by the best skill then available varied from 5 to 15 per cent. Owing to advances in the production of drugs, the disease has now ceased to be a menace, and no longer makes a large contribution to deaths in tropical Africa, though a certain number of people still die of it, coming for treatment too late, or living beyond the range of medical services. Several drugs, not chemically related, have contributed to this remarkable victory. A point in their favor is that the patient does not have to be admitted to a hospital, because he can be treated in his village by an itinerant team. The most recent drugs are not used in treatment of the sick, but for the protection (prophylaxis) of those who are exposed to the risk of sleeping sickness. With these drugs, all individuals, as far as possible, are given an injection which protects them completely for a large number of months, so that the chain of infection between man and fly is effectively broken.

Cattle, horses, and dogs bitten by *Glossina morsitans* carrying the "fly disease," or nagana, usually die. At first no effect is seen, but a few days after the animal has been bitten the eyes and nose begin to run, a swelling appears under the jaw and the muscles become flaccid. The animal begins to stagger and may go mad before it dies. It is found on dissection that the cellular tissues under the skin have become injected with air. The result of this fatal effect is twofold. There are severe losses on the margins of the fly belts in cattle country, as in East Africa. In the second place it is virtually impossible to introduce these domestic animals into the fly belts, and consequently mixed farming is not a practicable method of improving the management of the land and increase of crop yields.

Hookworms

It is probable that hookworm disease, or ankylostomiasis, occurs among a very high proportion of Africans, but, because very severe cases are few and it is rarely fatal, it has been much neglected. The tiny worms, when adult, live in the human intestines attached to the gut wall, from which they suck blood. Thus the victim suffers a continuous loss of blood. Extreme cases result in marked anemia, and there are many who believe that hookworm disease in milder but pernicious cases is responsible for much of the mental and bodily lethargy of many Africans. The eggs of the worms leave the human body in the faeces; the larvae develop on the ground and then enter through the skin of feet and ankles of persons walking unshod on contaminated soil. Europeans wearing shoes are rarely infected, and clearly proper sanitation would eliminate contaminated soil.

Water-borne disease organisms

Throughout tropical lands diseases of the intestines and stomach, ranging from mildly upset digestions to killing diseases, are much more common than in temperate lands. Climate is only indirectly responsible by favoring the rapid decomposition of foodstuffs and lowering man's resistance. Infection may be conveyed by dust, by the hands' coming in contact with infected material (hence the imperative need of washing before meals), by house flies, but above all by contaminated water, especially that which has been infected by human excreta. Danger may come from water even if one does not drink it; it may simply be used for washing cooking utensils or on vegetables to be eaten uncooked. For this reason salads, so popular in temperate lands, are particularly dangerous in the tropics. Fruit with a firm skin (for example, bananas or oranges) is safe, but bruised or damaged fruit should never be eaten. Milk is also very liable to contamination and should always be boiled.

The two forms of dysentery, the one caused by an amoeba living in water and the other by a bacillus, are very common. Various forms of diarrhoea are even more frequent.

The unpleasant disease known as bilharziasis, or schistosomiasis, of which one form is characterized by discharge of blood and mucus from the rectum and the other affects the bladder, is common throughout Africa. It is caused by drinking water contaminated by the fluke parasite *Schistosoma* or *Bilharzia*. The intermediate host is a water snail, such as *Planorbis* or *Isidora* (much enjoyed by ducks), and the obvious control is by elimination of these hosts. Fortunately, if water contaminated by *Bilharzia* is kept for two days, it becomes innocuous for domestic purposes. The disease can be cured with relative ease, but is a killing malady because of the disorganization of the internal organs. The snails flourish in bathing pools near villages and are able to live in water fouled by urine or excrement. Unfortunately, the disease has spread in Africa with irrigation works. Once again the control of the disease is dependent upon general improvement of sanitary conditions, and in this case calls for close collaboration between the irrigation engineers and the doctors.

Fortunately, diseases of the typhoid-paratyphoid group seem to be rare in Africa, and so is cholera.

The Guinea threadworm (*Dranunculus medinensis*), though only a millimeter in diameter, lives under the human skin and may reach a yard or more in length. It causes ulceration and much incapacitation. The embryo lives in a minute freshwater crustacean, and once again infected drinking water is the source of infection.

Lice, ticks, and fleas

Unpleasant as the unwelcome attention of these parasites of man and animals may be, it is the diseases they carry which are far more important. Relapsing fever is caused by a blood parasite (*Spirochaeta spp.*) carried by a louse or a tick. Although diagnosis is easy by a microscopic examination of the blood, the fever has symptoms closely resembling those of malaria and may not be suspected in time to prevent a severe epidemic. If diagnosed in time it is readily curable, and the disease can be controlled by delousing the population; but epidemics of unparalled intensity have occurred in the past. In 1921–1922 an outbreak in French Sudan and Niger killed at least 10,000 persons; in 1926 one district in Darfur (Sudan) lost 10,000 out of a total population of 20,000.

Another louse-borne disease is typhus, but this—by way of contrast—is a scourge of colder lands and rare in tropical Africa. It has affected Morocco and Algeria with some severity, as it did in 1942.

It is well known that murine plague is transmitted from rats to man by rat fleas. The domestic house rat, *Rattus rattus,* is the chief host, and fortunately is restricted in Africa to main ports, though a mouse, *Mastomys natalensis,* is known to be a host in certain areas. In World War I plague due to rats was a serious menace in Dakar, and in 1920 15,000 human cases were reported from French West Africa. Because of an energetic campaign waged against the rats, cases of plague and resultant deaths dropped steadily; in 1938 only four cases were reported in French West Africa and for the first time no deaths. Normally, about 60 per cent of cases are fatal. The other epidemiological form of plague, sylvatic plague, is confined to southern Africa (Figure 8.5). In that case the permanent hosts are certain wild rodents, mainly of the genera *Tatera* and *Desmodillus.*

Other human diseases

Africa does not escape the worldwide killing diseases of other continents. Tuberculosis is probably the most frequent cause of death in tropical Africa, despite the spectacular fall in mortality rates elsewhere in the world with the use of modern drugs. Pneumonia is especially dangerous to ill-nourished and scantily clad children liable to sudden changes of climate (as when the harmattan suddenly begins to blow); smallpox is likely to spread by movements of laborers and to assume serious proportions; gonorrhoea is very widespread; syphilis has become the commonest cause of admission to the hospital in many districts of Africa. Polio affects Africa as it does other con-

Figure 8.5   Plague in Africa. Plague is endemic, i.e., permanent, in the inland areas marked; small numbers of cases are reported in most years. (Map specially compiled by D. H. S. Davis.)

Sylvatic plague areas

Murine plague areas

• Outbreaks 1940-1950

0   600 miles

tinents, especially in transient labor camps, and so do influenza and trachoma. It would seem that Africans are particularly susceptible to epidemic diseases when away from their homes or when vitality is lowered by heavy manual work coming on top of indifferent feeding. Thus mortality on railway construction work has frequently been very heavy.

A disease particularly prevalent in tropical Africa and affecting children especially is yaws, caused by *Spirochaeta pertenuis*, closely allied to *S. pallida*, which causes syphilis; it is not, however, a syphilitic disease. The germ enters the body through cuts, abrasions, or sores. It causes skin eruptions and ulcers all over the body, which themselves may lead to other infections. We may here blame the climate to some extent, for in the tropics cuts and wounds do not heal as easily as in cooler lands and are likely to become the seat of other infections.

Leprosy, caused by *Bacillus leprae,* is another contagious disease widespread, though irregularly so, in Africa. According to figures collected on behalf of the British Empire Leprosy Relief Association, the known incidence of leprosy in East Africa in 1950 was 17.8 per thousand of population in Uganda; 10.2 in Kenya; 18.1 in Tanganyika; 14.0 in Nyasaland; 12.6 in Northern Rhodesia; and as high as 55.1 in the Belgian Congo. There were estimated to be 580,000 sufferers in the Belgian Congo alone and 265,000 in the other countries mentioned. Although the disease is now readily curable in early stages, lepers have so long been regarded as social outcasts that the difficulty is to persuade those who suspect they have the disease to come for treatment. Kimble, writing in 1960, estimates the sufferers in tropical Africa between one and two million—probably nearer the higher figure.

The mention of smallpox gives an opportunity of recording the very active steps taken by the French to combat disease in West Africa. In 1937 alone 2½ million persons were vaccinated, about a sixth of the total estimated population. Despite this, incidence is still distressingly high in many areas.

Locusts

So far we have been considering briefly the plagues which affect man directly; Africa has many others which attack his food supply—his crops and his animals. Many are pests and diseases of wide, if not worldwide, occurrence such as rinderpest and foot-and-mouth disease among cattle; some are ancient and well known, others seem to be new –like the swollen shoot disease of cocoa. We have already indicated that the tsetse fly makes impossible at present improvement of agriculture over huge areas of Africa. Similarly the wide prevalence of poultry disease has made poultry farming impossible over large areas. We cannot deal with the geographical distribution and possible causes of all these many pests and diseases, but for several reasons particular interest attaches to the study of the locust. Locusts are among the oldest enemies of mankind (Figure 8.6). The locusts brought by the east wind were the seventh of the plagues which Moses caused to harass Egypt in his effort to secure the release of his people from bondage. Throughout the Old Testament the destructiveness of the locust is proverbial. In Egypt, "Very grievous were they: for they covered the face of the whole earth, so that the land was darkened; and they did eat every herb of the land, and all the fruit of the trees: and there remained not any green thing in the trees, or in the herbs of the field, through all the land of Egypt."[2] Yet it was not until about

[2] *Exodus,* X, v. 14–15.

Figure 8.6   Desert locust. Maximum invasion area stippled. Known and suspected outbreak areas in black. (After B. P. Uvarov.)

1930, when a great locust plague seemed to be threatening Africa and western Asia (Figure 8.7), that several governments, including the British, French, Egyptian, and South African, realized the need for investigating not only the best means of killing locusts but also the reasons for their periodic swarmings. Later, in 1945, a permanent Anti-Locust Research Center was established.[3]

Tropical Africa is subject to plagues of three different locusts: desert locust (*Schistocerca gregaria*), African migratory locust (*Locusta migratoria*) and red

---

[3] B. P. Uvarov, "Some Recent Advances in Locust Research," *The Advancement of Science,* **VIII,** No. 29, 1951, pp. 17–22. This is a convenient summary of the official account, B. P. Uvarov, *Locust Research and Control, 1929–1950,* London, His Majesty's Stationery Office, 1951.

locust (*Nomadacris septemfasciata*). Each has its own "invasion area," though they partly overlap (compare Figures 8.6, 8.7, and 8.8). It has been found that the normal cycle of locust life in each breeding area is closely correlated with the climatic cycle, especially rainfall, whereas migrations of swarms between breeding periods are largely connected with wind systems. Where climatological data are adequate, it is now possible to forecast locust breeding and movement of swarms and so to warn areas of the impending danger. Where thermal convection currents develop over heated ground they provide a lift to locust swarms just as they do to birds or aircraft, and the swarms may fly at several thousand feet from the ground, maintaining a speed of about 11 miles an hour. Such swarms may travel hundreds of miles. Quite

Figure 8.7   Red locust: annual spread 1927–1934. Black areas show the swarms of 1927–1929. (After Uvarov.)

Figure 8.8   African migratory locust: annual spread 1926–1934. Black areas show the swarms of 1926–1927. (After Uvarov.)

different is the mass marching of millions of young locusts, or "hoppers" (Figure 8.9). They march actively when warmed by the sun and maintain direction by the sun's rays (though probably actuated by hunger, they may actually march for this reason into the desert), resting by night when temperature falls. Their activity is definitely stimulated by warmth. Each species of locust occurs in two phases—solitary, when the consequences are not serious, and gregarious, when the danger of swarming appears. It would seem that there exist certain permanent breeding grounds from which swarming periodically takes place. For example, small swarms of the African migratory locust were observed on the flood plains of the River Niger near Timbuktu in 1926–1927 over an area of some 50 by 120 miles. In 1928 the swarms invaded

Senegal and Sierra Leone; by 1929–1930 the whole of West Africa had been invaded; by 1930 the plague had reached Khartoum; and by 1932 swarms which had of course bred on the way reached Rhodesia and Angola. From the small initial center some 4 to 5 million square miles had been affected, and the plague lasted 14 years. Similarly, small swarms of red locust observed in Northern Rhodesia in 1927 1929 had become 6300 recorded swarms over 3,000,000 square miles by 1935. Although modern insecticides render the protection of a given area of crops comparatively easy, it needs a well-planned campaign to control a plague. In 1943–1947 coordinated campaigns, highly successful, cost roughly $5,000,000 a year. It may be that by intensive study of the ecology of initial breeding areas, human beings will one day master this powerful and baffling enemy.

The control of pests and diseases

With the constant spread of medical science (Figure 8.10), the teaching of hygiene, and the general raising of the standard of living, human mortality throughout Africa is being lowered. The survival rate has increased, and, unless there is a corresponding drop in the birth rate, the population of Africa

Figure 8.9 A plague of locusts in Morocco. As part of the international campaign assisted by the Food and Agriculture Organization of the United Nations, they are here being fought with the help of poison. (Courtesy FAO.)

Figure 8.10   The fight against malaria. Only recently was it found that the little-known *Anopheles melas* bred in these black mangrove swamps of Sierra Leone. (British Official Photograph.)

is bound to increase enormously. Despite the increasing measure of control over animal diseases and pests attacking agricultural crops (Figure 8.11), it is doubtful whether the output of food is keeping pace. There is increasing pressure on land resources which threatens the traditional methods of African agriculture. Over all Africa the readjustment of the people and the land becomes the primary problem. Nor does the problem end with the control of pests and diseases. In a preceding chapter we have seen the need for water control; we have seen the need for new methods of managing tropical soils and the failure of modern machinery designed for North American or European conditions.

There remains a whole range of diseases among plants, animals, and man himself due to some deficiency, often difficult to detect, in the land or the soil itself. Major deficiencies in the soil, such as low content of lime, phosphates, and nitrogen, can be detected by chemical analysis and to the trained eye may be apparent from the growth and form of plants themselves. It is much more difficult to detect absence or excess of "trace elements," the full significance of which is not yet fully known.

A deficiency disease of worldwide occurrence is goiter—not so much a disease in itself as a symptom of ill health due to an unbalanced diet deficient in iodine. The unsightly swelling of the neck is due to malfunctioning of the thyroid gland, and the influence extends widely into reproduction, growth rate, intellectual development, and deaf-mutism. The people of Africa, living close to the soil, are on the whole remarkably free from this disease, except in the Nile Valley and Delta, patches in the Abyssinian plateau, on high country near the source of the Niger, Northern Nigeria, round the Ebola River in northern Congo, and in the Katanga. In each case the incidence would appear to be due to the constant use of river water deficient in iodine. In a small but interesting area of the Langkloof Mountains near Knysna in South Africa local waters and soil are normal in respect to iodine content but very rich in available lime, though low in phosphorus. This lime-phosphorus unbalance seems to lead to increased demand for iodine and may explain the popular association of goiter with limestone areas elsewhere in the world.[4]

There were parts of Kenya where the mysterious disease "nakuruitis" swept away the settlers' cattle and sheep until it was traced to deficiencies of trace elements in the soil. With a dressing of cobalt the same land now carries excellent livestock.

If this chapter conveys one lesson, it is the need for continued study and research and the realization that Africa still holds many problems common to the whole world besides a number, often most baffling, of problems peculiarly its own.

[4] World Goitre Survey, *Iodine Facts*, London, April 1946.

Figure 8.11   A helicopter spraying cotton crops in the Sudan. The spraying is for control of jassid insects. (Courtesy of Pest Control Limited.)

BIBLIOGRAPHY

Much of the material on which this chapter is based has been supplied from unpublished sources, and I am especially indebted to Professor P. A. Buxton and Professor G. Macdonald of the School of Hygiene and Tropical Medicine (University of London), Dr. C. J. Hackett of the Wellcome Museum of Medical Science, Mr. H. S. M. Hoare of the Leprosy Relief Association, and Dr. H. S. Gear and Dr. D. H. S. Davis of the Institute of Medical Research, Johannesburg.

Under the direction of Dr. J. M. May the Department of Medical Geography of the American Geographical Society published 17 sheets of an *Atlas of Diseases,* the first comprehensive attempt to deal with the geography of the world's diseases. In 1951 the British Government for the first time collected for publication in one annual volume entitled *Colonial Research 1950–1951* (His Majesty's Stationery Office) reports which had been previously issued separately, dealing with insecticides, fungicides, herbicides, locust control, tsetse flies, animal health, and many other subjects. An excellent summary of the position is included by Kimble in two chapters of his great work. One is a factual statement in the chapter on "The Old Order," the other is a vivid account of the "Assault on Sickness."

CHAPTER NINE

Transportation in Africa

Those who are inclined to underestimate the importance of natural factors in the economic development of Africa would do well to study the means of transportation, past and present. In common with other Mediterranean lands, the ass was in common use as a beast of burden in North Africa from very early times. There is no need to do more than mention in passing the obvious association of the camel, the "ship of the desert," with the desert regions, nor is there need to stress the well-known but nevertheless striking adaptations of the animal for desert life—the broad spreading foot, the arrangement of the stomachs, the safety reservoir of food in the hump, the tongue and mouth able to laugh at thorns, the nostrils closing at will against sand and dust. That the camel is fully conscious of its successful adaptation to environment, so vastly better than that of clumsy-footed man, is clear from its supremely haughty bearing and supercilious expression.

South of the desert, in tropical Africa, where the tsetse fly reigns, there are no domestic animals which can be used as beasts of burden. The areas where they could have been used are so limited that broadly the attempt was not made. We may almost say in consequence that the wheel remained if not unknown at least unused until the advent of Europeans. In tropical Africa human porterage (where watercourses were not available for dugout canoes) was practically universal. So the routes from village to village, to the tribal meeting place, to the juju shrines in the forests were worn by human feet, traveling single file. There were no wheels, no wheeled vehicles, no cart tracks with the two deep wheel ruts so universal in India or Indo-China. In the forests or closer type of savanna country the tracks made by human feet were narrow (Figure 9.1). Suddenly the African realized in the early years of the present century that Western civilization had produced the ideal form of transport which he could really use, the bicycle. Millions of bicycles, of British and continental makes, at times also of Japanese, disappeared into the African bush.

Figure 9.1   A typical path through farmland, in Ghana, near Sekondi. These paths are ideal for bicycles. (Copyright L. Dudley Stamp.)

In the open savanna and the grass veld or steppe, vehicles with more than two wheels could also be used. In the south, where no tsetse fly hindered their use, the Dutch introduced at an early stage the lumbering ox wagon—the covered wagon of the Great Trek (Figure 9.2). With its standard "span" of sixteen oxen it was, until recently, still to be seen in parts of South Africa and the Rhodesias. Professor R. U. Sayce has claimed that the development of South Africa as a whole is intimately connected with the ox and has stressed the many thousands of ox wagons which were in use, notably in the period 1880–1890.[1] With the coming of the present century the bicycle proved its usefulness in South Africa as elsewhere in the continent, but after World War I it became clear that the modern automobile could go, at least in the dry season, over much of unforested Africa with but little in the way of formal roads. It would be too much to say that the drier parts of Africa have now a network of roads, but, except in the rains, most parts can be reached by automobile.

The qualification "except in the rains" may exclude a period of 6 or even 8 months in parts of tropical Africa. Human porterage is usable, although with difficulty, throughout the year. The same is true of the bicycle, but for all-the-year movement of passengers and goods overland, either railroads or all-weather roads are essential.

[1] R. U. Sayce, "The Transport Ox and Ox-Wagon in Natal," in *Studies in Regional Consciousness and Environment,* New York, 1930.

Railroads

In North Africa, Egypt, and South Africa, railroad construction began early. In South Africa the building of the line from Cape Town began in 1859. It was completed to Wellington in 1863, but it did not reach the Kimberley diamond mines until 1885, Johannesburg on the Rand until 1892, or Bulawayo until 1897. It may indeed be said that the "railway era" for tropical Africa began shortly after the partition of the continent and that strategic factors were stronger than economic ones in determining which lines were built. There was no coordination; gauges were chosen at the whim of the companies or of the governments who backed them. Most railways in tropical Africa were begun after 1890, and railway construction went on spasmodically and rather slowly until World War I. As the territories of the European powers became demarcated and widely accepted, so economic considerations (especially the exploration of valuable mineral deposits) replaced strategic as the main factors determining routes. It should of course be noted that Africa has many short lengths of line, especially in the Congo, constructed to join navigable stretches of waterway either by circumventing rapids and falls or by linking one waterway with another.

It was really not until after World War I, that the motor truck for goods,

Figure 9.2   An ox wagon of the old type on the High Veld. It has the full span of 16 oxen. Such ox wagons played a large part in the development of South Africa. Oxen are now often used for pulling cars and trucks out of mud after a sudden storm, but it is doubtful whether a full-span ox wagon still exists. (Courtesy South African Railways.)

Figure 9.3   Unloading ships at Accra, Ghana. Until the opening of Tema deep-water harbor in 1961 goods had to be offloaded into surf boats, seen in the background, and then carried by African porters to the shore. (Courtesy British Overseas Airways Corporation.)

Figure 9.4   Unloading at Accra. The automobile in the crate had just been lowered on two surf boats. (Copyright L. Dudley Stamp.)

the motor bus for African passengers, and the private automobile assumed first-class importance, and the construction of all-weather roads became more significant than that of railways. This change of emphasis is well illustrated by the famous Victoria Falls Bridge over the Zambezi. It was designed and built as a railway bridge and completed in 1904–1905. When I first visited the area in 1926 it was still a railway bridge, but the adventurous, with or without permission, would drive a model-T Ford (invaluable because of its high clearance) over the bumpy wooden surface. Later it was definitely converted to a rail and road bridge.

Some examples of early "strategic" railways may be quoted as interesting. The line from Lourenço Marques in Portuguese East Africa to Pretoria in the Transvaal, built by the Netherlands Railway Company, was completed in 1895. The Transvaal was an independent republic, but the line from Pretoria to Durban in the British colony of Natal was opened the next year. In 1891 the Imperial German government took over the administration of German East Africa from the German East Africa Company, and the Tanga railway was begun in the same year, though it did not reach far inland for many years. In 1892 the old Imperial British East Africa Company surveyed a railway route from Mombasa to Lake Victoria; construction was undertaken by and at the expense of the British government in 1896. In this case Britain's decision, made by Prime Minister Lord Salisbury, was based on a determination to suppress the slave trade.

Farther north the French in 1894 secured a concession to build the railway from their port of Jibuti to Addis Ababa, the capital of Ethiopia —still

Figure 9.5 African craft at Freetown, Sierra Leone. Many of the Africans of the West Coast are great seamen. (Copyright L. Dudley Stamp.)

Figure 9.6   A troop of young elephants in convoy in the Congo. African elephants are less easily trained than Indian but can be used.

the only railway link between Ethiopia and the outside world. It is perhaps indicative of the changing relative significance of road and rail that the Italians during their occupation of Ethiopia (1936–1941) built many motor roads but no railways and that at the end of World War II the Addis Ababa railway was not sufficiently important for through running to be resumed for some years.

Most of the railways in tropical Africa were begun after the Berlin Conference of 1884–1885. St. Louis was linked with Dakar in 1885; the line to link the Senegal River at Kayes with the Niger, though actually begun in 1882, did not reach Koulikoro on the Niger until 1906, and it was 1923 before there was through running from Dakar to the Niger.

It was Stanley who is credited with saying that "without railways the Congo is not worth a penny." He knew well the great navigable stretches of the mighty river and its tributaries and realized how those navigable stretches must be linked up by railroads circumventing the rapids and falls. Because the force of his argument was appreciated, the line from Matadi to Leopold-ville was opened in 1898, uniting the estuary with Stanley Pool and thus conquering the obstacle of the Livingstone Rapids. The short stretch of line from Stanleyville to Ponthierville around the Stanley Falls in the heart of the basin was opened in 1909.

Many years ago the late G. G. Chisholm, in his *Handbook of Commercial Geography,* first published in 1889, showed how expensive and inefficient is human porterage. A man carrying 100 pounds on his head might travel 15 or even 20 miles a day; two men driving a railway engine could haul, for example, 1,000,000 pounds 1000 miles in a day. Is it little wonder that goods valuable enough to stand the costs of human porterage were few in number—gold, diamonds, and ivory, to mention the traditional African ones—and the commercial opening up of Africa awaited the railroad? This is still largely true for such heavy commodities as minerals, though the truck and automobile have added greater flexibility and extended the range reached from a railroad. Sarraut[2] records that during World War I the French required to transport 4200 tons of cereals in the Ivory Coast. It took 125,000 porters 2,500,000 working days, with an incalculable loss in cultivation as a result!

The Cape to Cairo railway

Most of the continents have had their great railway romances. The destinies of California and of British Columbia were both in the balance before the forging of the railway links which bound them to the East, and the concept of the railroad as a unifying as well as a civilizing influence was uppermost in the minds of the great empire builders before the automobile and air age. The idea of a through railroad from Cape Town to Cairo is associated especially with the name of Cecil John Rhodes—scholar, financier, statesman, dreamer, philanthropist. Born in England in 1853, he was never a strong lad, and at 16 he went to Natal to join his brother on a plantation to lead an open-air life. Within a few months the brothers joined in the diamond rush to New Rush, afterwards named Kimberley, and soon Rhodes was averaging $500 a week. In 1873 he returned to England to try to get his degree at Oxford University. His scholastic attainments failed to gain him admission to the college of his choice, but the more discerning Provost of Oriel College admitted him. After a few months the climate affected his heart again and he had to leave, taking his Greek classics to the diamond fields. After 8 years, he did succeed in putting in enough terms of residence to qualify for his Oxford degree. By the time he had reached the age of 21, however, the bold young financier was already deeply involved in South African gold and diamonds and had begun reorganizing small companies into combines. Eventually, in 1888, he joined his great rival Barny Barnato after years of rivalry. There is no doubt Rhodes wanted to make a vast fortune to enable him to turn his dreams into reality.

Quite simply and with all modesty, he believed the English-speaking peoples had followed the highest ideals of justice, liberty, and peace and that God had called upon Britain and America to rule the world for its own good. He regarded the split between the United States and Britain as the

[2] *La mise en valeur des colonies françaises.*

Figure 9.7   The grave of Cecil Rhodes, Matopo Hills, Southern Rhodesia. This also illustrates the "onion weathering" of granite under the sun's action. (Copyright L. Dudley Stamp.)

greatest tragedy of history, one day to be remedied, and in the great task of bringing the whole world under one beneficent government he allotted himself Africa.

By long tradition the territories of the old British Empire, now the Commonwealth, had been colored red on political maps, and it has been said that it was Rhodes' ambition to "paint the whole of Africa red." He saw Africa on the road to progress and prosperity under the British flag. First he desired the union of South Africa and so, in 1881, entered the Cape parliament. He was largely responsible for extending control over Bechuanaland in 1884–1885. He became prime minister of the Cape in 1890. At the same time he was chairman and virtual dictator of the chartered British South Africa Company (founded 1888), which, after the manner of the famous old chartered companies such as Hudson's Bay and East India, acquired, developed, and ruled the vast heart of Africa now known as Rhodesia. This lasting memorial to his work is matched in his other sphere of interest by the Rhodes Scholarships he endowed to permit students from the United States and the British Commonwealth to study at Oxford University. He saw many of his hopes dashed by the Boer War in 1899–1902. He died on March 26, 1902, two months before the war came to an end.

Death came at the age of 48 from a particularly distressing form of heart disease in the great house, Groot Schuur, that he had built for himself on the slopes of Table Mountain, where he wandered from room to room trying in vain to get enough air to breathe. His home he bequeathed to South Africa to be the official home of future prime ministers, though he was not to know that his dream of a Union of South Africa would so shortly be achieved, largely through the efforts of Jan Christian Smuts, then fighting on the Boer side. He was buried, according to his wishes, amid the granite boulders of the lonely Matopo Hills near Bulawayo in his own Rhodesia (Figure 9.7).

Today Rhodes is sometimes regarded as an outdated "empire builder," but if he had put his life's aim and ambition into a single paragraph he might well have antedated Point IV (see p. 8) by more than half a century.

The two maps (Figures 9.8 and 9.9) reproduced here show the British sphere in southern Africa in the year 1881, when Rhodes entered parliament, and at the close of 1902, the year in which he died.

What of the Cape to Cairo railway? By 1885 it had reached Kimberley; five years later the territory in which Kimberley is situated (Griqualand West) had become part of Cape Colony. It was in 1885 that a British protectorate was established over Bechuanaland, and during 1896–1897 the railway was constructed right through Bechuanaland to reach Rhodesia. Rhodes had obtained a mineral concession from the chief Lobengula covering the whole of Zambesia (Northern and Southern Rhodesia) in 1888, which was thus proclaimed a British sphere of influence the same year. Lobengula's kraal was on the site of the modern Bulawayo. He was a great man and foresaw that the future of Africa lay in collaboration with the Western world. He sent two of his sons to be educated in England, something quite unique in 1892. At a small but famous private school in the heart of England's county of Kent they became fellow students of my eldest brother. Lobengula paid a state visit to

Figure 9.8   Africa in 1881   Figure 9.9   Africa in 1902
British territory in black.

Figure 9.10   The navigable waterways of Africa. This map shows in dramatic fashion how the navigable stretches of waterway are isolated by falls and rapids and that no river affords penetration deep into the continent.

England and saw his sons in school; he absorbed many ideas and ideals of the Western world and imported into his own country large numbers of top hats as appropriate symbols of authority. But his people, the Matabele, were restless. They rebelled, but their rebellion collapsed with an outbreak of smallpox, Lobengula himself dying in 1894. In 1896 the Matabele again murdered a number of settlers and were driven into the Matopo Hills. There Rhodes and three companions went unarmed and negotiated peace.

The next year (1897) the railway had reached Bulawayo, only a score of miles from the heart of the Matopos. Again construction was pushed on. In

1905 the Victoria Falls Bridge was opened, and Northern Rhodesia was linked directly with Cape Town. Construction continued across the territory to the mining area of Katanga on the border of the Belgian Congo and so to Bukama on the navigable Congo system, where the through route may be said to end. Bukama was reached in 1918. By this time the automobile had come to supply the really flexible link, and steamer services filled in other gaps. Before the end of 1902, the year in which Rhodes died,[3] only the existence of German East Africa interrupted the red on the map from the Cape of Good Hope to the border of Egypt, then a nominal vassal of the Turkish Empire. With the grant by the old League of Nations Mandate over former German East Africa after World War I, that territory became, if not red, at least pink. Before the outbreak of World War II tourist agents were issuing through tickets, using rail, road, and water links from the Cape to Cairo.

Roads in Africa

Speaking in general terms, the importance of the surfaced all-weather road did not come to be appreciated until the growth in use of the automobile, and particulary the truck and motor bus, after World War I. Prior

[3] Sarah Gertrude Mills, *Rhodes,* London, 1933.

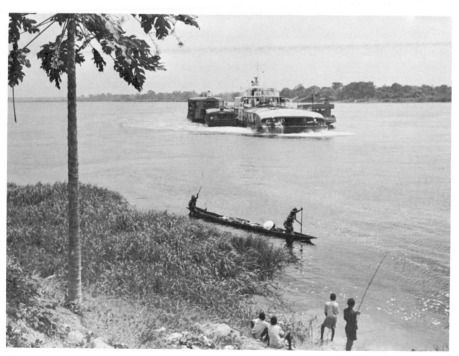

Figure 9.11   A typical African river steamer. This steamer is serving on the River Congo, but is typical of many African river services. (Courtesy United Nations.)

to that time reliance was placed essentially on the railroad for the "opening up" of territories. There is an interesting example of the road pioneer who was before his time in the story of the "Stevenson Road" planned by Mr. James Stevenson, a Glasgow business man and one of the founders of the African Lakes Corporation in 1878. It was designed to link Lake Nyasa (at Karonga) with the southern end of Lake Tanganyika near Abercorn and so to make river-road communication possible from the mouth of the Zambezi to the north of Lake Tanganyika. William McGowan, a young engineer who went to survey and assist in the construction of the road, has left an interesting diary kept from his arrival at Quelimane in 1884.[4] The road was never finished. The railway from Beira via Blantyre to Lake Nyasa superseded the proposed use of the Zambezi, whereas Lake Tanganyika was reached at Kigoma direct by rail (begun in 1905) from Dar-es-Salaam in 1914.

Transportation in Africa at midcentury

If it is true that the economic development of Africa depends on the existence of modern forms of transportation, what was the position in 1950, when the first edition of this book was being written?

With a network of regular airlines, especially British, French, and Belgian, all the main centers had been thrown into ready communication with Europe as far as passengers and mail were concerned. It had become relatively simple to hold pan-African conferences, the delegates traveling by air. European administrators, technicians, and scientific or other advisers could reach most African centers in a couple of days from Europe. There was an economy of time for the administrator going on leave. A West African tour of duty of 18 months, previously involving three weeks' sea travel each way, required only two days. There had grown up thriving African centers almost inaccessible by other means which air travel had made possible. A very good example was Kivu, then called Costermansville, in the healthy Lake Kivu area of the eastern Congo.

Freight of varied kinds can be and is handled by air, but for the development of ordinary commerce reliance is still to a considerable extent on railroads and navigable waterways, with roads acting as "feeders." Figure 9.13 shows by the thick black lines all parts of Africa within 20 miles of a railway or navigable waterway.

Among areas of modern development which would not have been possible without modern forms of transportation, we should note especially the goldfields of the South African Rand, the copper belt of the Katanga and Northern Rhodesia, the tinfields of the Nigerian Jos plateau, the peanut-

---

[4] *Scot. Geog. Mag.,* **LIX,** 1943, 31–36.

Figure 9.12 The Sierra Leone Railway near Freetown. Most African railways are 3 feet, 6 inches or meter (3 feet, 3⅜ inches) gauge, but this one is only 2 feet, 6 inches. The difficulties of railroad engineering in the wetter regions are well illustrated. In the rainy season the water here may be almost up to the rails. (British Official Photograph.)

cotton areas of interior West Africa, the cotton areas of Uganda, the Gezira irrigation area of the Sudan, and many others.

Although the importance of roads as feeders to the railroads has been mentioned in the preceding paragraphs, Africa like other continents has now its trunk roads and long-distance highways. It would now be quite misleading to regard the huge areas shown white on Figure 9.13 as "inaccessible." In the dry season, at least, it is possible for motor trucks to travel over the savanna or nonforested country almost without roads. Where all-weather motor roads have been built, there is an increasing tendency to desert the railroad for the road.

Figure 9.13   Africa, showing in solid black all parts within 20 miles of a railroad or navigable waterway. The railroads may be distinguished by comparing this map with Figure 9.10. The important systems are those constructed in northwest Africa, where there are no waterways, under French influence; the Sudan-Egyptian systems; the South African network; and the rival lines reaching south central Africa through Portuguese territories.

In South Africa especially it is increasingly the habit of many to journey exclusively by road, just as it is in North America, and to make little use of the railroads. Even in equatorial Africa, as described in Chapter 17, the French between the world wars built roads rather than railroads, and everywhere where Italian influence has been marked, roads, not railroads, have resulted.

With the development of roads has come the increasing neglect of waterways, but the Nile, the Great Lakes, and the Congo—with the Niger in part —remain as important highways of trade.

Transportation changes, 1950–1963

Undoubtedly the outstanding development in recent years has been the growth of air transport. Intercontinental travel is now in the main by jet planes cruising at 500 to 600 miles per hour at 25,000 to 40,000 feet, capable of very long "hops" between refueling, but requiring very long runways (up to 2 miles) for takeoff and landing, and hence only able to use well-equipped airports. The result is that each of the new national units endeavours to have at least one airport of the requisite international standard, and from these main ports there is a network of local lines. Also, the possession of a national airline has become a national "status symbol," though frequently such lines are linked in financial or other ways with one of the big world groups. As a result there is frequently a scheduled service of at least one plane a day, between most African cities and the outside world.

Air travel has become a commonplace for many Africans. Apart from its obvious importance in the governmental control of a widely spread territory, it makes possible very speedy transfer of troops, police, and labor. Air transport has proved itself very flexible. A clearing in the bush provides an adequate landing strip for light craft; often the chief danger lies in the wild animals which congregate on the improved grazing which results. Even on the international airport at Nairobi, a pride of lions straying from the nearby National Park has more than once hindered the landing of a jet.

The current African attitude towards railroads offers some curious anomalies. Some countries, notably the Sudan, are actively engaged in extending the railroad system, and Uganda, by pushing the main line westwards, has rendered the working of Ruwenzori copper ores an economic proposition. But a railroad is easily sabotaged: a bridge blown up or a length of rail removed and the railroad is useless. This has happened to the line from Dakar to Bamako at the Senegal-Mali border, and so what would appear a vital link in transportation services has been severed.

Political upheavals have had their effect also on roads. When the first edition of this book was published there were several regular trans-Saharan bus services from Northwest to West Africa, running through French territory and adequately serviced. These no longer function, but elsewhere it is generally true that more and more reliance is placed on transport by road.

The importance of transportation developments

Nothing has had a greater influence on African development than this increased mobility. At the opening of the present century very few Africans had ever been outside their tribal limits. Tribal organization was so strict

Figure 9.14   Main lines of labor movement in Africa. Most of the movement is towards the modern mining centers—the Rand, Katanga, and Jos Plateau of Nigeria. The important movement from the Rhodesias and Nyasaland should be added.

that, even had opportunity offered, permission would not have been granted by tribal chiefs. By 1950 the university colleges which had been established in East and West Africa drew students from so far away that they might spend three months out of their four-month-long vacation getting to and from their homes. Now they can make the same journey in a few hours by plane. It is recorded that in the year 1951 there were no fewer than 50,000 Africans from tropical Africa studying, visiting, and working in England. In 1961 there were at least three times that number. The labor in the Katanga copper mines, or the gold mines of the Rand, is drawn from a very large radius (see Figure 9.14), and it became common to find West Coast Africans who had received a missionary education working as clerks in the offices of Elisabethville in the heart of the Congo.

It is this increased mobility which has been mainly instrumental in disrupting the old tribal system of life, in depriving the chiefs of much of their authority, and in creating a class of Africans having no real roots in the soil. They tend to drift to towns and, as happens in so many parts of the world, social adjustment fails to keep pace. Bad housing conditions, inadequate sanitation, and the spread of the diseases of civilization, especially of venereal disease, result in an inevitable sense of frustration among these footloose Africans. The dignity of tribal life has been lost, and modern concepts of democracy have not yet taken its place.

On the other hand, increased mobility has made possible immensely rapid and beneficial economic development. As we have mentioned elsewhere, first the bicycle and later the automobile, especially the bus, have made the jungle African free to get about his country much more easily than ever before, and much faster. The bush farmer is able to get his surplus crops to a city market, where he has quickly learned to understand and appreciate the products of overseas factories.

There are perhaps two particular aspects of this increased mobility which may be mentioned. The first is the growth everywhere of the village shop or store, now to be found in practically every settlement, where it is possible to buy not only local produce but such universally used imported goods as soaps, patent medicines, cigarettes, cotton and rayon cloth, razor blades, and umbrellas. The shopkeeper not infrequently runs his own car and obtains regular supplies, and as soon as a settlement has become sufficiently large to have a village shop it is almost certain that a taxicab or a motor bus will link it with some larger center.

In the second place, the agents of government can reach with ease all parts of their districts. District commissioners or equivalent regional officials, for example, now cover in a single day distances which would formerly have taken at the average rate of travel of 15 miles per day a matter of weeks. So the great octopus of modern administration spreads its tentacles to the farthest corners of African lands, and along the same channels as law and order come education, social and medical services. In the opposite direction there comes an ever-increasing stream of surplus products available for export, which we will consider in the next chapter.

CHAPTER TEN

Africa and the World

In the last chapter emphasis was placed on the rapidity of change resulting especially from increased mobility of Africa's peoples and the opening up to international commerce of even the remoter parts of this vast continent.

With this increased mobility we can connect what is broadly to be described as a rise in the standard of living, which is evidenced in particular by the increasing variety of food which enters into the daily diet. In due course the old "hungry season" will have been forgotten. Kimble instances the typical case where twenty or thirty years ago the West African fishing village with more than sufficient for its own needs would perhaps be able to export a few miles inland a little dried fish. Today there are villages along the coast near Accra which between them need a fleet of forty trucks to handle their business, and some of their fresh fish is marketed as far as 300 miles upcountry. Thanks to the use of the airplane for commodities of high value, those who enjoy the amenities of higher incomes at such places as Leopoldville could, until the recent troubles, enjoy fresh strawberries, picked at dawn on the eastern highlands of the Congo a thousand miles away. The administrator, the trader, and others who can pay the price need no longer fear the dangers of isolation. When expert medical advice is needed, or hospital treatment is urgent, the helicopter is the answer.

With this increased mobility and the breakdown of old isolation it is becoming increasingly difficult to find even a small group of native Africans untouched by contact with Western peoples and Western ideas (see Figure 10.1). The pygmies of the Congo, the headhunters of the remote interior, the warring feudal tribes of the east, are scarcely to be found any longer. War dances may be remembered and are produced as a show for the visiting tourist. Kimble mentions his visit to a lake in which a former king of the Baganda people in Uganda threw his enemies to be devoured by his pet crocodiles. Today it is used as a swimming pool by his grandson, a graduate of Cambridge University in England.

Yet some of the old African customs are being incorporated with suitable modifications into modern life. The bush telegraph, or talking drum, about which so much has been written by travelers and explorers, is still used. Indeed it has been used to such effect for signaling along some of the tropical African railways that those lines have a better accident record than the finest-equipped lines in Europe and America.

It was one of the surprises of my own studies in West Africa to see in the bazaar at Lagos a druggist's stall, selling all the well-known brands of patent medicine from Europe and America, side by side with the stall of the witch doctor, where mysterious charms in dried skin and bone and hair, and mysterious preparations of roots and stems and seeds, or charms of bone and ivory were in equal demand. In a secluded grove in thick bush one may stumble accidentally upon, rather than be conducted to, a shrine of the fetish worshippers, perhaps to find a very life-like image of the local commissioner skillfully made from cow dung and mud and painted in life-like colors either to be revered or, as the case may be, to have symbolical needles and pins stuck into it. If one makes one's way into a village hut, there are the same uncertainties as to what one may find. It may be that the mud hut is almost devoid of furniture. On the other hand, it is equally likely to include a modern radio set run by dry battery—lately a Japanese transistor set—or a phonograph com-

Figure 10.1 A typical roadside store, Ghana. The coming of the village store, roofed with corrugated iron and with sheets of corrugated iron for sale, is a sure sign that Western civilization has reached an African village. (Copyright L. Dudley Stamp.)

plete with latest American records. In either case it is more than probable that the owner of the hut will possess a thoroughly efficient and modern three-speed bicycle.

As in other parts of the world, increased mobility and accessibility have resulted or are resulting in a decline of rural arts and crafts. The two-gallon gasoline container proves itself a far lighter, more efficient, and less easily damaged receptacle for water than an earthenware jar, and a discarded can the most efficient of dippers to be associated with it. Thus the old trade of making earthenware pitchers no longer exists. The same is true of woodworking, and even of metalworking, so that already government-sponsored or mission-sponsored schools are being established to keep alive the old arts and crafts. With house building the same is true. The great desire is for that curse of the tropics, corrugated or galvanized iron. The sheets which rust so readily in wet tropical climates are to be found everywhere, but even without attention they last longer than straw for the roofs. They are not inflammable and they keep out the wet, though anyone who has suffered through a night of heavy rainfall in a hut roofed with galvanized iron or has felt the heat which develops in the interior under the high sun of noon must be forced to doubt whether this modern progress is really progress.

The inevitable change everywhere is of course affecting clothing. The general tendency is for more clothing—incidentally, a greater demand on the world's factories; and there are those medical men who link the increase of certain diseases with this increase in the amount of clothing worn. The human skin does not suffer from being wet by heavy tropical downpours, but cotton clothing soaked through by a similar downpour and left to dry on the body may well be responsible for the growth in tuberculosis and other diseases of the lung which are indeed so serious in the wetter parts of tropical Africa.

African womenfolk, notably in West Africa, have tended to develop flowing styles in brightly colored and broadly patterned cottons and rayon which have now become characteristic. African men, on the other hand, away from the Mohammedan districts, tend to adopt the inevitable shorts or trousers and shirt of European pattern, wearing full European costume only on important occasions, or according to the dignity and importance of the position of the wearer.

Africa's contribution to world trade

For centuries the outside world has had an interest in African products. In the early days it was ivory, black ivory, and gold. Later came an appreciation of a wider range of African products, mahogany and wild rubber, gums from the bush country, or leather, such as the so-called Morocco leather from West Africa. Then there were the search for minerals and the realization that hidden away in the heart of Africa were vast deposits of copper, so much needed by the Western world, gold, and diamonds. So by the middle of the twentieth century we found the Congo-Rhodesian copper area producing nearly 20 per cent of the world's total and other fields in prospect of development. The largest diamond mines in the world, formerly claimed by Kimberly in South Africa, are now to be found in Tanganyika. The enormous deposits now proved of iron ore, of bauxite for the production of aluminum, and the important, if not outstanding, deposits of tin ore— the Congo and Nigeria producing approximately 20 per cent of the world's total—chromium, manganese, and cobalt are all indications of Africa's mineral wealth. In the first edition of this book, as recently as 1953, it was possible to say, "Of oil there is little and little likelihood of any." Only ten years later it is possible to point to the northern Sahara as one of the major oil-producing regions of the world and also to the considerable output of the coastlands of Nigeria. Of coal, except in South Africa and limited fields in Tanganyika, Nigeria, and Rhodesia, it is doubtful whether Africa has any great riches. On the other hand, there is general agreement that the potential hydroelectric power far exceeds that of any other continent; possibly Africa has one-third of the total water power potential of the entire world. In *Tropical Africa*, Vol I, pp. 251–263, George Kimble gives Burrow's estimate of 274 million horsepower, or about 41 per cent of the world total, as potential, and an already impressive list of hydroelectric plants installed though only using ½₅₀ of the estimated potential. Among the seventeen great projects described in *Tropical Africa* are the Coka Dam on the Awash River of Ethiopia; the Edea plant on the Sanaga River of Cameroun; the Zongo, Tshopo, and Ruzizi plants in the Congo, with the vaster Inga project; four projects in Angola; two in Mozambique; the Owen Falls plant in Uganda; the spectacular Kariba Dam on the Zambezi; and finally, the great Volta project in Ghana. Kimble deals only with tropical Africa, and his details do not include the Nile works in Egypt and the Sudan, the works in South Africa, or the northwestern countries.

If mineral deposits are expendable resources, this water power is not, and is a permanent asset of the continent. But the greatest of all the present and future problems of Africa is the development of the food-producing capabilities of the land.

The *Geographical Review* for October, 1961, includes a large folding map accompanied by a brief explanatory text on the source areas of export production in tropical Africa, prepared by Dr. W. A. Hance of Columbia University and two of his doctoral candidates, which is of very great interest. By taking the trade returns for 1957 from the United Nations *Statistical*

Yearbook, the total value of exports from the continent was found to be distributed as follows.

Union of South Africa and High Commission Territories.............	22 per cent
North Africa (Morocco, Algeria, Tunisia, Libya and Egypt).........	25 per cent
Madagascar..	1 per cent
Tropical Africa...	52 per cent
Commonwealth Countries.................................	26 per cent
French Community..	9 per cent
Belgian Congo..	8 per cent
Others...	9 per cent

Taking tropical Africa alone, the total value of all exports was $2,892,700,000. West Africa contributed 36 per cent of the whole, West Central Africa 27 per cent, British East Africa 12 per cent, and Central East Africa (Federation of Rhodesia and Nyasaland and Mozambique) 17 per cent. Tropical Africa contributed in 1957 2.93 per cent of total free-world exports (one-seventh of the United States' contribution) so that Africa as a whole contributed about 5½ per cent of world exports.

The main exports of tropical Africa are found to belong to a restricted range, and the chief are listed as follows:

Vegetable products	*64.9 per cent*
Coffee	13.4
Cacao	10.3
Peanuts	8.7
Cotton	8.6
Palm products	5.9
Timber and wood	3.6
Tobacco	2.7
Rubber	2.4
Sisal	1.6
Bananas	1.2
Tea	1.0
Animal Products	*2.8 per cent*
Hides and skins	1.2
Mineral Products	*27.1 per cent*
Copper	13.3
Diamonds	3.8
Gold	2.0
Tin	1.7
Cobalt	1.2
Manufactured products	*0.4 per cent*
Unaccounted	*4.8 per cent*

The map, says Dr. Hance, "displays a pattern of many productive 'islands' set in vast seas of emptiness." The "islands" are closely related to lines of communication; many are coastal or peripheral. Rather naturally the mineral islands stand in a special position, and twelve are listed.

1. The Katanga copper belt—the top-ranking export area of tropical Africa, with 15.5 per cent of the total value of exports.
2. Southwestern Ghana—manganese, gold, diamonds, and bauxite.
3. Sierra Leone—iron ore and diamonds.
4. Liberia—Bomi Hills iron ore.
5. Guinea—bauxite and iron ore.
6. Nigeria—Jos Plateau tin.
7. Kasai-Angola—diamonds.
8. East Congo and Ruanda-Urundi—scattered tin, gold, and tantalum.
9. Southern Rhodesia—gold, asbestos, and chrome.
10. Tanganyika—lead and diamonds.
11. Uganda—Kilembe copper.
12. Kenya—Lake Magadi soda.

It is indicative of the relatively undeveloped character of Africa's lands that Dr. Hance lists only four irrigation areas, with the Gezira as the only really outstanding one—1.8 per cent of tropical Africa's exports. The others are the inland Niger delta, the Gash-Tokar deltas in Sudan, and the pump schemes along the Nile in northern Sudan. To these might be added the works along the Limpopo in Mozambique. There is, of course, much irrigation in extra-tropical Africa—in Egypt, the northwestern states, and South Africa.

A special group of productive islands are highland areas (a quarter of the whole output), of which nine are listed, the chief being East Africa, Southern Rhodesia, Ruanda-Urundi, Cameroun, and Ethiopia.

The fourteen isolated coastal areas listed, not in order of importance of production, are:

1. Peanut area of Senegal and Gambia.
2. Bananas of Iles de Los and Guinea.
3. Firestone rubber of Liberia.
4. The rich Ivory Coast, with coffee, cacao, bananas, and forest products.
5. The rich cacao-timber area of Ghana.
6. Western Nigeria, with cacao and timber; Eastern, with palm products.
7. Timber of Gabon.
8. Gulf of Guinea islands.
9. Lower Congo—timber and bananas.
10. Angola fisheries.
11. Mozambique coastlands.
12. Tanganyika—sisal and cashew nuts.
13. Zanzibar-Pemba—cloves.
14. Somalia—sugar and bananas.

It is noted that the peanut-cotton area of Northern Nigeria, the scattered cotton lands of Chad and the Central African Republic, the gum arabic–millet zone of central Sudan, and the vegetable-producing areas of central Congo and southeastern Sierra Leone do not fit into the "island" concept.

Expressed in per capita terms, Africa's share in world trade is higher than that of the Far East, though somewhat below that of Latin America.

In certain commodities, however, Africa's output is very great: over 90 per cent of the world's diamonds, four-fifths of the world's cobalt, over half the world's gold, a third of the world's phosphates, a quarter of chromium ore and manganese ore, a fifth of copper. African production of iron ore and of oil have been increasing rapidly.

As regards agricultural production, Africa produces nearly three quarters of the world's cocoa and palm oil, 75 per cent of sisal, and 15 per cent of coffee.

Since World War II Africa has made immense strides politically, but at the expense of seriously disrupting trade and commerce, notably in the Congo.

The labor situation

The labor shortage led the Dutch East India Company as early as the seventeenth century to introduce laborers from the Far East. The process continued, and at a much later stage was followed by successive importations of Indian labor into Natal, Chinese labor into the Transvaal gold mines, and even labor from India, China, and Cuba for railway construction in the Congo. Apart from the fact that Africans had little reason to trust a prospective European employer, they had little or no incentive to exchange labor for wages. The position is now different. Such incentives are developing rapidly. The African naturally desires the products of modern industry, and the development of taxation makes it essential to earn money wages. It is interesting that the native reserves which have been set up, being maintained as areas of tribal life, are to a large extent cut off from the direct effects of development taking place outside. They have no internal capital resources, they become increasingly unable to support their growing populations, and they become exporters of labor.

In Africa as elsewhere in the world there is a drift of population from the country to the towns. Both Ghana and Kenya have reported a shortage of labor on the farms but unemployment in the towns. The migrant labor which has become a feature—for example, in the mining areas of Africa—is in fact relatively inefficient. Much time is lost traveling, much of it being done on foot over great distances in conditions which have bad effects on health. The womenfolk remain behind, with serious social results. There is thus an ever-increasing attempt, as at the steel works at Vereeniging, to retain a stable labor force of both Europeans and Africans.

The present position

Before proceeding to examine the countries and regions of Africa separately, emphasis must be laid on one dominant aspect of the present position. Africa is in the midst of changes so rapid, so kaleidoscopic, sometimes so unexpected, that inevitably parts of this book will be out of date before it can be published. But it would be a bold man indeed who attempted to anticipate events: much that seems likely may never happen; much that seems unlikely may come to pass within a brief span of time.

Late in 1963 UNESCO published from Paris a large volume entitled *A review of the natural resources of the African continent*, which is organized on a basis of topics and has extensive bibliographies of work through 1959.

PART TWO

The Countries and
Regions of Africa

CHAPTER ELEVEN

Egypt and the Nile[1]

Nearly every country in the world has its own individuality, but of Egypt it may be said that here is a country in many ways unique. Because it is unique, it is not in any sense typical of Africa. As the heartland of the Moslem lands of the Near East, and because the Suez isthmus is part of Egypt, it has long been involved in exchanges between the Occident and monsoon Asia. At present Egypt is acting as leader of the Arab states and plans to extend the United Arab Republic from the union of Egypt and Syria to embrace other units. It is then as a country very distinct from the remainder of the continent of Africa that we consider the Republic of Egypt.

The Republic of Egypt (Misr)

Although the total area of the Republic of Egypt is recorded as being 386,198 square miles, the settled and cultivated area comprising the Nile valley, the Nile delta, and the inhabited desert oases covers only about 13,500 square miles—less than a third the area of Pennsylvania. In its physical setting the whole of Egypt is in fact part of the enormous desert belt stretching from the Atlantic shores across the whole of the North African continent and, interrupted only by the Red Sea, into Arabia and Iran. It is in fact one long oasis, 700 miles from north to south, but only 10 to 15 miles wide, except where it is enlarged towards its seaward end into the delta (Figure 11.1). If Egypt of the Nile is thus to be described as an oasis, it is a unique oasis where two factors, the annual flooding of the Nile and the alluvial soils which have been deposited by that river, combine to render the oasis not only unmatched in natural fertility but, as long as the traditional "basin cultivation" was practiced, having that fertility annually renewed.

---

[1] I am greatly indebted to Professor J. H. G. Lebon for help in the revision of this chapter and to Professor Hasan Ahwad, Professor Hamdan, and their colleagues for personal help during visits to Egypt.

Figure 11.1   The Nile basin.

Whether Herodotus, when he wrote of Egypt some 3000 years ago, was already quoting some previous authority, or whether his *bon mot* was indeed original, it is to Herodotus that we commonly give credit for a statement which has perhaps been repeated more times than any other in geographical literature—that "Egypt is the gift of the Nile" (see Figure 11.2). However banal the statement may be, it remains eternally true. Thanks to the Nile, what would otherwise be a complete desert is a fertile and prosperous country with a history of human settlement unrivaled anywhere in the world.

Apart from a small and irregular amount along the Mediterranean fringe

Figure 11.2   A general map of Egypt.

Figure 11.3   The Nile valley in Upper Egypt at Thebes, Luxor. The air view shows very clearly the rocky wall of the Nile valley and the desert which lies beyond. It is clearly impossible to extend the irrigated land shown in the foreground. (Copyright Aerofilms Library.)

of the delta, Egypt receives practically no rain during the whole of the year.

The country as a whole falls quite simply into a number of physical divisions. The Nile itself runs between parallel lines of cliffs, in some places only 220 yards wide, but normally a few miles apart (Figure 11.3). From the edge of the bounding cliff on the east, the so-called Arabian Desert rises towards the shores of the Red Sea, culminating in a mountain range with peaks reaching between 4000 and 7000 feet. The drop to the Red Sea is sudden, and northwards where the Red Sea narrows into the Gulf of Suez the rugged relief is continued in the peninsula of Sinai. By contrast, to the west of the Nile valley, the Libyan hills subside gently into the broad flat plain of the great Libyan Desert. In places the surface of this plain sinks in shallow, broad depressions in which are to be found series of scattered oases. The Libyan Desert as a whole becomes lower in its general elevation from south towards the north, and it is in the north that, locally over a considerable area, its surface lies below sea level before rising slightly into the Libyan Plateau, which itself overlooks the Mediterranean Sea in the low scarp so well known to those who served in the North African campaigns in World War II. One depression in this western desert, lying near the Nile itself, is the famous oasis of El Faiyum, lying below sea level and in such a position that flood waters from the Nile can be directed into it. It is thus extensively cultivated and able to support a large population. Below Cairo the Nile divides into its distributaries which pass through the delta on their way to the Mediterranean.

As previously noted, the shape of the Nile Delta is the inverted capital Greek letter Δ (delta), and it may even be claimed that the word "delta" is one of the oldest geographical terms in existence.

Climatically, it may be said that the Egyptian year falls into two parts— a mild winter from about November to April and a hot summer from May to October, which is often ushered in by that scorching wind from the south known as the khamsin. As understood in midlatitudes there is no spring and no fall. The absence of the cyclonic disturbances which are so usual in midlatitudes results in a monotony of climatic conditions during most of the year; sudden variations in temperature are rare, except occasionally in winter. Since agriculture depends upon irrigation water, man has control to a very considerable extent over times of harvest. There is the end of the cool season when the midlatitude crops come to fruition (chetoi harvest) in April and May, followed by a second (nili) harvest when subtropical crops are ready for gathering, in July and August. Despite the fact that Egypt is 700 miles from north to south, stretching over some 8 or 9 degrees of latitude, there is little difference in the main crops which can be grown throughout the country. We shall consider later in this chapter the regime of the River Nile in detail with its spectacular seasonal flood, coming between July and December—a natural phenomenon long unexplained, but recognized for 5000 years as the basis upon which cultivation and settlement depend.

Historical outline

Such in brief is the physical background of the country whose history recorded in substantial monuments from the past is longer and less interrupted than that of any other land. Although some writers distinguish Upper, Middle, and Lower Egypt, the time-honored division is Upper Egypt—broadly speaking, the Nile valley above Cairo—and Lower Egypt, the delta below Cairo.

It was Menes, the founder of the First Dynasty, who united Upper and Lower Egypt, and from that time to the present day, between six and seven thousand years, Egypt has remained a unit and under a single government, except for very brief periods. Although this unity may be explained by saying that Egypt is an oasis naturally isolated by sea and desert, it remains a remarkable fact. It is true that where irrigation has to be planned and executed in terms of the country as a whole, unified control is essential. It may also be said that once the foreign invader has braved the sea and the desert and reached the fertile oasis his task of conquest is easy, and no natural barrier remains to prevent his hold over the whole.

The oasis-island which is thus Egypt has had another and most interesting effect upon its people. Though there are some slight differences between the people of the delta with somewhat lighter skins than the people of Upper Egypt, there is an essential unity throughout Egyptians in both their physical and mental characteristics. If one can judge from the representations of their ancestors in the days of the Pharaohs they have remained physically the same for thousands of years.

Through all the thousands of years of their history the Egyptian people have enjoyed, or perhaps one may say have suffered from, an essentially autocratic and highly centralized government. In Dynastic Egypt the Pharaohs were absolute rulers with a few carefully selected and autocratically appointed ministers. Their rule was absolute throughout the country. There was no tradition of local autonomy, no hereditary feudal aristocracy so general in other lands. It may be said that Egypt has known bureaucracy from its earliest days. The rank and file of the Egyptian people, the peasants, or fellaheen, of today have thus always been subject to a strict, sometimes harsh and oppressive, government. The effect of this has been clearly assessed by Professor Charles Issawi in his interesting book, *Egypt: An Economic and Social Analysis.* He suggests that ". . . the result has been greatly to weaken individualistic feeling and completely to uproot the spirit of municipal enterprise. Several millennia of centralized autocracy have accustomed the Egyptians to look to the government for the initiation of any business whatsoever. At the same time the rapacity of the governors has led to a proven distrust of the government, the effects of which are still unfortunately too visible. In addition to political oppression Egypt has always suffered from intense economic exploitation." He goes on to instance the enormous amount of human labor which must have gone into the erection of the pyramids and how at intervals even the long-suffering Egyptians attempted to unite in popular revolts.

The autocratic centralized government of Egypt has always, it may be said, been superimposed, and throughout practically the whole of its history the Egyptian people has been under foreign domination. In dynastic Egypt there was the invasion and the control of the country by the Hyksos or Shepherd Kings (1700 B.C.) from the heart of Arabia and also by Nubians from the south (c. 700 B.C.). Even if the Pharaohs of ancient Egypt are to be regarded as assimilating themselves with the people of the country which they ruled, and in that sense may be regarded as Egyptians, they often chose foreign advisers to carry out their designs. The favorite Old Testament story of Joseph is a most interesting example. Because it was reported that Joseph, languishing in prison, was an able interpreter of dreams, the Pharaoh of the day had him brought forth, and because his interpretations of Pharaoh's dreams appeared authentic and carried conviction he was immediately made second only to Pharaoh himself in control of the whole country.

Complete outside control of Egypt definitely came into existence with the Persian conquest in 525 B.C. The Persians in due course were ousted in 332

B.C. by the Macedonians under Alexander the Great, and in 30 B.C. the Romans took the place of the Macedonians. The varied interpretations which have been given to the story of Cleopatra, from Shakespeare to George Bernard Shaw, may serve to illustrate the relationship between Roman governors and Egyptian leaders. As the Roman Empire faded and Byzantium took its place, Egypt was left open to conquest by the Arabs, and to its lasting incorporation in the Moslem world. The Arabs acquired the country in A.D. 642 and controlled Egypt for two centuries, always from outside the country, from Medina, from Damascus, and from Baghdad. In A.D. 868 the first Turkish dynasty was established. Almost exactly a century later the Moslem Fatimite king—this time from the west—overran the country, but it was a Kurdish successor to the Fatimites who saved Egypt from the Crusaders. Although the country was conquered again by the Ottoman Turks in 1516, Egyptian rulers preserved their identity and acknowledged in a somewhat perfunctory way the nominal authority of the Sultan of Turkey.

When Napoleon I turned his attention to Egypt and the French expedition of 1798 reached the country, Egypt was a poor, isolated, and neglected backwater of the Ottoman Empire. Its once prosperous trade centered on the ancient port of Alexandria had been ruined by the diversion of world trade routes from the Mediterranean to the Atlantic after the discovery and development of the Americas. Although the conquest of Egypt by Napoleon Bonaparte was itself ephemeral, it was the beginning of a new era in Egyptian development. It marked the return of Egypt into the sphere of European commerce and laid the foundation for the future role of Egypt in the life of the world around the Mediterranean Sea.

Napoleon was less interested in the internal development of Egypt and the restoration of the age-old agriculture of the country than he was in the possibilities of developing Egypt on a colonial model, its destiny being to supply such tropical products as cotton and cane sugar which could not be produced in the homelands of France herself, but which were of enormous importance in the Napoleonic French World Empire. The seeds were sown, and when, a few years later, the dynasty under Mohammed Ali (an Albanian) became established, Egypt herself went ahead, and more and more the economic prosperity of the country became linked with the expansion of cotton cultivation, the development of the delta, and commerce with Europe. Although Egypt remained nominally a part of the Ottoman Empire, the influence of the Sultan at Constantinople became less and less. Mohammed Ali himself, following the autocratic procedure of his innumerable predecessors, attempted to create an industrialized, closed, and state-controlled economy, and to expand Egypt so as to include part of the remains of the Ottoman Empire.

But in the meantime European powers had come to have other interests in Egypt, and Mohammed Ali's plan was defeated by those European powers in 1841. This is another key date in Egyptian history.

It was a design of Napoleon Bonaparte who first, if he did not originate, brought to the fore the concept of a canal through the isthmus of Suez to link the Mediterranean Sea with the Red Sea and thus to provide a seaway from Europe to India and the Far East. As British interests in India expanded and were consolidated it was naturally they who would appear to have had the main interest in such a project. Actually British personnel of the great East India Company passing to and from Britain and India were taken by ship to Egypt, to the old port of Alexandria. They traveled by river boat up the Nile to a point above Cairo, where they transferred to desert caravans for the land passage across to the shores of the Red Sea, there to embark on the second sea stage of the journey to their Indian destinations. The ships of the old Peninsular and Oriental Steam Navigation Company (P. and O.) provided the means, and when any such route, however tedious and inconvenient, has become established, vested interests are unwilling to see such a radical change as would result from the construction of a canal and a through route. We deal below with the story of the Suez Canal, but, although the British even more than the French had become concerned with the destiny of the project, so essential to the development of easy communication from the home country to India and the Far East, the British government officially opposed the scheme!

In 1870 came the defeat of France by the Prussians, only one year after the opening of the Suez Canal. Britain's interest in Egypt immediately became a positive one, the desire—indeed the need—to secure effective control if not over Egypt herself at least over Egypt as part of the vital sea route to the east. The opportunity came in 1882 when the Egyptian ruler asked for Britain's help in quelling a nationalist revolt marked by antiforeign riots in Cairo and Alexandria.

From 1882 to 1914, although remaining nominally a vassal of the Turkish Empire, Egypt became in effect a British protectorate. British troops were stationed in the country to maintain order and in particular to guard the Suez Canal. With the outbreak of World War I in 1914, Turkey allied herself with Germany and thus became ranged on the side of Britain's enemies. Consequently Egypt was declared on December 18, 1914, a British protectorate. This was a wartime expedient, and the protectorate came to an end on February 28, 1922, when the Sultan of Egypt became hereditary ruler and was proclaimed king on the fifteenth of March. From that date Egypt has been an independent state, and steadily the evidences of independence have become more and more marked. Extraterritorial privileges enjoyed by European powers were abolished in 1937. Later, after the conclusion of World

War II, when Egypt so nearly became a victim of German invasion, British troops were withdrawn from Egypt. They left the quarters which they had so long occupied in Cairo, a small number remaining for guard duties along the Suez Canal.

Thus with the proclamation of the late King Fuad I as king in 1922 the dynasty established by Mohammed Ali became the recognized ruling house of Egypt, and the declaration of 1922 established the succession of kings in the direct male line by primogeniture, after the European model. A constitution was introduced in 1923, and, although suspended from 1935 onwards, it was reintroduced in 1945. In 1952 a military group, focusing widespread discontent, forced the abdication of Fuad's successor, and though for a year his infant son was nominally accepted as king, in 1953 a republic was proclaimed, and in due course the military leader, General Nasser, became president. A treaty of 1936 had defined relationships with Britain and recognized Britain's right to station troops to guard the Suez Canal. This treaty Egypt declared to be at an end in 1951. Troops were withdrawn and the canal nationalized in 1956. In 1958 Egypt and Syria joined as the United Arab Republic (U.A.R.). This was dissolved in 1961, but was reformed in 1963.

The population problem of Egypt

Few populations are as homogeneous throughout as the people of Egypt. The fundamental element is constituted by the fellaheen, or peasants, which form some 82 per cent of the total. From earliest times they have kept their Hamitic type almost pure. Moderately tall, slightly built, with long limbs and broad shoulders, and a pronounced nose, they are very strongly contrasted with their Negro neighbors to the south. Although there has undoubtedly been some mixture with the Arabs of the north and the Negroes of the south, this seems to have exercised but little influence on physical type, and still less on manners and customs. The habitation of the fellaheen is still built as it was in the time of the Pharaohs of dried mud over a framework, a house often without any opening save the door, and the sole furniture of which is a chest for clothes, a low table and a few cushions and mats. There is an advantage in the absence of other openings, for the smoke which accumulates within acts as a deterrent to the eternal plague of mosquitoes.

The fellaheen were converted to Mohammedanism, and consequently Egypt is a keystone in the great Moslem world. Next in importance is that element of the population represented by the Coptic Christians, descendants of those ancient Egyptians who adopted Christianity in the fourth century, and whose head is the Coptic Patriach of Alexandria. They are grouped especially in Middle Egypt, around Assiut (Asyut), which is sometimes called the Coptic Capital, and in the Faiyum. Unlike the fellaheen, who are almost exclusively farmers and who remain essentially dwellers in the country, the

Copts have tended to drift into towns and become artisans, traders, merchants, and money lenders. Until recent times they often lived in walled and guarded enclosures, as in Cairo. Together with Greek Orthodox Christians they number well over a million.

These are the two essential elements in the indigenous population of Egypt as far south as Aswan. South of Aswan lies Nubia; the people of the valley are Nubians with strong Negro affinities. There are besides half a million mixed Bedouin Arabs in the deserts of Lower Egypt, and pure Bedouins in the Nubian Desert.

The population of Egyptian towns is much more mixed. There may be found by the side of indigenous Egyptians, Arabs, Nubians, Turks, Greeks, Syrians, Armenians, and Jews, and especially that mixture of races so typical of the ports and bazaars of the eastern Mediterranean, commonly called Levantine. To this total it is necessary to add 100,000 French, English, Belgians, Italians, and other Europeans.

In common with other countries of the Mediterranean the population of Egypt has shown a remarkable rise in the last century and a half. The French mission of Napoleon Bonaparte estimated the number in the whole country rather under 2½ million people. In 1821 Mohammed Ali found a little over this figure—2,536,000. Under the wise agricultural policy for which he was largely responsible, the population grew rapidly. Incidentally, Egypt is the only African country for which adequate and accurate population statistics exist over a considerable period. In 1846 the population had reached nearly 4½ million, in 1882 nearly 7 million; by 1927 this had doubled to 14¼ million. In 1937 the census gave a total of no less than 15,932,694; and ten years later, in 1947, the staggering figure of 19,087,304 was recorded. The increase continues; the census of 1957 recorded more than 23,300,000 and the estimate for 1 Jan 1960 was 25,625,000. The population density reaches 1900 per square mile in the so-called "settled" area. Although Egypt exhibits the worldwide tendency towards urbanization, there are still only two really large cities[2]: Cairo, which approaches 4 million according to the estimate of January 1964, and Alexandria, which had reached 1.4 million by 1959. The modern port of Port Said at the entrance to the Suez Canal approached 230,000, the older port at its southern end, Suez, only a little over 156,000. Figures for other urban centers will be found in the Appendix.

The rapid population increase combined with the already extremely high

[2] The use of the word "city" involves a problem in Africa. In English-speaking countries, an urban agglomeration would be referred to as a town, the word "city" being reserved for those which have been accorded a certain important status, following the usage in Britain. Thus Nairobi is often referred to as the first and only "city" in East Africa, having been created a City by Charter.

density on the cultivable land gives Egypt a population problem which seems well-nigh insoluble. Along the margins of the valley and delta, by lifting the water higher, the area of the irrigated land may be extended a small amount, and there are some areas where the old basin irrigation may be replaced by the more efficient perennial irrigation, but any increase in food output which might result would not match the needs. Moreover, in contrast to other parts of Africa, crop yields are already very high, and from the point of view of yield per acre Egyptian farming is already so efficient that there is little hope of an adequate solution in this direction. Although the new Aswan high dam may increase the cultivable area by 50 per cent, the Egyptians look to increasing industrialization as their main hope. Much money has been spent on the development of various textile factories—cotton, wool, rayon, and silk—and manufactures include also glassware, soap, fertilizers, leather, metalworking, pottery, sugar, cigarettes, and alcoholic beverages (Figure 11.4). Still newer developments are iron, steel, automobiles, and aircraft. How far these devel-

Figure 11.4 Inside a modern Egyptian cotton mill at Mehala el Kobra, one of the industrial developments of Egypt. (Copyright Deane Dickason from Ewing Galloway.)

opments will go towards supporting a surplus population running into millions is another matter. Modern Egypt is now fully alive to the value of the tourist trade; luxury hotels are among the many fine new buildings of Cairo, Aswan, and elsewhere.

The regions of Egypt

For a consideration of the country as a whole, we may regard Egypt as divided into: the Western Deserts (Libyan Desert); the Eastern Deserts (Arabian and Nubian Deserts); the Nile valley, or Upper Egypt; the Nile delta, or Lower Egypt; the Faiyum. The two great desert tracts represent 97 per cent of the surface of the country but have less than 2 per cent of the population.

The Western Deserts (Libyan Desert). The plateaus which make up the greater part of the surface of the country consist in the extreme southwest of the ancient metamorphic rocks and granites of the great African Massif. These are covered as we proceed northward by gently inclined sheets of sediment, giving rise, as a result of weathering, to great flat-topped, table-like hills or mesas. The sedimentary rocks dip gently northward, but at a slightly higher angle than the surface of the country, so that geologically the beds become younger and younger as one goes towards the Mediterranean. North of the southern outcrops of ancient rocks are found the wide stretches of Nubian sandstone, then northward wide expanses of limestone. This explains the essential structure of the Libyan Desert to the west of the Nile valley. In the south the surface is covered with superficial deposits of sand. It is one of the least habitable parts of the whole Sahara, avoided by nomads and caravans alike, no oasis relieving its arid surface, no settlement of significance existing.

The northern portion of the Libyan Desert formed by the lower plateau surfaces of limestone is relatively more habitable. A long line of oases, shown in Figure 11.2, occupies the depressions over a distance of 600 miles. There are numerous salt lakes, but in places wells reach fresh water. Where this is the case the oases can support populations which run into thousands. The oasis of Dakhla, for example, has at least 15,000 people and a permanent capital town with as many as four mosques. Between the actual oases several nomadic tribes contrive to find sufficient pasture for their camels and provide means of transport for the oasis inhabitants. It is one of the great features of life in the Mohammedan world that the pilgrimage to Mecca demands movement, and even these remote oases supply their quota of pilgrims for the sacred journey. Catering for pilgrims is one of the great occupations throughout the Mohammedan world. Thus these oases of the northern Libyan Desert are linked by a regular and frequented route, leading particularly to the capital.

The Eastern Deserts (Arabian and Nubian Deserts). To the east of the Nile, to which is naturally attached the Sinai Peninsula, the desert tract between the Nile and the sea is relatively narrow, but its surface is much more varied, and the country has in places considerable natural resources. The mountain belt, partly of volcanic origin, which borders the shore of the Red Sea is continued along both sides of the trough or rift valley of the narrow Gulf of Suez, and so into the southern part of the Sinai Peninsula. As any voyager by steamer down the Gulf of Suez is able to recognize, the arid shore is far from hospitable. Actual access to the shore is rendered dangerous by coral reefs, so that there is no port between Suez, the southern end of the Suez Canal, and the little harbor of Quseir or Cossair. Here and there in little basins amid the rugged sandstone or basalt mountains are little agricultural villages; and along the south there is an inhabited trench, the depression of Keneh, lying between the volcanic belt and the true Arabian Desert.

In the Peninsula of Sinai the desert plateau fades northeastwards into the Negev or Israeli desert, inhabited by a few nomadic pastoralists. In the southwestern parts of the peninsula, along the shores of the Gulf of Suez and the Red Sea, there are little cultivated basins among the rocky mountains and numerous fishing villages. The Peninsula of Sinai is indeed a land of transition. The east looks to and fades into Asiatic lands, the west looks towards and is dependent upon Egypt proper.

The eastern deserts of Egypt and the Peninsula of Sinai are not without economic significance. There are precious stones, also the famous turquoise, some deposits of phosphate rock and nitrate and the small but significant oil fields which have long been worked along the western shores of the Gulf of Suez. To this must be added the larger oilfields discovered from 1949 onwards at Sudr, Asl, and elsewhere in the peninsula. There are salt deposits, too, and from the mountains of the Arabian Desert Egypt obtained and still obtains some of those magnificent building stones—porphyry, granite, and sandstone—used in Egypt's famous monuments dating from the time of the Pharaohs, though the most famous of all is the pink granite of Aswan.

The Nile valley or Upper Egypt. This valley is the Khem (signifying "dark") of the Egyptians, a name which points the contrast with the white shimmering desert stretches on either side. The Nile is navigable throughout Egypt as far south as the town of Aswan at the First Cataract. The navigable Nile is paralleled also to Aswan by the main railway. The Aswan dam, just above Aswan, holds back the Nile waters to form a long narrow lake almost to the Egyptian southern border, and this stretch of water is navigated by river craft and steamers of the Sudan railways to the town of Wadi Halfa just inside the Sudan Republic and below the Second Cataract. Wadi Halfa is the northern terminus of the Sudan Railways running to Khartoum and Port

Sudan. The long-discussed plan to build a new high dam above Aswan, actually started in 1960 with Russian help, will flood riverside villages, together with such famous monuments as the Abu Simbel temples, and also Wadi Halfa itself, though it will enable important additional areas in Egypt to be brought under irrigation. Above Aswan begins the ancient land of Nubia—included in what the French would call *Afrique noire*, the Africa of the Negroes.

Upper Egypt consists of a succession of irrigated basins marked off from one another by those points where the two cliff-like walls of the river valley approach close to one another. Those who distinguish a Middle Egypt regard Upper Egypt as stretching as far northwards as the Thebes Basin. This basin, the ancient site of Thebes, was perhaps the richest of all the basins of the Nile valley in ancient times, and it was around it that the Middle Empire developed. The incredible richness in ruins of temples and palaces of this part of the Nile valley, at Thebes, at Karnak, and at Luxor in particular, is lasting evidence of ancient glories. At the present day the ancient system of basin irrigation has been almost completely replaced by perennial irrigation from the Aswan dam. This area has become the principal region of cultivation of the sugar cane and the site of the principal sugar factories, which have given new prosperity to modern Egypt.

On the whole the valley widens northwards and is lined by a succession of towns and large villages, among which one may regard Asyut as the chief of this very rich region of Middle Egypt.

The Nile valley stretches as far as Cairo (Figure 11.5). Curiously enough, Cairo has been the capital of Egypt only since 1863, unless one regards Cairo as merely the resiting of ancient Memphis after the Moslem conquest. The fact that Cairo has become the heart of Egypt is due to the economic development of the delta in the past century and a half. From the point of view of modern Egypt, Cairo is perhaps the most rationally situated capital in the world. Its predecessor, Memphis, was on the western or left bank of the Nile, nestling under the low limestone cliff on which were built the great pyramids (Figure 11.6) and the Sphinx. In contrast, Cairo originated on the right or eastern bank of the river, on or below a projection of the desert plateau. There the Arab conquerer of Egypt, 'Amr, built a mosque on the site of the former Roman citadel. To the Arab town was added later the Turkish town, the citadel built by Saladin and, in due course, the Levantine town built by Mohammed Ali and his son. The modern cosmopolitan city of Cairo flowed from the foot of the hills, across the alluvial plain, to the Nile itself, and its suburbs have crossed over the river to the western side and now stretch all along the road from Cairo to the pyramids, displacing the cultivation of the Nile alluvium.

Figure 11.5   The site of Cairo. With the recent growth of the city to over three million inhabitants, suburbs have spread westward over the cultivated lands, and development is almost continuous to the pyramids at El Giza. East of the Citadel a new garden city, Muqattam or Mokkattam, is under construction on the surface of the plateau.

The Nile delta or Lower Egypt. The area of the delta is double that of the Nile valley or Upper Egypt. If, therefore, the whole could be placed under cultivation it would play a prominent role in Egyptian economy. Whereas Upper Egypt, the Nile valley, has a history of cultivation going back for thousands of years, the final conquest of the delta is the result of the comparatively modern activity of man, armed with the knowledge and the tools of science. For long the outer delta of the Nile was simply an immense area of sand, traversed by the seven branches of the river, two of them reasonably navigable, interrupted by long lagoons, or land periodically flooded or impregnated by salt. Ancient Egypt used only the inner delta lands. The outer delta in fact remained a desert barrier between Upper Egypt and those centers of commercial activity, the ports of Alexandria, Abukir, Rosetta, and Damietta. The branches of the river were the commercial routes which linked the Mediterranean ports with Egypt proper. Today modern perennial irriga-

Figure 11.6   The Great Pyramids of El Giza from the air. (Copyright Geographical Publications.)

tion and the drainage of marshes and lagoons have made the delta the principal economic region of Egypt, with cotton as the chief cash crop. The population has become widely distributed and dense, but it is the land and not the sea which matters. Much of the delta coast itself is still deserted and cut off by lagoons from the cultivated lands.

Alexandria, founded by Alexander the Great in 332 B.C., was a naval base against the Persians as well as an outlet for Egyptian commerce, and it remained for over 2000 years the largest city in Egypt. Like most ports associated with the world's great deltas it lies not on the delta but to one side —in this case the western side—where it is free from silting up, which would have resulted in the past from deposits of Nile alluvium. Thanks to the Island of Faros, the port enjoys shelter from Mediterranean storms and suffered an eclipse in fortune only when the Atlantic sea routes replaced the Mediterranean. Although it might be thought that the opening of the Suez

Canal would have taken trade and traffic exclusively to Port Said, Alexandria has more than shared in the great redevelopment of Mediterranean commerce.

The Faiyum. Properly speaking, the Faiyum is a depression in the Libyan Desert comparable with those previously mentioned in which are found the oases. The only difference—but it is an essential one—rests in the fact that it lies below sea level, and by a connecting channel with the Nile valley receives the vitalizing waters from the main river. Although this connecting channel is doubtless natural, it has been carefully remade and controlled by the hand of man. It is a large basin, over 500 square miles. Already in 1882 it had more than 200,000 inhabitants; by 1927 the total had reached over half a million, and in 1957 over three-quarters of a million. The capital, Medinet el Faiyum, is a town of considerable size, surrounded by numerous villages in which the inhabitants live by the exportation of fruits, baskets made from local oziers, and pottery made from local clay. In addition to the ordinary crops cultivated throughout Egypt, the oasis of the Faiyum specializes in fruits such as oranges, lemons, grenadines, figs, apricots, nectarines, olives, and the traditional grape. As a result of this fruit cultivation, the area has a delightfully wooded appearance, quite different from that of the open Nile Valley.

Irrigation and agriculture

In its course through Egypt the Nile runs smoothly and evenly, usually nearer the eastern side of its valley. The river level falls slightly from January to May and June, when it reaches its lowest level. In July the water rises rapidly and continues to do so through August and September, reaching its highest point in Lower Egypt in the month of October, when it is normally 7½ meters or about 25 feet above its low level of May–June. The level of the river then falls rapidly through November and December, more gradually through the succeeding months.

As in so many eastern countries, water can be lifted from the river and equally from wells by the shadoof, which consists of a bucket, or bag of skin, suspended from the end of a long pole balanced by a counterweight. By the shadoof water is commonly and easily raised 7 to 10 feet or more, and a succession of lifts may raise water considerably higher. Another method of lifting water a short distance is the Archimedean screw, and the more elaborate types of lift operated by cattle or donkeys are still widely used, including the *saqia* or Persian waterwheel, although small mechanical pumps are now common. The traditional form of irrigation in Egypt, however, is basin irrigation. The waters of the river at the time of flood are led off into carefully constructed inundation or flood canals, from which the water passes into a basin where the flat field or fields are enclosed by low earth banks. These basins vary in size and may be anything up to 100,000 acres. The Nile waters at time of flood are rich in a reddish-gray silt, which is naturally deposited and left behind in the basins. Unbeknown to the ancient Egyptians, the slime or ooze to which Shakespeare refers is derived from far-away Ethiopia. It represents the results of natural geological as well as soil erosion from distant areas, and, as much of the silt is derived from areas of basic volcanic rocks, it is naturally rich in mineral salts.

The peasant sows his seed broadcast in the damp mud which is left when the waters are led off from one basin into the next. There follows for the cultivator a period of comparative rest until the harvest is ready. The corn which has been sown at the beginning of November is ripe by early February. Other plants, sown a little later or with a longer vegetative period, may not be ready until April or May. This is the natural winter harvest, the so-called *chetoi.*

It happens naturally that the borders of the valley are too high to be covered by the river floods which inundate the basins. Water must be lifted to these higher fields by a shadoof, or a succession of shadoofs, or by other means. The water which is thus distributed is free from sediment, and it becomes necessary to fertilize the fields with such material brought to the spot as dung and organic debris from the villages. There is more work for the peasant, and he sows his seeds later; the harvest, in this case known as the *nili,* is also later.

The traditional crops of Upper Egypt, sufficient for feeding—and clothing —of a dense population, are cereals (wheat, barley, maize), cotton, vegetables (beans, peas, lentils, onions), and especially lucerne or bersim for cattle. Grapes, date palms, and olives are perennial plants, likewise made possible by irrigation.

It will be seen that such a system of basin irrigation is dependent upon the height of the flood, which fortunately in the case of the Nile is remarkably constant, and also on a system of cooperation between landowners, which will permit the development of a system of basins.

It was Mohammed Ali in the early part of the nineteenth century, following doubtless upon the lead given by the members of the French Commission, who saw the possibilities of a system of permanent irrigation by canals. The French were not interested so much in extending the existing production of traditional Egyptian crops as they were interested in securing from Egypt those products of warm climates which Europe needed, notably cane sugar and cotton. The concept of Mohammed Ali was that every peasant should have enough land to support himself and his family, which he calculated to be between a hectare and a hectare and a half, or 2½ to 4 acres. Two factors made the materialization of such a partition of the land impossible. In the first place the Islamic law ordains that property shall be divided between all the heirs, and hence the subdivision of land. On the other hand, large-scale perennial irrigation is only possible under some unified system either of land ownership or land control. The question is so important that careful statistics are kept of land ownership.

As recently as 1948, 95 per cent of Egyptian landowners were small holders with less than 5 acres of land but holding between them less than 35 per cent of the cultivated land surface. By contrast, there were about 2000 landowners holding over 50 acres but between them one-third of the whole. The Agricultural Reform Decree of September 1952 limited agricultural ownership to 200 feddans (207.6 acres) and by the end of 1959 about 350,000 acres had been distributed among 111,000 farmers.

The modern system of canal irrigation may be regarded as having begun with the construction of the Delta barrage, at the head of the Delta below Cairo, from 1861 onwards (replaced in 1942 by the great Mohammed Ali barrage). The barrage of Zifta was added to this system in 1901, and the year 1902 marked the completion in Upper Egypt of the great Asyut dam, followed in 1909 by the barrage at Esna (Isna) and still later, in 1930, by the dam at Nag Hammadi 150 miles above Asyut.

Although these various dams both increased the area of cultivable land during flood water and assured more abundant harvests, what was needed to provide water during the long dry period when the level was low was a reservoir along the southern border of Egypt. It was for this purpose that the great dam at Aswan was constructed. Completed in 1903 at an original cost of $15,000,000, it was sucessively enlarged in 1907, 1912, and 1933. It is now being replaced by a new high dam. The old basin irrigation utilized the flood season so that both water and silt were spread over the land. So that the silt-laden waters of the main flood will not choke the reservoir, the sluices at Aswan are not closed until the latter part of November, when the water is almost free from silt. The water is used in the early summer (the "timely" season) and makes a second harvest of tropical products possible.

Thus the old peasant irrigation is now responsible for less than one-fifth of the land actually irrigated (mainly in Upper Egypt), permanent canal irrigation for the remaining four-fifths. Permanent irrigation has made possible an extension both of the crops possible and of the harvest season. In particular, even in the delta where the soil is slightly salt, there are large rice fields. In the neighborhood of the towns market gardening is extensively practiced, often by Greeks and Italians rather than by Egyptians, for the production of vegetables—artichokes, tomatoes, onions, etc. The great system of permanent irrigation has of course rendered necessary strict control by a large government department, the Water Supply Department. The principal food crops now cultivated in Egypt are corn (maize) and wheat, followed by rice, barley, beans, lentils, and millet, with extensive areas under sugar cane and numerous vegetables.

An interesting study of irrigation and land use in Upper Egypt has been made by Douglas D. Crary (*Geographical Review*, **XXXVII**, October, 1949). He gives a map to show the extreme fragmentation of the land in a particular basin (that of Zeiniya-Bahari, watered from the Esna barrage), and notes that the age-old methods of sowing seed broadcast by hand and then turning them into the soft mud by dragging with a piece of wood are still followed. This is especially the case with the first crops sown in the mud left by the receding waters, which are the forage crops, particularly white clover (bersim) and flat peas (gilban) and fenugreek (hilba). Land from which the water has been drained off after 10 or 15 days is firm enough to support animals, so that it is plowed before the sowing of the food crops—wheat, barley, cow peas, and lentils with small quantities of safflower (for orange dye from the flowers and oil from the seeds). It should be noticed that crop rotation between cereals and leguminous crops is practiced.

Since animals are taken to the source of feed rather than the feed carried to the animals, the land also benefits from natural manuring. This may even result in a form of transhumance, and the use of temporary housing units, known as ezbah.

As a result of this intensive hand cultivation acre yields in Egypt are very high, and the country affords an excellent example of efficient peasant agriculture, albeit prodigal in the use of manual labor.

Egypt's economy and commerce

In Upper Egypt practically the whole production from the irrigated lands is needed for the feeding of the people. Improved supplies of irrigation water, better agricultural techniques, and a knowledge of fertilizers have resulted in increased output, but this has been more than balanced by increase in population. It is the development of the delta lands over the last 100 years which has made possible the production for export of those agricultural commodities on which Egypt depends for foreign currency. Even the greatly increased output of cane sugar has been consumed within the country itself. So too has the increased output of corn and to an increasing extent that of rice. More than 65 per cent of the total exports are commonly represented by cotton, produced in the delta and exported through the great port of Alexandria. From an acreage of just under a million in 1945 it climbed to a postwar peak of 2,000,000 in 1950, or a third of all the cultivated land of Egypt. Troubled political conditions were later reflected in a drop, but acreage climbed again to 1,977,000 in 1958 (1,790,500 in 1963).

Two main types of cotton are grown, the long staple and the medium staple. For a long time the famous long-staple cotton with a silky luster (1½ inches staple) known as *sakellarides,* usually contracted to *sakel,* was recognized as being second in quality only to the famous Sea Island cotton of the West Indies. From 1935 onwards a new and heavier-yielding variety perfected at the experimental station at Giza, opposite Cairo, and consequently known as *Giza 7,* surpassed *sakel* both in acreage and yield. More recently a worm pest has impaired yields (in 1961 and 1962). Other long-staple cottons have been produced, and the possibilities are by no means exhausted. The shorter-staple cotton, *cashmuni,* though of good quality, is not up to the standard of *sakel.* It is grown to some extent in Upper Egypt. A remarkable feature of cotton production in Egypt is the very high yield per acre. The average between 400 and 500 pounds of ginned cotton per acre is still well above the average American figure, despite recent improvements, and more than five times that of the yield common in India.

Though spinning and weaving mills have been developed in Lower Egypt, notably in the delta at El Mahalla el Kubra, the bulk of the crop is exported as cotton, particularly to the U.S.S.R., China, Japan, India, and the cotton-consuming industrial countries of Europe such as Czechoslovakia, Poland, and Germany. Formerly the largest customer was the United Kingdom.

It was the American Civil War which, by cutting off supplies to Europe, especially to Britain, was mainly responsible for the rapid development of the Egyptian cotton cultivation and export.

The varied range of imports into Egypt reflects the demands of a country with a high and growing standard of living for the manufactured products of Europe and America. The recent trend has been towards reliance on the communist countries.

Communications

Naturally the Nile, in addition to its function in supplying irrigation water, has from time immemorial been the main highway of the country. Shallow draft steamers ply regularly as far as Aswan (the First Cataract), where connection is made with various services offered by the Sudanese government southward. Many thousands of sailing vessels ply on the Nile and the waterways of the Delta (Figure 11.7). The Egyptian State Railways focusing on Cairo comprise some 3000 miles of standard gauge line, contrasting with the usual 3 ft. 6 inch gauge of Africa south of the equator. Lines run south through the whole length of the country to Shellal just above Aswan, the terminus of the Sudanese steamers; they run north to Alexandria, to Ismailia and along the west bank of the Suez Canal to Port Said. There is also a direct line from Suez to Cairo. In addition to standard gauge lines there is a considerable mileage of narrow gauge lines serving the agricultural regions of the delta.

The Arab countries, including Egypt, refuse to recognize the existence of

Figure 11.7   The Nile near Cairo. On the left are date palms along the bank. The picturesque Nile sailing boats (*feluccas* or *dahabiyas*) carry a large proportion of the goods transported by the Nile waterway. (Copyright Ewing Galloway.)

Israel as a separate state and remain technically at war; the frontier is closed and guarded by U.N. troops. The through railroad connection which was established between Egypt and Turkey thus no longer functions.

The focal position of Cairo has been emphasized since the development of international air transport. On high ground east of the city is the fashionable and wealthy suburb of Heliopolis, and nearby the main airfield, which became one of the main air junctions of the world, with regular services to the chief capitals of Europe several times daily, services through East Africa to the south, services east to Iraq, Iran, India, and Far East, and Australia at frequent intervals. With the disputes which followed the seizure of the Suez Canal, Egypt lost, but only temporarily, the advantage of this focal position together with much of the tourist traffic. It would be surprising if Egypt had failed to respond to the development of modern motor transport. Good motor roads connect Cairo with Alexandria, Port Said, and Suez, so that each of these points may be reached in the minimum of time from the capital.

The Suez Canal

So long as the world's commerce was focused on the countries around the Mediterranean Sea between Europe on the north, Asia on the east, and

Africa on the south, the existence of the isthmus of Suez was mainly of importance as providing part of the land route between Egypt and its Asiatic neighbors, or from farther afield between the extremes of the Arab domains of the Middle Ages and the Turkish Empire which succeeded it. With the extension of European interest in India and the Far East, the isthmus became a barrier, interrupting the natural line of sea communication from the Atlantic seaboard and the Mediterranean to the Red Sea and the Indian Ocean. A glance at a physical map shows that the Gulf of Suez and equally the Gulf of Aqaba (Akaba) on the other side of the Sinai Peninsula are continuations of the system of rift valleys so marked throughout East Africa. From the head of the Gulf of Suez to the Mediterranean sea coast is less than 70 miles in a straight line. The land between is flat—at most only a few feet above sea level and in part occupied by shallow salt lakes, the so-called Bitter Lakes. It is not always realized that the Suez Canal as we know it today was not the first waterway to unite the Mediterranean with the Red Sea. The earlier idea, of course, was to link the heart of Egypt with the Red Sea at a time when the largest ships then in use were shallow-built, using the lower branches of the Nile. Consequently a canal was constructed—a fresh-water canal, known as the Canal of the Pharaohs—leaving the Nile in the neighborhood of Heliopolis, following a course due east to the neighborhood of the modern Ismailia, whence it passed southwards to the Gulf of Suez near the present site of the town of Suez. In the days of the later Roman Empire, it fell into disuse, but was resuscitated in the days of the Arab domination, since the Arabs always had the great idea of trading between the Mediterranean and the East. The Ottoman Turks, seeking always to preserve the isolation of the Moslem world and to interrupt any means of communication between Christians and Moslems, abandoned the canal. With the discovery of the Cape route to India the former canal seems to have been completely forgotten.

When France at the beginning of the sixteenth century took the initiative for eastern development and exploration, and when Richelieu founded the *Compagnie Générale du Commerce,* the idea of a canal came under consideration. The idea remained, however, one of a route from Alexandria, using the Nile, and thence from the neighborhood of Cairo to the Red Sea. It was the struggle between the French and the British in the time of Napoleon Bonaparte which gave birth to the idea of a direct canal from the Mediterranean to the Red Sea in order to enable the French to wage war against England in Indian waters. Mohammed Ali, as in so many other things, took up the idea left him by Napoleon Bonaparte, and it is recorded that he referred to making "a Strait of Bosphorus in the Desert of Suez."

After the idea had been discussed for some 50 years it was the Frenchman, Ferdinand de Lesseps, who brought the plan to realization, securing the approval of Napoleon III and the support both of the Turkish Sultan and of the Egyptian ruler, Mohammed Saïd, successor to Mohammed Ali. Britain under Prime Minister Palmerston opposed the whole scheme. But the *Compagnie Internationale Maritime de Suez* was formed, with a capital of 200 million francs.

The Canal was constructed rapidly from 1860–1869, and on November 18, 1869, a flotilla of 68 ships carrying the Empress Eugénie of France, the Emperor Francis Joseph of Austria, the Khedive of Egypt, and many other dignitaries passed through the Canal and inaugurated it, after it had received both a Christian and a Moslem blessing. It is interesting that the British themselves played no part, other than one of opposition, in a project afterwards of greater importance to them than to any other country. The original shareholders in the Suez Canal Company included the Khedive of Egypt. Knowing that the Khedive was particularly hard up for funds and anxious to dispose of his holding, the British Premier, Disraeli—afterwards Lord Beaconsfield—in 1875 made an instantaneous and personal decision to acquire the Turkish holding on behalf of the British government. He borrowed $20,000,000 in the name of the Cabinet and presented the British Parliament with what was virtually a *fait accompli*. Had it not been for this bold stroke of an individual, the opportunity would doubtless have been lost by which the British government held 295,026 shares out of a total issued of 652,932 and had three representatives on the governing board of 32. The concession granted to the Suez Canal Company was for 99 years from the date of inauguration; hence it was due to expire on November 17, 1968. On July 26, 1956 President Nasser, however, proclaimed the nationalization of the Suez Canal Company. It was clear that Egypt would no longer observe the convention of 1888, whereby the canal was open equally to vessels of all nations, by excluding Israel. Britain and France landed troops to protect their interests, but this show of force was not fully endorsed by the British people or by Britain's allies, and the troops were withdrawn. In 1958 Egypt agreed to pay £28 million in compensation to the shareholders of the Suez Canal Company, spread over a period of years. In 1959 the World Bank granted a loan of US $56.5 million for the general improvement of the Canal.

The Canal runs straight through Egyptian territory (Figure 11.8). It is 103 miles long, including 4 miles of approach channels for the harbors, which have been added since its original construction. In the early days there was no traffic by night, and vessels had to tie up until daylight and could pass only in certain places. As improved by 1950, the Canal had a depth of 34 feet and had cost about 90 million dollars (30 million pounds) to construct. Depth was increased to 37 feet by 1962, and some miles of twin canal have been constructed.

At the northern end of the Canal, on the western side, stands Port Said. It is built on a low sandy island between a vast lagoon and the Mediterranean

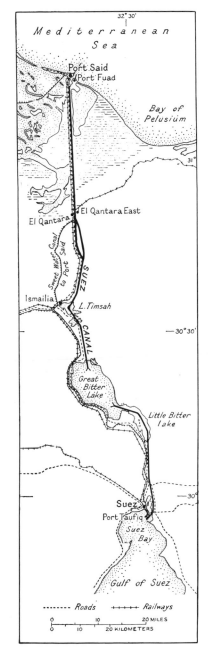

Figure 11.8   The Suez Canal.

Sea. Facing Port Said on the eastern entrance to the Canal is Port Fuad, but the population and the development remain concentrated in Port Said. The majority of vessels passing through the Canal halt at Port Said for Canal formalities, for oiling or coaling, or perhaps for revictualing, and Port Said has grown into one of those curious international refuges of mankind, associated only with the great seaways of the world. Luxury hotels, bazaars, and shops, operated by members of almost every nation, are likely to be just as active in the middle of the night as during any of the daylight hours. From Port Said is the railway to Cairo, which at first parallels the Canal as far as Ismailia. It was during World War II that a steel swing bridge was built at Kantara across the Canal and made through running possible from Uskudar (or Haida Pashar) opposite Istanbul to Tobruk in Libya.

South of Ismailia the Canal passes through the great Bitter Lakes, through a deepened channel marked out by buoys and where there is no longer any need for the speed restriction imposed in the Canal. At the southern end of the Canal is the Port of Suez, again linked by road and rail with Cairo.

In the period between the two world wars nearly 5000 steamers a year, with a net tonnage of some 30 millions, passed through the Canal in a year. More than half of them were British, followed in order by Italian, German, Dutch, French, Norwegian, and Japanese. In the years which followed World War II, tonnage passing through the Canal had doubled, taking merchant shipping alone. By 1958 the number of vessels had reached nearly 18,000, totalling 154 million tons. Although British ships easily outnumbered those of any other nation, the proportion had dropped to a fifth. In addition government vessels, warships, and transports also passed through the Canal in great numbers. It is obviously unnecessary to stress any further the enormous strategic as well as commercial importance of the Suez Canal.

The Canal has the great advantage that there are no locks; it is open to the sea at both ends.

The River Nile

So far we have considered only the course of the River Nile as it passes through Egypt. From time immemorial, as the life of Egypt depended upon the annual flooding of the Nile, the behavior of its waters was carefully studied. The Nile in Egypt affords us the earliest known examples of river gauging, by the famous Nilometer at Cairo. The annual flooding was accepted perforce as the gift of the gods. It was not indeed until the nineteenth century was far advanced that this water regime came to be understood and the source of the Nile itself discovered (Figure 11.9). With a total length of 4060 miles, the Nile is one of the world's greatest rivers. It ranks second in length only to the Missouri-Mississippi (4500) unless the Amazon can be found to be slightly

Figure 11.9 The regime of the Nile, showing flow at selected points.

longer than the 4000 miles commonly claimed. The basin of the Nile falls naturally into some seven major divisions (Figure 11.10).

The lake plateau. The Nile has several sources rather than one, but the farthest headstream may be regarded as the Kagera, which rises in the highland of Burundi over 4000 miles from the Mediterranean, and flows into Lake Victoria. Lake Victoria is a huge though shallow lake. There is little variation in its level. Though it lies in the equatorial region of well-distributed rainfall, there is a great loss of water by evaporation. The Nile flows out of Lake Victoria at Jinja over the Ripon Falls (now submerged), followed at a short distance by the Owen Falls, site of a large dam and power station. The dam has raised the waters of Lake Victoria several feet and has made the Lake immeasurably the largest storage reservoir in the world. Below the Owen Falls the river, known as the Victoria Nile, traverses Lake Kioga and then flows over the magnificent Murchison Falls before entering the northern end of Lake Albert.

The waters which drain into Lake Albert form another source of Nile water. Unlike Lake Victoria, Lake Albert is a deep, narrow lake, with precipitous, mountainous sides. At its lower end it receives the Victoria Nile before the united waters pass on northwards as the Albert Nile. A dam to increase the storage capacity of Lake Albert would maintain an enormous reservoir of water to serve the whole basin.

The basin of the Bahr-el-Jebel. This is a huge, almost level expanse of land lying some 1200 to 1500 feet above sea level through the center of which flows the mainstream, here called the Bahr-el-Jebel (literally, Mountain River). The extreme flatness of the basin results in enormous areas becoming inundated during and after the rainy season, promoting the growth of enormous quantities of swamp vegetation, including tall grass and giant reeds, known as sudd. The sudd is very likely to choke the mainstream completely and to cause difficulties to navigation. This tendency has been aggravated since 1957 by the rapid spread of the South American water hyacinth (*Eichornia crassipes*). Much more serious is the huge loss of water by evaporation from this great basin, with the result that the White Nile leaves the basin unenriched by the rainfall over this huge area, and possibly with a smaller volume of water than that which passed into it 500 miles farther south. Part of the scheme, therefore, for the regulation of the Nile is the cutting of a straightened channel through this basin and its maintenance as an open waterway. This would also reduce evaporation.

Actually, numerous streams, especially from the southwest (from the Sudan-Congo border), drain into this basin. One, the Bahr-el-Ghazal, joins the Nile at Lake No. Other streams drain from the Ethiopian mountains to the southeast, collecting together as the Sobat which joins the White Nile a

Figure 11.10 The profile of the Nile. Fractions show drop in units per 10,000 of distance.

229

short distance above Malakal. The Sobat is a more important source of water than the left bank tributaries and makes good the loss of water through evaporation in the marshes.

The White Nile valley from Malakal to Khartoum. Here the White Nile passes through the increasingly arid region of the central Sudan. Throughout the whole of this stretch it receives no tributary of importance.

The Blue Nile basin. The Blue Nile drains from the lofty mountains of Ethiopia north-northwestwards, to join the White Nile at Khartoum. Whereas the White Nile at Khartoum is a river of almost constant volume, it is the Blue Nile which, receiving the monsoon rains from Ethiopia, contributes that volume of water in the high-water season which is later responsible for the Nile floods in Egypt. The Blue Nile has in the heart of the Ethiopian mountains a natural reservoir in Lake Tana. Quite obviously the agreement of the Ethiopian government is an essential part of a comprehensive regulation of Nile waters, yet there is little reason why Ethiopians should have any interest in what happens after the Nile leaves their territory. On the Blue Nile at Sennar has been constructed the magnificent dam which has made possible the irrigation of the Gezira (see "Sudan," Chapter 15).

The desert cataract course. Below Khartoum the united Nile flows at first northwards until it reaches the Sixth and highest Cataract and, after receiving the important but seasonal Atbara, commences the succession of descents to its lower levels over the Fifth, Fourth, Third, Second, and First Cataracts, each of which marks the outcrop of resistant granitic rocks of the ancient African complex. This desert course of the Nile serves mainly to transport the life-giving water from Khartoum to the Egyptian border. The land on either side, for reasons which will be discussed at length in Chapter 15, is unsuitable for extensive irrigation, and so the water reaches the Egyptian border. We expect the new high dam at Aswan—the First Cataract —in creating a lake extending right back to the Second Cataract and flooding Wadi Halfa has already been noted. It still remains true that there is a considerable loss of water from these great lakes by evaporation.

The Nile in Upper Egypt. Since this course of the Nile has already been described, no further comment is necessary, except to emphasize the utter dependence of Egypt on the waters received from Ethiopia even more than on the waters received from the southern Sudan and the plateau of East Africa. During the low-water season 80 per cent of the water is derived from the White Nile, but during the flood season only 14 per cent, leaving 70 per cent at that season to come from the Blue Nile, 16 per cent from the Atbara.

The delta course. The map given above (Figure 11.1) illustrates the existing and projected control points for the Nile waters. It reinforces the discussion in Chapter 3 which suggested that the essential division of Africa for purposes of development must be on a basis of river basins. Unity of purpose within the whole Nile basin among all the peoples concerned is obviously a *sine qua non* for future African development and peace.

BIBLIOGRAPHY

H. E. Hurst and O. Phillips, *The Nile Basin*, Vol. 1, Cairo, 1931.

H. E. Hurst, *The Nile*, London, 1952, 2nd Edition 1957.

Alan Moorehead, *The White Nile*, London and New York, 1960, and *The Blue Nile, ibid.*, are pleasantly written accounts of the White exploration of the Nile lands and their political history.

J. Ball, *Contributions to the Geography of Egypt*, Cairo (Survey and Mines Dept.), 1939.

C. W. Hallberg, *The Suez Canal*, New York, Columbia University Press, 1931.

C. Issawi, *Egypt: An Economic and Social Analysis*, Londong, 1947 and later editions.

D. Warriner, *Land and Poverty in the Middle East*, London, 1948 and later editions.

CHAPTER TWELVE

Mediterranean Africa
or the Barbary States

In many respects the three principal countries, Morocco, Algeria, Tunisia, which together make up northwest Africa may be regarded as an island cut off from the rest of the world. To the northwest is the Atlantic Ocean, to the north and northeast the Mediterranean Sea, to the south the great wastes of the Sahara (Figure 12.1). But from earliest times the Mediterranean Sea has exercised a unifying influence on the countries by which it is bordered. It has permitted travel from one shore to another of peoples, of their religions and cultures, at times of their conquering armies. Northwest Africa was long called on the older maps "the Barbary States" from the name "Barbars" or "Berbers" then commonly used for the inhabitants. Northwest Africa of today bears the impress of several distinct cultures resulting from its geographical position. Developments in the past hundred years have been mainly under French influence, but the title French North Africa ceased to be appropriate with the independence of Tunisia and Morocco, followed by Algeria in 1962.

The basic substratum of the population, the Berbers, reached the area overland along the North African desert coastal routes. So too did the Moors, or Arab conquerors, and the Moslem religion. The Moorish hordes found no reason to be stopped by the Atlantic Ocean when across the narrow Strait of Gibraltar, from one Pillar of Hercules to the other, they could see the lands of Spain which lay beyond. They extended their conquests and their influence over most of the Iberian Peninsula. But the Moors superimposed their culture and religion on a pre-existing pattern of life which had been brought across the narrow waters in the heart of the Mediterranean Sea. Carthage—the modern Tunis—was established by a sea power. When Rome overcame Carthage, the Romans in their turn left their impress upon the Berber peoples (Figure 12.2). In due course, when the great Arab domains gave place to the Ottoman Empire, northwest Africa became nominally part

Figure 12.1 Physical sketch-map of northwest Africa.

of the Turkish domain. Too remote to be under direct control of Constantinople, as the Turkish power waned the Barbary States became the prey of local upstarts of Turkish or other origin, and it was the piratical behavior of these local potentates in menacing harmless merchant shipping proceeding on its lawful way through the Mediterranean that led to interference in North African affairs by European powers. The task did not prove to be simple. Both British and American naval expeditions failed to produce decisive results in the suppression of the Barbary pirates, and it was for this reason that the French appeared on the scene. French influence began to be felt about 1830.

The territory now known as Algeria was proclaimed a French colony in 1834, but seventeen years of guerilla warfare were necessary before the

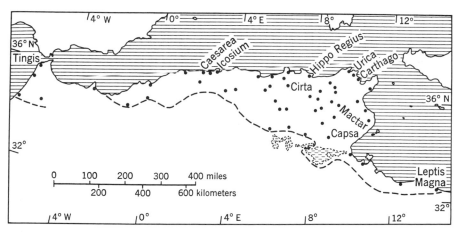

Figure 12.2 Roman Africa. The dots show the principal towns established by the Romans, and the broken line the limits of control.

country came effectively under French control. The year 1951 thus marked the centenary of the real French hold over Algeria, but in the early part of that hundred years economic progress was slow. The railway line from Algiers to Oran was begun in the year 1860, and from that event the development of agricultural and mineral resources may be regarded as beginning and, at first slowly, later more rapidly, continued to expand. French influence extended southwards over the great desert area now forming Southern Algeria. In 1881 the Sultan of Tunis transferred his allegiance from Turkey to France. But it was not until 1912, after a long period of dispute, that the appearance of German claims led the Sultan of Morocco to accept French protection, and Morocco became a French protectorate. There remained Spanish interests and Spanish influence, rather naturally to the southern side of the Strait of Gibraltar, so that there a small tract was recognized as Spanish Morocco, and the Port of Tangier came internationally under French, British, and Spanish control.

After World War II developments were rapid. On March 20, 1956, France recognized the full independence of Tunisia, retaining rights only to the Bizerta naval base. In 1957 the monarchy was abolished and Tunisia became a republic. In March and April 1956 France and Spain relinquished their protectorates over French and Spanish Morocco respectively, and later in the year the international status of the Tangier Zone was abolished so that the whole of Morocco became a sovereign independent state under a king who holds both supreme civil and supreme religious authority. The king is also prime minister and chooses his own National Consultative Committee and ministers. Spain retains control of five towns, including the ports of Ceuta and Melilla (see Figure 12.3).

When de Gaulle was recalled to power in France in 1958 and the constitution of the Fifth Republic was adopted in 1960, the "French Republic" was constituted so as to include A. Metropolitan Departments, B. Algerian Departments (Algeria), C. Saharan Departments (Sahara), D. Overseas Departments, and E. Overseas Territories. Thus the distinction was maintained between the old Northern Algeria and the vast area of the Sahara previously called Southern Algeria. Northern Algeria had become the home of a million Frenchmen—many second and third generation—or about 10 per cent of the total population, estimated at just under 10 million on January 1, 1960. The principle of self determination would mean handing over control to the Moslem majority, but was accepted by a general referendum throughout France. A joint Council was set up in 1962 after agreement had been reached with the Moslems who had been waging a war of independence, but French extremists with their cry "Algérie française" and an underground army inaugurated a reign of terror and destruction. However, de Gaulle persisted with his policy of self determination. A referendum in Algeria was, as

Figure 12.3 Northwest Africa. Main roads, railroads, and towns.

expected, overwhelmingly in favor of independence. An independent republic was accordingly declared on July 4, 1962. It is estimated that by late 1963 fewer than 100,000 Frenchmen remained in the country.

The physical background

The Arabs called their great country of Arabia the Isle of the Arabs, recognizing that the desert isolates as much as the sea. They gave the name Djezira-el-Maghrib, or the Western Isle, to that area of northwest Africa isolated by sea, ocean and the great desert. Maghrib is indeed a convenient name and a better one than the Barbary States. The island, if we regard it as such, is structurally a part of Europe. The great folded mountain ranges which form such conspicuous features in the European lands bordering the Mediterranean Sea, the Alps, the Apennines of Italy, the Sierra Nevada of southern Spain, are continued in North Africa, where they form not one continuous mountain range but a succession of mountain ranges separated by lofty plateaus or at times by narrower mountain basins. Collectively this is the Atlas system, the alignments of which run, broadly speaking, from west-southwest to north-northeast, that is, roughly parallel to the sea coast, and are cut across by the political divisions of Maghrib. Perhaps the simplest way to regard the structure of the whole area is as a lofty plateau wider in the west, narrowing towards the east, with a corrugated surface, and flanked by great ramparts to the north overlooking the Mediterranean, and to the south overlooking the Saharan wastes. Thus a traveler, journeying from the north, from the Mediterranean shore southwards, will pass through a succession of mountain ranges and intervening plateaus from the relatively well-watered Mediterranean coastal slopes, across mountain ranges often capped with snow, to basins which become increasingly arid, until at last the real desert is reached. Such a traverse made by a geographer was described by him. A succession of east-west belts stands out impressively. The reference is to Professor Griffith Taylor's article entitled "Sea to Sahara: Settlement Zones in Eastern Algeria," *Geographical Review*, **XXIX**, 1939, pages 177–195.

The arrangement of the mountain ranges affords a natural division for the whole area, and it is usual to distinguish some ten regions for descriptive purposes on this basis. Starting in the west, in Morocco, the central and highest range is the Great or High Atlas, with a core of crystalline rocks, reaching in its highest points some 12,000 feet. South of the High Atlas lies the triangular depression known as the Sous, being broadly the valley and plain of the small river of that name. The Anti-Atlas range to the south is considerably lower and of less extent. To the north of the High Atlas is the parallel range of the Middle Atlas, and between the High and Middle Atlas lies the Moulouya depression. Both the Great and the Middle Atlas are separated from the Atlantic Ocean by a broad plateau roughly 1000 feet in elevation, dropping gradually to the coast. This largely cultivated plateau watered by snow-fed streams from the high mountains is a well-settled agricultural region, familiar to many travelers because it is traversed by the main road from the great port of Casablanca to Marrakesh, an old capital of Morocco, which lies almost in the shadow of the High Atlas.

To the north the plateau passes into the plains, likewise well settled and cultivated, with the magnificent old walled cities of Rabat, Meknes, and Fez, until a new mountain rampart is reached in the curved range of the Rif Mountains (otherwise Er Rif). This range was obviously formerly continuous with the Sierra Nevada of Spain before the cutting of the Strait of Gibraltar.

Eastward into Algeria the High Atlas of Morocco fades out, and instead two parallel mountain ranges, the Tell Atlas, continue the line of the Rif in the north; and the Saharan Atlas continue the line of the Anti-Atlas in the south. Between them they enclose a broad plateau generally known as the Plateau of the Shotts. A "shott" (in French, "chott") is a shallow lake, frequently salt and frequently only semipermanent. Along part of the Algerian coast the Tell Atlas drops steeply to the Mediterranean, the northward slope often being known as the Tell. A separate coastal range is sometimes developed, as near Oran, separated by a deep valley from the Tell Atlas itself.

Still farther east, in Tunisia, the two main ranges of Algeria approach close to one another, thus almost eliminating the Plateau of the Shotts. The mountains reach the eastern shores of Tunisia in high cliffs, Cape Blanco marking the termination of the Tell Atlas and Cape Bon that of the Saharan Atlas. Between these two promontories is the Gulf of Tunis, which afforded such an attractive, protected site to the builders of Carthage as well as to its successor, the modern town of Tunis.

Climatically the whole of the Atlas lands experience a Mediterranean climate of winter rainfall associated with cyclonic disturbances and a summer when Saharan conditions spread over the whole, and a hot, sunny, rainless period results. Almost everywhere more than 80 per cent of the total precipitation comes in the winter half of the year. With such varied relief local variations in climate are very marked and often very sharp. The Moroccan coast is washed by the cold Canaries current flowing southwards, and the cool air from over it lowers the summer temperatures, resulting in considerable fog (as on the Californian coast) but only a moderate rainfall. The Moroccan coastal plain and plateaus are indeed dry and depend largely on irrigation water, but the lofty mountains attract a high-relief precipitation of 60 inches and more (Figure 12.4).

The western coastlands of Algeria form a sort of rainshadow area, the bulk of the rainfall having been precipitated on the Rif Mountains, but farther east the Tell Atlas is well watered and contrasts strongly with the dry

Figure 12.4 Annual rainfall.

enclosed plateau, with only some 10 to 15 inches of rain. Despite nearness of the ocean in terms of miles, the Plateau of the Shotts with an elevation of 2000 to 3000 feet is so cut off from maritime influences as to experience great extremes of temperature. Rapid changes in natural vegetation as well as of agricultural development reflect these climatic contrasts.

On the best-watered regions, as on the slopes of the High Atlas, the Middle Atlas, and the Rif and in eastern Algeria, there are forests of cork oak, holm oak, and conifers (the Aleppo pine, cedar, and juniper) together with stretches of grassland. Much of the former forest cover, however, has been destroyed, leading to soil erosion and an arid appearance of the mountainsides which is not justified by the actual rainfall. In the drier areas, or where the soil is poor, the forests give place to that characteristically Mediterranean bush vegetation commonly called *maquis,* closely comparable to the Californian *chaparral.* It has stunted oaks together with numerous evergreen bushes and flowering shrubs, among which the heaths (*Erica*) are conspicuous. The *maquis* often forms very dense thickets. On such areas as the plateau of western Morocco and other dry areas, the *maquis* becomes impoverished, the shrubs are scattered, there are coarse wiry grasses, but small palms appear. With a still smaller rainfall we find a very stunted Mediterranean vegetation which is sometimes described as *steppe* or *dry steppe.* It is here that the wiry, tufted, drought-resisting grasses of the alfa or esparto types occur. The esparto is of some economic importance as a source of paper-making material.

South of the Anti-Atlas and the Saharan Atlas the whole merges into true desert, often with considerable stretches of erg, or sand. A conspicuous feature is a line of mountain-foot oases, most of which are now reached by modern means of transportation and form the outposts of civilization from which the trans-Saharan journeys may be attempted. Throughout the whole area abundant and assured sunshine favors the ripening of cereal crops and fruits wherever adequate water is available. Wheat and barley are the principal cereals; and among fruits the grape, with very extensive production of wine, especially in Algeria, and the olive take pride of place, with date palms in the oases. On the semiarid pastures and maquis, sheep and goats are numerous, especially the Merino and other wool-producing sheep. Though the irrigation works of North Africa are small rather than large and spectacular (there are no large rivers), irrigation has been practiced at least from Roman times onwards. The French in the last century did much to extend the cultivable area by their careful, systematic control of available water supplies.

Reference has already been made to the population of the Barbary States. A large proportion of the population is a mixture of Arab and Berber stocks, usually known as Moors. The more purely Arab population has come to be associated with the desert margins and the more arid areas, whereas the Berbers are the cultivators of the damper highlands. The Berbers even more perhaps than the Moors are European both in paleness of skin and cast of countenance, and it is not surprising that with the mixture of blood in Spain they should closely resemble Spaniards, or indeed the southern Italians. This alone marks off Maghrib from the rest of Africa, and yet the American or North European tourist to Morocco or Algeria is able to find in the flowing white robes of the people, in the characteristic architecture, in the prevalence of mosques, in the inevitable bazaars, with their mingling of camels, mules, and donkeys, an oriental flavor far more distinctive than anything which he is likely to find in the Far or Middle East.

Morocco (Maghrib-el-Aksa, that is, the Farthest West)

Morocco is a kingdom over which the king, formerly Sultan, exercises supreme civil authority as well as, in his capacity as Commander of the Faithful, the supreme religious authority. The present dynasty has been in existence for some three centuries, and prior to that Morocco, from the time when Islam was introduced at the end of the seventh century, and more especially from the time of the great Arab influx of the eleventh century, had a colorful history, with the rise and fall of various Arab and Berber dynasties. Many rulers of the past have left their mark in the great cities. Fez (Figure 12.5) was founded early in the ninth century (808), Marrakesh in 1062, and a number of other walled towns have remained well preserved to the present day. Perhaps one of the most colorful of them all, because of its situation on the seaboard, is the capital Rabat (Figure 12.6). It is here that the king normally resides, though occasionally also at Fez, Marrakesh, and Tangier.

From 1912 to 1956, the Empire of Morocco was divided into three

Figure 12.5 The main entrance to the walled city of Fez. (Copyright L. Dudley Stamp.)

unequal zones. The French zone, by far the largest, had an area of approximately 200,000 square miles, and in it the effective authority was exercised by the French as the protecting power, represented by a resident-general, with headquarters at Rabat.

The Spanish Zone, the Rif, was an area of about 8000 square miles. The sultan's powers were here delegated to a caliph, whom the sultan chose from two candidates presented by the Spanish government. The Spanish high commissioner resided at Tetuan. The Rif Mountains include some wild and inaccessible country where tribesmen were brought under effective control only in 1927.

A third zone was the International Zone at Tangier, only some 225 square miles in area, around the well-situated and well-equipped port of Tangier, the natural gateway from Europe into Morocco.

The former Spanish Zone, which may be called now the Northern Zone, with a population somewhat over a million, has rather less than 100,000 Europeans and Jews and is an area of very limited natural resources. In the western coastal part, especially around Larache, there are small areas of arable cultivation, but the area is not self-supporting and imports foodstuffs. The pastoral highland zones yield wool, hides, and skins, mainly from sheep and goats, but such forestry resources and mineral resources as exist have been little developed except for the recent production of iron ore.

The short railways running inland from Ceuta and Rio Martin to Tetuan have become in recent years of little importance because of the construction of some good motor roads. Mention may be made of Melilla, which serves as a port for iron-ore mines in the vicinity, some of the iron ore going to Britain.

Along the Atlantic seaboard in the extreme south of Morocco is an enclave which remained Spanish territory, known from 1958 to 1963 as the Province of Ifni. The coastlands in the same latitude as the Canary Islands are designated officially by the Spaniards as the Province of Sahara, divided into two zones. Sekiall Hamra (formerly Cape Juby) and Rio de Oro in the south.

The Southern Zone of Morocco, formerly French Morocco, comprises an effectively occupied area of some 90,000 square miles, with a population between 8 and 10 million, mostly Berbers, Moors, and Arabs, but including some 20,000 Moroccan-born Jews, and a population of "foreigners," mainly from France and Algeria, which total half a million. The French and other Europeans are mainly in the towns, more than a third of them in Casablanca alone, mainly interested in trade and commerce.

The French took an active part in conserving what remains of the formerly more extensive forest lands, a conservation rendered necessary both from the shortage of timber and fuel and from the dangers of soil erosion where the forest cover has been removed.

Agriculturally Morocco is a country of considerable existing importance and of marked possibilities. To date crops have depended very largely on the

Figure 12.6   A glimpse through one of the gateways of Rabat. A good example of the charming walled cities of Northwest Africa. (Copyright L. Dudley Stamp.)

Figure 12.7 Old and new in Morocco. A modern block of apartments behind an old Moorish arch. Notice the use of donkeys as pack animals. (Copyright Geographical Publications Limited.)

winter rainfall, which is scarcely adequate, and the annual spring flooding of rivers controlled to a small extent. Naturally, yields, especially of cereals, fluctuate widely from year to year. This is important because cereal farming of barley and wheat takes leading place (Figure 12.8). The Moroccans have in the past had no effective weapon against serious locust plagues, which play havoc with the crops from time to time. When I was working in Morocco some years ago, a locust plague occurred. The locusts were so thick and were killed in such numbers by one of the slow-moving railway trains that they formed piles before the engine large enough to stop the train. In the journey across by small steamer from Ceuta to Algeciras, every passenger was mobilized to kill the locusts which had got on board ship and to sweep them overboard before permission to land in Spain was given.

There are some interesting points in connection with the development of agriculture in Morocco. Food is already produced in excess of home needs, and there is a surplus for export. Crops which pay the heavy costs of transportation are fruit and vegetables. Morocco can place these on the French market two or three weeks in advance of comparable Algerian products, but the bulk of the Moroccan harvest clashes with the harvest of Algeria. If large-scale irrigation is extended there could be a greatly increased output of cereals, vegetables, fruits, wine, and olive oil, as well as cotton and possibly also silkworms, dependent upon mulberry plantations. Casablanca and Rabat offer attractive local markets, and more intensive development has naturally taken place around these centers.

In the drier areas Morocco has a very large number of sheep and goats, as well as considerable numbers of cattle, mules, donkeys, horses and camels.

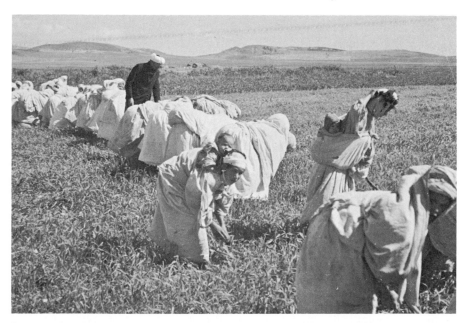

Figure 12.8 Moroccan women weeding the wheat fields. They work in gangs of thirty or forty. Later in the year they will work at harvesting beans, peas, and other crops. (Copyright Geographical Publications Limited.)

Among the hill peoples transhumance is commonly practiced, and the same is true on the intermontane plateaus where seasonal growth of vegetation is followed to different levels.

Off the coast of Morocco are very valuable fishing grounds. Fishing vessels from France, Portugal, Spain, and even distant Britain fish in Moroccan waters, but the coastal fishing industry is largely in the hands of Moroccans, who have adopted European methods for sardines, anchovy, and tunny fishing. The canning of sardines has become an important industry at Casablanca and the smaller ports along the coast.

Morocco has relatively few metallic minerals, apart from some manganese, but very extensive deposits of phosphatic chalk. Where the proportion of phosphate reaches a certain percentage the deposits form resources of immense actual and potential value. The workings are in pockets scattered over the middle west of the country, and an electric railway connects some of the most important with Casablanca. At Casablanca is a factory for the manufacture of superphosphates, and in a world hungry for fertilizers it is difficult to overemphasize the importance of Moroccan deposits. Between one-half and one-third of the total exports of the country are represented by phosphates going almost entirely to those countries of Europe where intensive agriculture is practiced, such as Denmark and Holland, or where poor soils benefit enormously by phosphatic dressing, as in Spain, Italy, and France.

The old Moroccan railways of narrow-gauge lines which the French constructed for military purposes mainly between the years 1911 and 1915 have almost all been replaced by standard-gauge lines, but it is the growth of the road network in this relatively dry country where road construction is easy that has been the outstanding development of recent years. Although Tangier is reached by excellent roads as well as by railway, this has not succeeded in diverting the bulk of the traffic from Casablanca and Rabat.

Apart from towns already mentioned, the great inland market of Marrakesh, or Morocco City, is by far the largest, with over 250,000 people, though only a small proportion of Europeans. It stands in the midst of rich agricultural though rather dry country and is an ancient walled city, still an epitome of the life of the country, with large markets and an important fair, also with local industries such as carpet making, oil pressing, leather, silk, metal work, and butter making.

Both Fez and Meknes are also large and again are walled cities acting as collecting and distributing centers for their regions.

Casablanca stands apart from all the other Moroccan cities not only because it is a great port, but also because it is a fine cosmopolitan city with a million people; it has modern electrical power stations, supplying electricity to the railways as well as to the town, modern factories for superphosphates, cement works, oil and soap factories, a sugar factory, and numerous others.

Kenitra, the second port, handles only about one-tenth of the trade of Casablanca. Agadir, the port for the Sous basin, is a development dating from 1930, but it was largely destroyed by earthquake in 1960.

Algeria

The vast territory long shown as Algeria on the maps of Africa, and as covering more than 850,000 square miles, falls clearly into the vast stretch of Southern Algeria until 1962 known as the Sahara departments and the settled country of the north or Algeria proper now to be considered. The line of oases along the Saharan foot of the Atlas ranges is broadly the dividing line between the two. Algeria proper, some 295,033 sq. km or 114,000 square miles, has a population of 10 million.

In contrast to Morocco, Algeria was a French possession. The thirteen *départements* into which Algeria was divided in 1959 were organized into *arrondissements* and *communes,* with administration on French lines, the inhabitants electing representatives for all local and national assemblies.

In the century of French occupation Algeria became a field for French settlement and colonization (Figure 12.9). More than one million Europeans,

Figure 12.9   Home of French settlers at Guyotville near Algiers. Along the fertile raised beach are carefully cultivated plots with "primeurs" or early vegetables, including tomatoes, potatoes, and beans, as well as grapevines and fruits. Most of such land has now been taken over by Algerians. (Copyright G. M. Hickman.)

mainly French, resided in Algeria, and these immigrants from Europe and their descendants constituted between 10 and 15 per cent of the total population. From 1871 to 1962 the numerous Jews were regarded as French citizens. Reference has already been made to the exodus of more than four-fifths of the French settlers in 1962 consequent upon the grant of independence.

Five parallel zones may be distinguished in the country. These, as already mentioned, comprise the Tell, the Tell Atlas, the Plateau of the Shotts, the Saharan Atlas, and the Saharan Oases Zone. Algeria is essentially an agricultural country, and under the French occupation the cultivable areas were greatly extended. There are no permanent streams in the country, but by drainage and improvement of the distribution of existing waters, large areas, especially in the coastal plain, previously almost unoccupied, have been rendered attractive and support a large population. Attention has had to be paid to the elimination of salt from some of the former salt-encrusted soils, but over the wide lands rendered cultivable, cereals take the first place. A large surplus of wheat and barley is produced on an area over 10 miles across, though climatic conditions result in much fluctuation in yield from year to year. Commercial agriculture, however, is attracted especially to the cultivation of the vine. There is an enormous production of wines to be broadly classed as *vin ordinaire,* and the value of the export of wine is five to ten times the value of the next most important export, cereals. Algerian red wines tend to be a little heavier than those of France and are often blended with French wines on arrival. Total production from Algeria was between one-third and one-half of that of the whole of France.

Most of the vineyards are around Algiers and Oran (Figure 12.10). French growers evinced some fear that Algerian output would seriously overtake French and world demand and lead to a depression in the wine industry in France itself. With the departure of so many French growers and the fact that the Moslems do not drink alcohol, many vineyards have been torn up.

Other exportable products include tobacco, olive oil, early fruit and vegetables, as well as dates from the oases. Much of this commercial agriculture is in the hands of French settlers.

The pastoral occupations which are dominant outside the Tell, especially on the plateaus, by way of contrast are in the hands of Moslems. Here again irrigation plays a part because, with the provision of fodder, a great improvement can take place in the livestock industry, especially of dairy cattle.

The mineral wealth of Algeria is by no means negligible. There are especially rich iron ores, free from phosphorus and so suitable for steel manufacture, which are mined at intervals along the Tell and exported especially from many of the coastal ports, notably Oran, Algiers, Bougie, Philippeville, and Bône. This is an important source of supply to Britain and formerly to

Figure 12.10   Terracing on the steep slopes to the Mediterranean near Algiers. The steep slopes are planted with vines, various fruits, and vegetables. (Copyright G. M. Hickman.)

Germany. Phosphates in quantity are also produced and exported. The construction of oil and gas pipelines from the Saharan fields to the Mediterranean ports of Bougie and Bône has led to their rapid expansion.

It is perhaps a little difficult to convey a right impression of Algeria as a country which is so strongly oriental in its general aspect and character, but has so many of the amenities of modern life—well-equipped railways, excellent motor roads, and numerous good hotels, both large and small. The hotels are or were frequently owned and kept by Frenchmen, who ran them as they would have in their native France. It will be interesting to see how much the strong French cultural influence will now survive under independence —perhaps much, to encourage the tourist trade. It is of course most noticeable in the larger towns or cities, such as Constantine, the largest inland center, where half the total population was European. This city is a natural fortress and the natural outlet for the grain-growing lands of the high plain of Setif.

Algiers, where again half the population was European, is the largest city of the Atlas lands and the principal port. Its original harbor—not a very good one—has been so extensively modernized as to be almost entirely artificial and it deals with a third of the total trade of the country. Notwithstanding that, its attractive situation makes it a tourist center also (Figure 12.11).

Oran is almost as large and has almost as large a trade as Algiers. Again

Figure 12.11   Contrasts in the city of Algiers. To left and right are blocks of apartments of different stages of architectural development; in the background a building showing Moorish architecture. The traffic cop in uniform contrasts with the women in white Moslem garb and the men in part Arab, part European clothes. (Copyright G. M. Hickman.)

more than one-half the people were European. It is from Oran that the railway to the Saharan oases (Colomb Béchar in particular) may be extended to form the trans-Saharan route, but modern road construction has tended to displace that of railroads.

Tunisia

With an area of rather under 50,000 square miles and a population of some 3 million, about 90 per cent of the people are Moslems, born and bred in the country. Of these inhabitants of European stock the French are now the most numerous, but there are large numbers of Italians and smaller numbers of Maltese, Spaniards, and Greeks, together with a large Tunisian-born Jewish population.

Tunisia, like its neighbors, is primarily an agricultural country, though mineral wealth, particularly of phosphates discovered in the Gafsa region in 1885, and reached by railway, supplies important exports. As in Algeria, there are large areas sown with wheat and barley, but the development of vineyards and of olive groves is smaller than in Algeria, although some of the largest olive orchards in the world are inland from Sfax and Sousse.

Road transport is not as well developed as in Algeria, and the country has suffered from the passage of armies in World War II. The experts say that the surpluses of cereals, vegetable oils, minerals, and wine again suggest possibilities for future development, though not to the same extent as in the larger and richer territories of Morocco.

Tunis, the capital, is connected with its outport of La Goulette by a 6-mile channel across a lagoon. It stands in a favorable position relative to a wide hinterland, and this same nodal position was doubtless responsible for the choice of the near-by site for the ancient city of Carthage, the ruins of which lie just out of La Goulette. Only one-third of its population is European, and it far exceeds in size any other town in the country. Sfax on the northern side of the Gulf of Gabès is a phosphate port, though there is also a trade in olive oil and fish.

Bizerte (Bizerta), which became so well known during World War II, may be regarded as an alternative outlet for Tunis for some of the oils and agricultural products of the interior.

There are no inland towns of any size (see Figure 12.12), though one of great interest is Kairouan, an old Moslem capital, and now a center of mineral working.

Figure 12.12 Rooftops at Bou-Saade, a small town on the dry plateau. (Copyright G. M. Hickman.)

It should be noted that in addition to phosphates Tunisia has deposits of metalliferous ores, especially of iron, lead, and zinc, and these are particularly at the edge of the Sahel around Kairouan.

The economic development of northwest Africa

The foregoing descriptions will have made it clear that Morocco, Algeria and Tunisia, though situated in Africa, form a region so apart from the remainder of the continent that they might almost have been excluded from a book dealing with Africa, the tropical continent.

Whatever their future, the three chief countries of northwest Africa must remain a monument to the influence of French enterprise and French culture. That influence was especially marked over the first half of the present century and may be measured especially by some of the changes in the three decades of 1921 to 1951. In those thirty years the population of Morocco increased from 4 to 9 million; of Algeria from 5.5 to 9 million; and of Tunisia from 1.9 to 3.5 million—in all from about 11.5 million to 21.5, or practically double in 30 years.

In the first place the French brought peace to countries harassed for centuries by internecine strife. The pacification of the Saharan areas of southern Algeria was only completed in 1934. The isolated forts on the desert routes— usually with their little cemeteries—bear witness to the patient, self-sacrificing work of many units of the French Army, as well as the glamorous, now disbanded Foreign Legion.

In the second place the French introduced Western standards of hygiene and medicine. It is doubtful whether there has been any great change in the crude birth rate, but the result has been a big drop in the death rate and greatly increased longevity.

In the third place there has been a great advance in agriculture (Figure 12.13). Cooperatives among the indigenous population and later "rural amelioration societies" have played a large part.

In the same period mineral working increased from virtually nothing to a level of world importance, notably in iron ore and phosphates. From 33,000 tons of phosphate exported from Morocco in 1921 the total topped half a million tons in 1951. With this has gone the marked though localized development of manufacturing industry, itself linked with the settlement in North Africa of large numbers of French. The French population approached the 2 million mark in 1951. The settlement of small French farmers on a large scale was officially encouraged in many ways. Villages in expropriated land were often built in advance, especially after the dreaded phylloxera disease destroyed the vineyards of southern France and left so many small farmers without a means of sustenance.

Road construction and port development have given the area, Algeria in

Figure 12.13 Irrigated seedbeds under date palms in the oasis of Touggourt. The water is brought by the pipe in the background from an artesian well. (Copyright G. M. Hickman.)

particular, magnificent roads and ports second to none of an equivalent size anywhere in the world.

In some ways social change and education have moved more slowly. The vast majority of the indigenous people are devout Moslems. The women are heavily veiled, and in general education is not for them. But by 1951 even the old Islamic university of Fez was demanding modern studies, and the University at Algiers was crowded.

It is too early to say what will be the effect of independence on economic development in the three countries, accompanied as it has been by the large-scale departure of the French. It must not be overlooked that the peoples of northwest Africa are Moslems and their language is Arabic. Egypt is exercising an increasing influence, notably in Morocco, and a closer union of Arab states is a distinct possibility. In particular there is a move towards the establishment of a united Maghrib state.

BIBLIOGRAPHY

There is a very extensive and detailed literature on French North Africa in the French language. The accounts in the *Géographie universelle* are naturally very full, and later material will be found in J. Blottière's *L'Algérie* (Paris, 1948). In English there is A. H. Brodrick's *North Africa* (New York, 1943). The detailed studies on which Bernard based his account in the *Géographie universelle* were his own *Le Maroc* (Paris, many editions), his *L'Algérie* (Paris, 1931) and de Lanessan's *La Tunisie* (Paris, 1917). Later works include J. Célérier's *Le Maroc* (Paris, 1948). All these works, even those written since World War II, are to a large extent of historical interest; the story of Morocco and Tunisia since independence needs to be followed from current records. For Algeria see *Focus*, February 1961. For Morocco see D. E. Ashford, *Political Change in Morocco*, Princeton Univ. Press, 1961, and J. T. Milge, *Morocco*, New York, 1953. Unfortunately L. Laitmans *Tunisia Today*, New York, 1954, was published before independence.

CHAPTER THIRTEEN

The Sahara

The world's greatest desert, the Sahara, stretches right across the north of the African continent from the shores of the Atlantic Ocean to the shores of the Red Sea (Figure 13.1). The long, narrow Red Sea serves only to interrupt the desert stretch, to be continued on its Asiatic side across Arabia and into Iran. Three thousand miles from east to west across Africa, the Sahara is nowhere less than a thousand miles wide; in round figures, the desert occupies more than 3 million square miles, or between a quarter and a third of the whole continent. Not by any means the whole of this vast area is "true" desert. There are very large areas of "tame" desert or poor scrub and steppeland, where at least some vegetation can exist and the margins fade into steppeland supporting sparse nomadic pastoral populations.

Such an obvious unit geographically has no separate political existence. The southwest quadrant is occupied by the welter of states which have arisen from the former French West Africa, the northwest forms the territory of Spanish Sahara along the coast, Mauritania, and the southern extension of Algeria inland. The northeast quadrant lies in Egypt and the former Italian Libya, now the Kingdom of Libya; the southeast section lies in the old Anglo-Egyptian Sudan, now the Republic of the Sudan, and, surprisingly enough, in the Chad Republic, part of former French Equatorial Africa. Though the boundaries between these political units are but lines through the desert wastes, they are clearly defined by treaty and in some cases demarcated. The geographical unity of the whole is such that a general description seems justified.

Every traveler by one of the desert caravan routes is familiar with the spectacle of bleached bones showing through the sand, grim reminders of some unfortunate camel or ass which perished by the way, in a country where nature is hard on the weak and unprepared.

In somewhat the same way, on a gigantic scale, there appear at intervals through the desert plains of sand and gravel rocky mountain ridges which

Figure 13.1 The Sahara. The Sahara may be regarded as lying between the annual rainfall line of 10 inches in the north and 15 inches in the south; the true desert within somewhat narrower limits. (Map in part after A. Bernard.)

are the bare ribs of once huge mountain chains formed early in the earth's history. Some of these mountain remnants are still mighty masses in their own right, especially the Tibesti and Ahaggar mountains, rising to heights of 10,000 feet in the very heart of the Sahara. By the trend of the folds in the rocks and the ridges to which they give rise, geologists distinguish the remnants of several distinct periods of earth movement, at least two of which are well marked. Much of the higher ground is actually of volcanic material, and many of the peaks are extinct volcanoes.

The old idea that these mountain masses were once islands and that the sands of the Sahara were of marine origin, and that its salt lakes were the remnants of a once extensive ocean, is entirely without foundation. The features of the Sahara as they appear today are the results of atmospheric weathering. Nowhere in the world are there better opportunities for the study of the phenomena of arid lands. Although the desert is broadly the area with an average of less than 8 inches of rain a year, with decreasing average fall there is increasing irregularity. The regime along the Mediterranean border is naturally that of the neighboring lands, with the rare rains coming in the cold season, whereas along the Sudan border the season of possible rain coincides with that of the neighboring tropical lands. In the heart of the Sahara the mountain masses exercise a distinct influence of their own, and many storms of great violence have been observed, for example, at Tamanrasset in the Ahaggar massif. Short, sharp storms may occur two or three times a year, or it may be that several years will pass without one. When such storms do happen, the mechanical action of the rain on the unprotected ground is at a maximum, and the normally dry watercourses are filled with turbulent muddy water.

With its normally cloudless skies and the consequent intense radiation, most of the Sahara is characterized by a great range of temperature from day to night. The range even of shade temperature may be over 60 degrees; it is double that on surfaces exposed to the sun. Consequently, bare rocks are intensely heated by the sun and expand so that they crack away from the underlying cooler mass, often with a loud report like a pistol shot. Where rocks such as granite are composed of different minerals, each mineral may have its own coefficient of expansion, and the rock may be broken in small fragments by no other action than that of insolation—exposure to the sun. At night the temperature of the ground may be 15 degrees or more less than that of the air and so may record as much as 20 degrees of frost. The "skinning" of rock surfaces which results is clearly seen in the case of granite.

At least along the northern part of the Sahara the thermometer commonly falls below freezing in the winter, and every year ice forms at places like Touggourt or Biskra, much more frequently than along the Mediterranean itself farther north. In the summer the Sahara can lay claim to have recorded the highest known shade temperatures on the earth's surface. Azizia in Tripolitania recorded 58°C. or 136.4°F. in September 1922. There are other records at least as high as 133°F. These extremes of temperature are associated with a clear atmosphere and dry air; relative humidity may drop below 10 per cent.

Returning to the rocky deserts which form a large part of the Sahara, we may distinguish:

1. The ancient crystalline rocks with associated granites and ancient volcanic rocks folded in pre-Cambrian times into the mountains known as the Saharides, trending roughly south to north.
2. The older Paleozoic rocks grouped around earlier rocks but also folded by Hercynian movements into north-south folds—these are the Altaïdes.
3. Sandstones and other rocks, especially the well-known "Nubian" sandstone of Cretaceous age, and also limestones, laid down in arms of the sea, not in the heart of the Sahara but in peripheral basins.
4. Huge basins occupied by sediments of continental origin laid down by wind or in shallow fresh or saline waters.

It would seem that quite late in its geological history, probably at the same time as the formation of the rift valleys of East Africa, the Saharan area was rent by great faults. Some blocks of country were elevated, others depressed. Through the cracks great sheets of lava were poured out or volcanoes piled up to great heights. As a result of the differential uplift of the blocks, cliff-like scarps are of frequent occurrence.

The wind plays a very important part in sculpturing the desert surface. Apart from strong constant winds such as the harmattan, violent whirling storms produce the dreaded sandstorms. Particles of rock, already detached by insolation, are constantly rolled against one another, gradually rounded, reduced in size, and smoothed until, when desert sand is examined under the microscope, even the smallest grains are rounded and polished. But before this happens angular fragments are hurled against rock faces, undercutting them and sculpturing them into fantastic shapes. Some hard rocks appear polished by this action, but nature has here its own protection. The sun, bringing to the surface of the rocks, by capillary action, any moisture contained in the surface layer, causes the water to evaporate, and a thin hard skin of iron and manganese salts is formed to protect the rock surface. This desert *patina* or crust is often black in color and suggests that fire has passed over the rocks. The process is not fully understood, and it is probable that some of the moisture comes from dew.

Rock and gravel surfaces occupy the largest part of the Sahara. Sand dunes which have so fired the public imagination do not in fact occupy more than about an eighth.

In detail, the character of the desert is the result of a combination of several factors. There are, first, the character of the underlying rocks; second, the force of torrential water erosion produced by the rapid runoff after the occasional severe storms; and, third, the conflicting character of desert weathering consequent upon a rapid alternation of heat and cold, which results both in the formation of the protective hard crust or desert patina and also in the shattering of the rocks.

Broadly speaking, there are three main types of surface and resulting scenery. The *Erg* desert is the desert of shifting sand dunes, the distribution of which is shown in Figure 13.1. A distinction is there made between those areas where sand movement is still active and what may be called "fossil" sand dunes, where movement appears to have ceased. The famous area of the Great Erg may be regarded as the most intractable part of the whole Sahara, and the area of sand which is most avoided by the cross-desert routes.

Then there is the *Reg* desert, a firm-surfaced naked plain, where the surface is strewn with an accumulation of stones and boulders (Figure 13.2), representing the detritus from rock outcrops resulting largely from the sun's action.

Figure 13.2   The *reg* type of desert, Sahara. (Courtesy of the Départements de la France d'Outre-Mer.)

Third, there is the *Hamada*, or rocky, desert, where bare rocks outcrop.

From the point of view of caravan movement preference is for the finer types of reg, or gravel plains.

In contrast to some of the deserts of Asia there are no great stretches in the Sahara of fine alluvium, and even if water were available there are not the stretches of land suitable for irrigation that we find, for example, in Iraq, or in Western Pakistan in the Indus basin.

A scanty vegetation is to be found over most parts of the Sahara except the erg. Naturally in the north it is a very stunted and attenuated representation of the vegetation of neighboring Mediterranean lands, whereas in the south it is the tropical grassland with scattered spiny shrubs, which fades gradually into the true desert. Both the coarse wiry grasses growing in tufts and the spiny bushes, and more especially the succulent plants, afford some rough pasture for camels, and few areas are completely despised by the desert nomads.

Oases occur wherever water is sufficiently near the surface for vegetation to be able to reach it, and often desert plants have amazingly long roots. It would be wrong to think of the typical oasis as a well surrounded by a clump of palms. Although the date palm is the characteristic tree of oases large and small, the oasis often has a margin of coarse shrubs and grass, the larger have tracts of land which can be cultivated by permanent settlers. Water is not always reached in depth from wells, but by striking horizontal channels into the surrounding country at a higher level and there reaching the water table so that the water flows into the oasis in the hollow by gravity. These

Figure 13.3 Section through a *foggara*. The foggara, shown by a heavy line, taps the underground water table at X, and the water flows by gravity to the grove of date palms.

horizontal channels are found especially in the west in Mauritania, and are known as foggara (Figure 13.3). They are similar to the karez of Baluchistan.

Most maps of the Sahara indicate the extensive watercourses which may, on rare occasions, be occupied by surface water. Many of them do mark the lines of underground streams, and from the air it is often possible to distinguish whole underground river systems by the sparse but nevertheless distinct lines of vegetation, plants with roots long enough to reach the water below. At intervals the vegetation becomes richer, and an oasis develops wherever the water table is near enough to the surface. The linear arrangement of oases is thus explained. Taking southern Algeria as an example, it would seem that water from the Atlas ranges drains as underground rivers southeastwards, water from the Ahaggar massif by a system of radial drainage. The underground water can of course be reached by wells and is usually cold, fresh, and pure in contrast to the occasional scanty surface supplies impregnated with magnesium sulphate (Epsom salts) and other salts. There has been some discussion, as in deserts elsewhere, whether the water tapped by modern French wells is "fossil" water and therefore exhaustible, or is fresh water renewed from rainfall or snow on distant mountains and therefore inexhaustible. The water obtained along the trans-Saharan routes discussed below suggests that the latter is true. The use of the water in irrigation has made possible a doubling of the size of the palmeries in several oases.

On the whole the numerous peoples of the Sahara belong to Euro-Asian groups rather than African. The core of the Sahara, with its focus in the massif of Ahaggar, is occupied by Berbers, a Hamitic group, of which the principal people are the Tuareg. The Tuareg are the "People of the Veil," so called because the men wear veils. The Tuaregs stretch right through the country of Air almost to the Nigerian border, and they are essentially nomadic camel men. Over the whole of the western desert and the northern area the people are of Arab stock, and are often called, very vaguely, Moors.

In contrast to the Tuaregs, who are nominal but unlettered Moslems, the Moors know and observe the Moslem religion, its history, and Islamic law. They fall into three occupational groups—the camel nomads, the semi-nomadic cattle raisers of the northern Sudan stretch, and the cultivators of the oases. Their habitation is essentially the tent; their connection with the peoples of northern lands is suggested by the appellation *Beidan,* or white, in contrast to the appellation *Sudan,* or black.

The Tibu (literally rock people from their home in the Tibesti Mountains) inhabit the southeastern desert, north and east of Lake Chad, and are obviously people with much Negro blood, though they too are Moslems. They may perhaps be regarded as Berbers who have intermarried with Negroes and adopted a Sudanese language.

It is natural that the French, who have controlled such a large proportion of the Sahara, should have paid particular attention to the problems of the desert and of its peoples. More than 10 pages of the great French *Géographie universelle* are devoted by Professor Augustin Bernard to a consideration of the Sahara. For details of the many regions into which the vast area can be divided, reference should be made to this work.

So long as France had possession both of the north and south, interest centered upon routeways across the Sahara. Those of importance at the time of World War II were discussed by W. E. Rudolph.[1] His map showed clearly the great east-west route lying to the south of the desert region through the grasslands of the Sudan, a route followed by Moslem pilgrims from the Islamized parts of West Africa through the Republic of the Sudan on their way to Mecca. By way of contrast is the modern military road skirting the Mediterranean Sea, of such significance in World War II. The trans-Saharan desert routes were thrown into fresh prominence by wartime conditions, with the need of communication for the Free French territories of West Africa at a time when communication by sea was difficult or impossible.

In the years between the wars the French had built motor roads equipped with rest houses, refueling stations, and a system of telegraphic communication to prevent the possible loss of tourist cars. One of these main desert highways (*piste automobile*) linked Colomb Béchar, at that time the railhead of the Algerian railway system, with Gao on the Niger River, and connected from there with Timbuktu and other points in West Africa. Another route, the Hoggar route, ran southwards from Algiers, through the remarkable center of Tamanrasset and Agades, to Zinder and so to Kano in northern Nigeria, thus linking with the Nigerian railway system. A third trans-Saharan route was from Tripoli across the southern part of Libya, through the oases of Fezzan, and thence across hundreds of miles of desert, virtually without water and pasture, to the neighborhood of Lake Chad. Other routes are shown on the map, Figure 13.4. It is notable that the first follows along the course long proposed by the French for the trans-Saharan railway. This rail-

[1] "Strategic Roads of the World, Notes on Recent Developments," *Geog. Rev.,* XXXIII, 1943, 110–131. The routes he discussed, as well as some later additions, are shown in Figure 13.4. A valuable study of trans-Saharan transportation routes has been made by Benjamin Thomas of U.C.L.A.

Figure 13.4   Trans-Saharan and other strategic routes in North Africa.

way was constructed southwards from the Algerian system to Colomb Béchar, within desert territory but separated by 1400 miles from the proposed terminus of Gao on the Niger in French Sudan (now Mali), whence an extension to Niamey lower down the Niger was also planned, while a branch line was intended to reach Timbuktu and the great irrigation area of the Niger inland delta.

The second, or Hoggar, route passes through Tamanrasset and skirts the Ahaggar massif—a remarkable region in the heart of the Sahara—actually in the administrative area of Southern Algeria. In general the region is an immense plateau averaging more than 3000 feet high; more exactly a succession of platforms separated by abrupt edges and consisting of ancient schists penetrated by basic rocks. These are remnants of the pre-Cambrian (Algonkian) mountain chains known as the Saharides. Local peaks are formed of old volcanic necks and reach their highest point in Tahat (9840 feet). This island mountain mass in the midst of the Sahara is also a climatic island with violent thunderstorms which from time to time fill the deep watercourses before the streams lose themselves in the surrounding desert. Bernard has described Atakor, as the highest part of the Ahaggar is called, as a formless mass, without harmony, without line; a skeleton robbed of its flesh yet transformed by its colors into country of wild beauty. Black basalt plateaus rest on a foundation of rose-colored granites; the volcanic peaks take on at sunset a lilac tint. The scene is so different from those to which we are accustomed that it appears entirely unreal. On the flanks of the mass lies the remarkable settlement of Tamanrasset, a town with poplar-lined avenues, electric light, and a modern hotel where passing travelers mingle with the various local officials.

In 1941 the position of the Vichy Government was such that to tap the resources of West Africa by an overland route became vital, and active consideration of the railway scheme was decreed. However, the fortunes of war soon changed the urgency of this position. Details of the route are found described by R. H. Forbes in a paper entitled, perhaps rather prematurely, "The Trans-Saharan Conquest"[2] He notes that the great desert route to be followed by the railway has often been called the "Rue des Palmiers" from the numbers of date palms to be found in the favored locations along the route. He mentions the occasional floods and surface water, the wells operated by shadoof to supply water and also in places the use of foggaras. This old slave route had already become a well-traveled route with comfortable French hostels at convenient distances and even competing gas stations, though certain sections are waterless and cars were required to be

[2] *Geog. Rev.*, **XXXIII**, 1943, 197–213.

equipped with radio and a competent operator, and certain points had been equipped with desert lighthouses to guide travelers.

In the early thirties I was planning to lead a small party of geographers across the Sahara by this route and to make halts on the way for geographical observations. A young couple who set out in a car to explore the position before our party made the attempt disappeared into the desert and were never heard of again, and it was largely in consequence of this that the later careful precautions were introduced. It may perhaps be claimed that the Sahara has not yet been fully conquered.

Economic developments in the Sahara

Although the Sahara was carved up by France, Spain, Italy, and Britain in the latter part of the nineteenth century, and French "pacification" of the 1,500,000 square miles of French territory went on almost until the outbreak of World War II, little change took place in the life of the desert. Neither nomadism nor the Moslem concept of indivisibility of Moslem territory were compatible with fixed political boundaries—they were just lines on a map. The whole position has been changed by the rising tide of nationalism and the suddenly enhanced importance of boundaries consequent upon discoveries of oil, gas, metallic ores, and underground water (Figure 13.5). There are reasons for the late geological exploration of the Sahara: first, the difficulty of working in waterless deserts many miles from a base; second, the mantle of sand and superficial deposits masking so much of the underlying geology. Modern equipment, notably air conditioning; specialized transport, including helicopters; and new techniques, notably aerial photography and geophysical prospecting, have led to numerous and often spectacular discoveries. It must be remembered that even now only the very rich deposits are economically exploitable. On the whole the metallic minerals fall into the category of future reserves; even the huge iron ore deposits of Mauritania at Fort Gouraud have produced only a rather slow development. With oil it is different. The first discovered was in 1956 at Hassi-Messaoud at a depth of 11,200 feet. At first a short pipeline was constructed to a railhead at Touggourt and later a 400-mile line direct to a new oil terminal at Bougie in December 1959. Production from this field reached 6.5 million tons from 54 wells in 1960.

Seventy-five miles farther south the field of El Gassi-El Agreb began producing in 1961; 300 miles southeast of Hassi-Messaoud a rich group of fields lies within a few miles of the Libyan border; and from Edjelé, Zarzaitine, and other fields oil is being sent by pipeline (completed in 1960) to the new port of La Skhirra north of Gabes in Tunisia. On the whole Saharan oil is heavy and yields much less motor fuel than Persian Gulf oil. No oil has been dis-

Figure 13.5 The oilfields, gasfields, and pipelines of the Sahara.

covered in Tunisia, and several of the main groups have abandoned the search. Libya, by way of contrast, has been the scene of an unprecedented oil rush, with all the major world groups represented among the concessionaires, and it is estimated that in one year alone, 1960, over $150,000,000 was spent in prospecting. Although important Algerian fields arc near the Libyan border, it is not here that the Libyan exploration has been so successful but in the discovery of fields within a hundred miles of the coast of the Gulf of Sirte. From fields at Zelten, Dahra, and Beida the oil is being piped to new ports of which Marsa el Brega (from Zelten) was the first. Other fields have been proved in Libya, but development is being concentrated on the more accessible.

The natural gasfields of the Sahara so far located are in three areas of southern Algeria—at In Salah, 600 miles from the coast, at Hassi-Messaoud and at Hassi R'Mel. The last mentioned may be the richest deposit in the world and is only 280 miles south of Algiers. A gas pipeline reached the coast at Arzew from Hassi-Messaoud and Hassi R'Mel in 1961.

Specially constructed tankers are being built to handle the gas, and Britain is a large potential consumer. Pipelines may be extended under the Mediterranean via Sicily to serve Italy and possibly via Spain to other countries.

There are obvious possibilities of oil and gas in other parts of the Sahara. Neither Egypt and Sudan in the east nor Morocco and Mauritania in the west have yet been successful in the search, but suddenly exact desert boundaries have assumed a great significance.

It may be of some value to terminate this chapter by some notes on the political divisions recognized in the Sahara.

Spanish Sahara (Territories of Rio de Oro and Sekia el Hamra). This area of little over 105,000 square miles has a population of about 14,000, but some 30,000 nomads are estimated to enter with their flocks after the rains. The name of the southern part, Rio de Oro, signifying River of Gold, must be an example of supreme optimism, fertile imagination, or a facetious wit.

Farther north, as an enclave of 741 square miles in Morocco, is the Ifni Territory, with a population approaching 40,000.

Mauritania. This territory was administered as a part of French West Africa until it became an independent republic in 1960. It is discussed in the next chapter.

The vast tract of Southern Algeria has already been considered in connection with Algeria itself, and much of the descriptions on the preceding pages refers to the Algerian Sahara.

The Kingdom of Libya. Libya may be regarded as a wholly Saharan country. Along the borders of the Mediterranean Sea are those parts which enjoy a sufficient rainfall or can command sufficient water to make habitation possible. In the extreme south is the land of Fezzan, where isolated oases of considerable size are cut off by great stretches of desert. The Mediterranean coastal fringes fall into two main parts—Cyrenaica and Tripolitania. Cyrenaica includes Benghazi, Tobruk, and Derna, towns which became familiar in the North African campaigns of World War II. The western parts of the Mediterranean coastlands, likewise capable of settlement and some development, form Tripolitania, centering around the attractive town of Tripoli (Figure 13.6). Tripolitania came under Turkish domination in the sixteenth century, and, although the Arab population retained or later secured some measure of independence, the country in 1835 was proclaimed a Turkish vilayet or province. In 1911, when a quarrel had broken out between Italy and Turkey, the Italians occupied Tripoli, established an army there, and shortly afterwards the Italian chamber passed a measure which decreed the annexation of the country, later confirmed by treaty. Though there had been earlier Italian settlements, this marks the beginning of a period of rapid development of Libya as an Italian colony.

By 1938 there were 90,000 Italian settlers in Libia Italiana, that is, in Tripolitania and Cyrenaica. The land hunger at home, the extreme pressure of population on the resources of the home country, had long resulted in a constant stream of emigrants from Italy to the New World, and in large numbers of Italian laborers seeking work in France and elsewhere. But there was still the great problem of the need for land. In her colonies in Africa, all of them in desert tracts—Somaliland, Etritrea, and Libya—it cannot be said that the Italians spared money or materials in their efforts to develop their

Figure 13.6   Tripolitania, showing main regional divisions and tribal areas. (From Jean Despois, *Geog. Rev.*, 1945. Courtesy of the *Geographical Review*, American Geographical Society.)

new territories for settlement. The Italians are great road builders, and they gave Libya some excellent roads through areas capable of settlement. There are now motor roads well served by buses the whole length of the coast, out to the Zelten oilfield and to Sebha in the Fezzan and to Ghadames. The buildings in the towns and the farms, if not on a palatial scale, were ambitious. There was a touch of grandiloquence in some of the monuments which were erected rather in advance of successful colonization and development. In 1962 it was estimated that 29,000 Italians remained, largely in Tripoli.

The whole of Libya has an area of approximately two-thirds of a million square miles, and the boundaries were fixed after agreement with Egypt in such a way that Italy secured the oasis of Giarabub (Jaghbub or Jarabub) in 1926, in exchange for which Egypt's claim to a rectification in the frontier at Sollum on the Mediterranean Sea was accepted. This vast territory, according to the Census of 1954, had 1,088,889 people (the United Nations' mid-1960 estimate was 1,950,000), Arabs and Berbers as well as a considerable Egyptian population. The North African campaigns were fought through its deserts, and after a dingdong struggle the Germans and Italians were expelled in 1942. Tripolitania and Cyrenaica were placed under British military administrations and the Fezzan under French, with the idea that the future of the area should await development of events. The British government recognized the Amir Mohammed Idris el Senussi as Amir of Cyrenaica in 1949. Representatives from other parts of Libya met as the Libyan National

Figure 13.7 Section across Tripolitania from south to north. (From Jean Despois, *Geog.*
Rev., 1945. Courtesy of the *Geographical Review*, American Geographical Society.)

Assembly in November 1950, and declared their desire to have the Amir as
king of all Libya. Thus Libya became an independent kingdom, unifying the
three traditional areas. Under treaties of friendship Britain and America
have air bases, the United States paying an annual rental of $12,000,000
for the Wheelus base.

An interesting account of Tripolitania, in English, has been given by Jean
Despois,[3] together with several instructive maps (Figures 13.7 and 13.8). The
rainfall map shows at once the small area of the country which enjoys more
than 8 inches of rain on an average, and how very tiny is the area just
around Tripoli itself which receives the not particularly large total of 14 inches.

Strung out along the seacoast between lagoons and the sands of the dunes
are oases with numerous palms, dotted with villages. Their existence is possible through the thousands of wells from which water is constantly being
obtained. Immediately behind are the plains of the Jefara, sandy steppes
with stunted vegetation and occasional muddy depressions into which water
seeps at times. The Jefara is bounded on the south by the bare rock cliff known
as the Jebel, or the mountain. Its steep edge, which we may look upon as the
beginning of the inevitable African plateau, is serrated by dry watercourses.
In places the Jebel is 2500 feet in height but falls eastwards.

On the heights of the mountain, altitude has resulted in an increased pre-

[3] "Types of Native Life in Tripolitania," *Geog. Rev.,* **XXXV,** 1945, 352–367.

Figure 13.8 Tripolitania—rainfall. (From Jean Despois, *Geog. Rev.*, 1945. Courtesy of the
Geographical Review, American Geographical Society.)

Figure 13.9   An air view of the ruins of Cyrene. The ancient Greek capital of Cyrenaica is a good example of early European influence in North Africa. (Copyright Aerofilms Library.)

cipitation, and some dry farming is possible in a land with stunted Mediterranean plants; but otherwise from this area—known as Dahar or "the back" —the country fades quickly into the desert itself.

Cyrenaica has points of comparison. There is a main coastal plateau and the southern zone or depression of the Kufra. On the coast, Benghazi (Figure 13.11) has about 10 inches of rain a year, and the Italian population was concentrated in the agricultural zones of the oases at the foot of the hills along the coast. Once again the area capable of settlement and development is extremely limited. A brief but lucid account of Cyrenaica is found in the *Report of the Proceedings* of the International Geographical Congress held at Cambridge, England, in 1928. Along the coast, sometimes called the Marmarican coast, are one or more systems of terraces ending seawards in cliffs, diminishing in general from west to east. A few miles from the coast is a water parting, south of which are the flat, bare surfaces of the highlands region tilted slightly southwards and consisting of a limestone *hamada*. This gives southwards to a depression in part below sea level, in which are found the Siwa oasis (in Egypt) and the oases of Jarabub and Jalo. Finally, to the south, is the great Libyan erg with long lines of sandhills. The Jarabub oasis is described as occupying a rock-girt basin some 350 square miles in area in which there are three large intercommunicating irregular basins, each in turn subdivided into small *hatiya*. A hatiya has a flat bottom with a salty alluvial soil, covered with halophytic vegetation and sometimes with a salt lake. There are occasional springs which give potable but bitter water, and all the numerous wells have a high proportion of magnesium and calcium salts. A

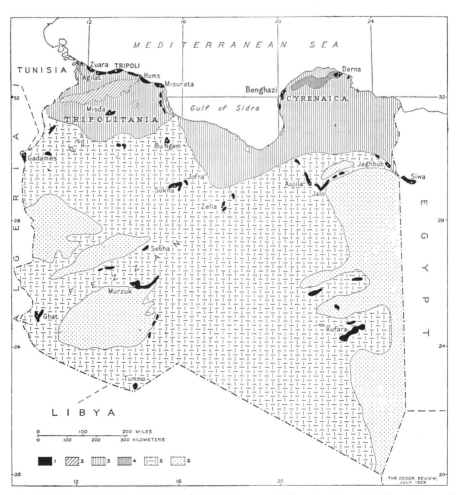

Figure 13.10   Libya. (1) Cultivated land and oases. (2) Dry farming with olives, figs, and barley. (3) Steppes and scrub used for pasture. (4) Dense scrub. (5) Rocky desert (*hammada*) and pebbly desert (*serir*). (6) Sandy desert. The boundaries are those that existed when Libya was an Italian colony. (From S. Dainelli, *Geog. Rev.*, 1929. Courtesy of the American Geographical Society.)

Figure 13.11   An air view of Benghazi. Most of the modern buildings were constructed by the Italians during their occupation—a good example of modern European influence in North Africa. (Copyright Aerofilms Library.)

few hundred people at most live in the *zawiya* enclosure focusing on a small mosque; there are palm groves and some small vegetable gardens.

Such a description might be applied widely to the oases of the Sahara.

BIBLIOGRAPHY

Earlier descriptions of the Sahara dealing with its physical geography have a permanent value and so has much of the material on desert life. But recent political and economic developments, especially those based on exploration of oil, have been so rapid that it is difficult to keep up to date. For Libya see *The Economic Development of Libya* (International Bank, 1960). Progress in the oil industry is recorded in the periodical press, notably the *Petroleum Review*. In their monthly *Overseas Review*, Barclays Bank DCO, which has offices throughout Libya, gives details of current developments.

CHAPTER FOURTEEN

West Africa[1]

West Africa forms a well-marked division of the continent, whether it is defined geographically or politically. Geographically it may be defined as stretching from the westernmost point of the continent, Cape Verde near Dakar, for some 1750 miles eastward to the Cameroons mountains. There in the east the natural limit is a line of volcanic mountains and uplands trending along fault lines from northeast to southwest, including the mighty volcanic peak of Cameroon Mountain itself (13,350 feet) and extending out to sea to embrace Fernando Po, Príncipe, São Tomé, and Annobón. The southern limit of West Africa is undeniably defined for all purposes by the Atlantic Ocean, or that large section of it commonly called the Gulf of Guinea. Speaking generally, the coast trends east and west and, roughly parallel to the coast, there exists in West Africa a succession of vegetation zones. Forest and swamp of the coast give place inland to savanna and scrub, until some 600 or 700 miles from the coast cultivable West Africa fades into the Sahara desert. This is the geographical limit, and where the rainfall drops to 15 inches or less the desert may be said to begin. This great block of country, offering a variety of environmental conditions to its human inhabitants but broadly all permanently inhabited or capable of supporting a settled population, has an area of about a million square miles.

Politically West Africa comprises the series of republics which have replaced the vast lands of French West Africa (Afrique occidentale française) with the four enclaves of former British Colonial territory (the Gambia, Sierra Leone, Ghana, and Nigeria), Portuguese Guinea, and Liberia. On the eastern limit the islands of Fernando Po and Annobón are Spanish, São Tomé and Príncipe Portuguese. The States succeeding former French West Africa

[1] I am greatly indebted to my colleague Dr. R. J. Harrison-Church for his meticulous care in making suggestions during the revision of this chapter.

do not, however, recognize the existence of the Sahara, and several stretch across the barren wastes, there to adjoin the southern boundaries of North African territories (especially Southern Algeria). If, therefore, one uses the boundaries of former French West Africa to define "West Africa," one includes another million square miles of desert to the north of what is geographically West Africa.

Geographical West Africa consists of a succession of strips running east and west. This is clear at once from Figures 14.3 to 14.6. The lowland coastal strip gives place to a rolling plateau; the normally wet coast gives place to parallel bands merging into one another, but becoming steadily drier inland until the desert is reached. Equatorial rainforest is succeeded by deciduous forest, savanna, scrub, and then desert, each with its own characteristic products.

Historical background

Whoever may have been the original human inhabitants of West Africa, perhaps people of pygmy stock, the West African Negroes came early on the scene and penetrated to the coasts, taking their system of shifting cultivation in forest clearings wherever they went. From the Barbary States, Egypt, and the Sudan successive waves of adventurers came, helped greatly from Arab times onwards by the possession of camels. They included Hamites and Semites. Especially noteworthy were the Hamitic cattle-keeping Fulani who, like the other cattle keepers, rarely penetrated the tsetse-infested forest belts. The nomads mixed freely with the Negro peoples, often adopting their language and sometimes their customs, but it was the nomads who brought Islam to West Africa. The marked distinction between the agricultural, pagan, pure Negro, coastal peoples and the inland pastoral-agricultural Moslem mixed peoples is thus very old and very fundamental. For knowledge of West Africa in the Middle Ages we owe much to a Moor, Leo Africanus, who was born at Granada in Spain in 1494 or 1495, but was brought up in Fez (Morocco) and subsequently traveled extensively and left written accounts of the great Negro empires of his day.

The first great empire was the Ghana Empire (Figure 14.1) which reached its zenith about A.D. 1000. Its capital was at Ghana, now in the desert some 250 miles west of Timbuktu. This empire was succeeded by the Mali Empire (from its thirteenth-century capital Mali on the left bank of the Niger above the modern Ségou) but more commonly from its ruling race the Mandingo Empire. The Keïta family, to this day providing small chiefs in the Bamako area, can be traced back to the seventh century, and in the fourteenth century ruled over the greatest Negro empire the world has ever known and one of the world's great empires. In 1660 the last Mandingo emperor was forced to abandon Mali, the site of which is now a waste of scrub.

Figure 14.1   Ancient empires of West Africa.

Figure 14.2   Later kingdoms of West Africa.

The Gao or Songhaï Empire lay to the east of the Mandingo Empire, with its capital at Gao on the Niger. It came to an end in 1591 by conquest from across the desert by a Moorish army largely composed of European mercenaries and equipped with cannon. The Songhaï and Mandingo Empires gave place to many small kingdoms, some ephemeral, some like the Mossi Empires or the Fulani Kingdoms of remarkable and lasting stability.

The story of these Negro empires is important for at least two reasons.[2] In the first place they demonstrate the governing abilities of the African. Pride in their former glories led to the adoption of the name Ghana for an entirely different area (the Gold Coast) when it became independent and the similar resuscitation of the name Mali. In the second place they were based on a mixed economy in areas which today have become semidesert. Does this prove the desiccation of Africa?

The foregoing descriptions make it clear that the natural geographical divisions of West Africa run east and west. In sharp contrast the majority of modern political divisions run north and south. Each major political division thus tends to be a transect of the whole. Political boundaries cut right across environmental zones and in fact take no notice of human distributions. Frequently a single tribe, such as the Ewe, discussed later, is divided by a boundary created during the European partition of Africa but perpetuated by modern national units.

The physical background

Using West Africa in the geographical sense, we see that this great section of the continent partakes of most of those features common to the whole continent south of the Sahara. There are the usual huge plateaus with level or gently undulating surfaces, though the general elevation is here less than most parts of tropical Africa—500 to 1000 feet above sea level (Figure 14.3). The desert country of the north lies mainly at about 1500 feet above sea level, with occasional hill masses rising above the general level. South of this lies the shallow depression or basin, an ancient sea and later lake bed, through the heart of which the River Niger makes its great northward bend via Timbuktu. Westward a low divide separates the basin of the middle Niger from the basin of the Senegal; to the east a somewhat similar divide separates the Niger from the basin of Lake Chad. Southward of the central Niger basin the land rises again to rolling country 1000 to 1500 feet above sea level, and this higher country forms the divide south of which are rivers, mainly

---

[2] The Ghana Empire is believed by some to be the origin of the word Guinea (as a corruption), later applied to the whole west coast. The British gold coin, the "guinea," took its name from the fact that it was minted from gold from the Guinea coast. The guinea, equivalent to 21 shillings, is still used in Britain by some trades and professions as a unit of price, though no coins or notes have been issued for a very long time.

Figure 14.3   Physical map of West Africa.

Figure 14.4   Drainage of West Africa.

short, draining direct to the Gulf of Guinea. At both ends this higher land
rises to considerably greater heights. To the west are the Futa Jallon–Guinea
Highlands; to the east the Jos Plateau. The two maps here reproduced (Figures 14.3 and 14.4) show respectively the relief, or physical regions, and the
drainage.

Reference has already been made to the inhospitable, harborless character of much of the African coasts. West Africa is no exception. Where the
desert reaches the sea, north of St. Louis and Cape Verde, longshore drifting
has caused long curving sandy beaches offering no shelter (except at Port

Etienne), with dangerous offshore shoals and heavy surf. Cliffs are rare on much of the African coasts, so that those of Cape Verde, behind which Dakar seems to hide, call for comment. Southward the coast is largely one of mud flats with mangrove forests intersected by innumerable channels, but a number of estuaries, though with variable channels and impeded by sandbanks, offer shelter and access to the interior. Most important of these are the mouths of the Gambia, Casamance, Cacheu, and Rokel rivers—respectively in Gambia, Guinea, Portuguese Guinea, and Sierra Leone.

Geology

In common with the greater part of the continent, West Africa consists essentially of an ancient crystalline complex, widely exposed, with various groups of overlying sediments in certain regions. The basement complex includes great masses of granite-gneisses, ranging from true granites to ortho- and para-gneisses, and highly folded metamorphic rocks which show trend lines broadly termed Huronian, from north to south. Sediments, usually gently folded and only slightly if at all metamorphosed but believed to be pre-Cambrian, rest on these and are sometimes important because of the inclusion of gold-bearing conglomerates (as in Ghana). There are also groups of Paleozoic sediments, likewise gently folded but into northeast to southwest folds. Later sediments include Mesozoic and Tertiary. The sediments of the lower group, known to the French as *Continental Intercalaire* and broadly contemporary with the Nubian sandstones of Egypt and Libya, were probably laid down in an inland basin over a very long period of time from the Permian to the Lower Cretaceous. Later a shallow sea invaded the interior or occupied gulfs extending from the eastern part of the present Gulf of Guinea. At a later stage there were the huge inland Quarternary basins, such

Figure 14.5   Average annual rainfall of West Africa. Figures are in inches.

as those of the Middle Niger and Chad, in which were deposited various lacustrine, fresh-water, and terrestrial deposits. Volcanic rocks of various ages add the final major feature to the long geological story.

Although substantial mineral deposits are know to lie in former French West Africa, many localities are remote, and not all the ores are high grade or worth exploiting. The impressive output up to World War I was essentially from British West Africa. Though the gold-bearing "bankets" of Ghana are not known in neighboring territory, there are some alluvial and eluvial deposits, especially in the Republic of Guinea. Alluvial diamonds, probably derived from some ultrabasic rocks but not yet traced to their source, are widespread and industrially important in Ghana, the Ivory Coast, Sierra Leone, and Guinea. The local exploitation of highly ferruginous laterite as iron ore has long been widespread, and such ores are now of commercial importance near Conakry in Guinea. Hematite iron ores of international significance worked in Sierra Leone are now worked elsewhere, as in Liberia and northern Mauritania. Bauxite is widely distributed, and some is of high grade and now being exploited in the Los Islands off Conakry and in Ghana. Though the working of manganese ore up to 1950 was restricted to Ghana, (then the Gold Coast), there are known deposits in the Ivory Coast and Niger. Mineral-bearing sands with ilmenite, zircon, rutile, and titanium ores occur along the Senegal, Sierra Leone, and Ivory Coasts. There are phosphates which rank with the lower grades of Morocco now being exploited near Thiès in Senegal and in Togo, and deposits occur elsewhere. Unfortunately limestones suitable for making cement or agricultural lime are rare, and thus the works near Dakar, Enugu, and Abeokuta are of special significance. Rock salt and saline earths by contrast are common and worked in Mauritania, Senegal, Mali, and Niger.[3]

Natural regions and political divisions in West Africa

The relief features shown in Figure 14.3, which afford a series of strips roughly parallel to the coasts, are reinforced by the character of the natural vegetation itself dependent upon climate—shown in Figure 14.6. The general arrangement of vegetation belts is agreed, but several different detailed schemes have been proposed. It is indicative of the isolation in which each national group worked in Africa before World War II that even the scientists and technical officers such as foresters and agriculturalists in the French and British spheres rarely met, scarcely ever collaborated. Even in the study of

[3] P. Légoux, *Esquisse géologique de l'Afrique occidentale française.* Bull. 4, Service des Mines. Gouv. Gen. de l'Afr. O.F. Dakar, 1939. Colored map. Reviewed at length in *Geog. Jour.,* **CV,** 1945, 129–133.

Figure 14.6   Natural vegetation of West Africa.

natural vegetation it is difficult to correlate the work of the British[4] and the French.[5] In general terms, however, there is a *coastal belt* of mangrove woodlands and sand-bank grass forest with coarse grasses and screw pines. Floristically the French have distinguished a Casamancian area of forest in the west, where the coast trends northwest to southeast. Inland the *evergreen rainforests* extend as a broad belt except where interrupted by the Ghana dry belt and are succeeded inland by *deciduous forests* with much grass—the *Guinea Zone*—which gives place to the drier savanna or *Sudan Zone* with the conspicuous Bombax. On the higher plateaus the natural vegetation is of somewhat different type, and *montane forests* may be distinguished. The Sudan Zone fades into thorn scrub and desert.

The important point is, of course, that each of these zones forms a distinctive environment to which the human response has been very different. The shifting cultivation of the formerly pagan or animistic Negroes of the coastal zones contrasts utterly with the life of the Moslem Fulani cattlemen or the sedentary Hausa of the northern zones. Yet political divisions cut right across all these natural zones.

---

[4] T. C. Chipp (Editor), *Aims and Methods of Vegetation Survey,* 1928, but see R. W. Keay, *Vegetation Map of Africa,* UNESCO, O. U. P.

[5] A. Aubréville, *Climats, forêts et désertification en afrique occidentale,* 1949.

Until the emergence of the independent African states in 1958–1960, politically West Africa could be regarded as French territory occupying the whole vast interior and reaching to the coast in four main areas: (1) Senegal, (2) French Guinea, (3) the Ivory Coast, and (4) Dahomey with Togoland, separated by enclaves not under French control.

The first enclave was the narrow British territory of the Gambia; Senegal and French Guinea were separated by the enclave of Portuguese Guinea; French Guinea from the Ivory Coast by the broad enclave of British Sierra Leone and Liberia; the Ivory Coast from Dahomey by the British Gold Coast and the trusteeship territories of Togoland.

The French approached West Africa both by sea and by land, and French West Africa administratively met Southern Algeria in the heart of the Sahara. The British and Portuguese approached West Africa from the sea, and Liberia, too, was established by coastal settlements. From the coasts there was gradual penetration inland, but the four British enclaves of the Gambia, Sierra Leone, Gold Coast, and Nigeria, like Portuguese Guinea and Liberia, were based essentially on coastal settlements. The same was true of the former German Togoland and Kamerun (Cameroon). The fact that French West Africa formed a continuous tract encouraged unification of the territories, whereas the British areas, cut off from one another, each developed along individual lines.

French West Africa at the midcentury and after

The reorganization of the former French Empire into the French Union (Union française), completed after World War II, had certain important effects in West Africa. The seven former "colonies" of Senegal (Sénégal), Mauritania (Mauritanie), French Sudan (Soudan Français), French Guinea (Guinée), the Ivory Coast (Cote d'Ivoire), Dahomey (Dahomey), Upper Volta (Haute-Volta, resuscitated in 1947), and the Niger Territory (Niger), all became "territories" within the Federation of French West Africa with its capital at Dakar. The trusteeship territory of Togoland remained outside the Federation. As already explained briefly in Chapter 2, the recall to power of General de Gaulle in 1958 and the framing of a constitution for the Fifth Republic had speedy and far-reaching effects for French West Africa. The eight territories listed above were offered a choice between complete independence or autonomy within the French Community (La Communauté). French Guinea voted for independence and became the Republic of Guinea (République de Guinée, with French as the official language) on October 2, 1958. The other seven voted to remain in the French Community, but before the end of 1960 each had become a republic with the titles respectively of Senegal (République du Sénégal), Mauritania (République Islamique de Mauritanie), Mali (République du Mali, formerly French Sudan), Ivory

Coast (République de Côte d'Ivoire), Dahomey (République du Dahomey), Upper Volta (République de Haute-Volta), and Niger (République du Niger). The former French trusteeship territory of Togoland became the independent Republic of Togo on April 27, 1960 (Figure 14.7).

Under the earlier constitution of the French Union, crystallized at the Brazzaville Conference of 1944, each territory elected its deputies (African or French) whose duty and privilege was to reside in Paris and sit in the National Assembly, there to legislate both for French home affairs and for African or other territories. The African deputy thus began to play an important part in the government of France itself. The Africans settled down to European ways of life in Paris; conversely, French settlers established themselves as private traders, shopkeepers, and craftsmen in considerable numbers in tropical Africa. They took with them French ways of life and gave a remarkable atmosphere of metropolitan vitality and racial cooperation to the towns of French West Africa where they settled. By 1950 there were 30,000 Europeans, mainly French, in the unique city of Dakar (12 per cent of the population) and 10,000 in the Ivory Coast capital of Abidjan. After 1945 new building and modernization took place in Dakar on a scale unparalleled in Africa, and the changes in Abidjan, especially with the opening to traffic of the deepwater lagoon port in July 1950, were almost equally staggering. There was keen competition for the African farmers' groundnuts, coffee, cocoa, palm kernels, palm oil, and bananas; keen competition among middlemen and exporters. The big jump was in coffee growing—80 per cent on African farms and less than 20 per cent on European-owned plantations —with a guaranteed market in France. There was proportionately less production of palm oil than in British West Africa, some being made into soap locally in Senegal and the Ivory Coast. The same postwar period was marked by such industrial growths as oil-seed crushing of peanuts on a large scale in

Figure 14.7 Political map of West Africa.

| Palm oil, northern limit | Camels, southern limit | Cocoa, main areas |
| Horses, southern limit | Cattle, southern limit | Peanuts, main areas |

Figure 14.8   Economic map of West Africa.

Senegal, cement and lime making, brewing, boot and shoe making. These industries were run both by Africans and by French.

The development of iron ore and bauxite mining in French Guinea was large-scale private enterprise, but the social services and public works were financed by the Metropolitan Government, through the organization known as F.I.D.E.S., comparable with the Colonial Development and Welfare of Britain.

The French system in Africa was designed to make the African a good citizen of Greater France, to bring him into partnership even to the extent of governing France. There was no place in the scheme for the conservation of any indigenous African social structure. The coming of independence found a considerable number of French-speaking Africans with experience in matters of government and organization, with a tradition of interracial co-operation, and so the transition has been made with remarkable smoothness.[6]

British West Africa at the midcentury and after

The trends in British West Africa after World War II offered some remarkable contrasts to French West Africa. The introduction of universal franchise leading to democratic self-government would seem the quickest way of completing the disappearance of the British Empire, which indeed it was. Whereas the French until 1958 held up the ideal of citizenship of Greater

[6] See Virginia Thompson and Richard Adloff, *French West Africa*, 1958, and *The Emerging States of French Equatorial Africa*, 1960 (Stanford: Stanford University Press).

French—just as the Romans did 2000 years ago, by the lure of the magic words, *civis romanus sum*—the British held to the ideal of a Commonwealth of Free Nations.

Progress was rapid. Before 1939, broadly speaking, the administrations of the British colonies were largely bureaucratic and almost entirely white. The governors were appointed by the Colonial Office in London, and ultimately policy was the responsibility of the British Parliament acting through the Secretary of State for the Colonies. Not unfairly the British colonies were described not as countries but as collections of tribes in a steel framework of British administration.

It was during World War II that Africans entered in large numbers the higher circles of administration, notably in financial committees, but in an advisory capacity.

In the postwar period the rapidity of African cultural and political development was recognized by the successive establishment in each colony of entirely new constitutions based essentially on democratic principles as understood in Anglo-Saxon countries. The form varied slightly from one area to another, but the principles were the same—a large legislative council, elected directly by universal adult (or adult male in Northern Nigeria) suffrage or through electoral "colleges"; African ministers in charge of departments and forming a cabinet in complete control of the countries' affairs, except for the governor's right of veto—the governor appointed as before. The changes were accompanied by the development of a party system, the rapid Africanization of the civil service and the development of local government. The old distinctions between "colony" and "protectorate" largely disappeared.

General satisfaction with the new constitution was tempered by one consideration. Africans had no direct representation in London, where the Colonial Office appointed governors and where Parliament determined policy.

In the Gold Coast the 1951 elections (see page 149) under universal adult suffrage for the House of Assembly put into power Kwame Nkrumah, leader of the Convention People's Party, who at the time was in prison for seditious activities. He was immediately released and took office as Leader of Government Business.

Clearly the people of the Gold Coast now understood the system of democratic elections and the party system, so that the country was ripe for independence with the goodwill of both main parties of the British Parliament. The General Assembly of the United Nations agreed in December 1956 that the new country should absorb the trusteeship territory of British Togoland; the new country chose the title Ghana from the ancient African empire of that name (though not in the same area; see page 272); and the British Parliament passed the Ghana Independence Act. The State of Ghana thus came into existence on March 6, 1957, choosing dominion status within the Commonwealth. On July 1, 1960, it was declared a republic within the Commonwealth with Dr. Kwame Nkrumah as president.

The story of Nigeria is not dissimilar. It became a federation under a governor-general on October 1, 1954; six years later to the day the Federation was declared a sovereign independent state within the Commonwealth.

The question of the trusteeship territory of the British Cameroons on Nigeria's eastern borders—in two separated portions—was left open, to be decided by the vote of the people. The small northern area was added to the Northern Region of Nigeria; the southern portion elected to join the Cameroon Republic, the former French trusteeship territory.

Sierra Leone presented the problem of the viability of a much smaller state, but independence was achieved on April 27, 1961. Of the British areas in West Africa only the Gambia remains with colonial status. There the problem is the tiny size—less than 4,000 square miles and with a little over a quarter of a million people—and the enclave character within French-speaking territory.

It is not of course to be expected that all should go smoothly in the newly independent countries. Some outside critics are concerned at the treatment of the minority or opposition parties by the ruling party in Ghana, and when the Queen, as titular head of the Commonwealth, was slated to visit West Africa with Prince Philip in the summer of 1961, some sections of the British public counselled against the visit. But in each of the four countries of West Africa the visit was acclaimed with tremendous enthusiasm, and proved a great personal success for the Queen and her Consort.

Although political divisions between French and British territories cut indiscriminately across tribal areas, there is little if any tendency either for realignment of boundaries of the newly independent states or for mass migration one way or the other. In general there is little restriction of movement across the frontiers. There continue to be seasonal movements of labor, such as the "strange farmers" in the Gambia and a general movement of men from Mali, Upper Volta, and Niger into the richer coastal states.

The British developed, notably in Nigeria, a system of government-controlled marketing boards for the chief export crops. In Nigeria such boards were established for cocoa, peanuts and palm oil products. The boards fix the price to be paid to the producer, who therefore knows in advance what he will receive. It is held that this is conducive to an even spread of wealth, to a balanced cropping and to fair prices in times of depression. There is no lure of a sudden high price to tempt the cultivator to neglect to grow food nor in times of boom is there danger of the rise of a "Kulak" class. The marketing boards use the "profits" they make on world markets for the benefit of the industry; it is in fact a form of taxation. The upsurge in coffee production in the Ivory Coast and cocoa in Ghana suggests that producers appreciate the benefits, though there are those who argue that the minimization of the profit motive lowers the incentive of the progressive individual. Somewhat later the French introduced a system of guaranteed markets (in France) and prices.

The Gambia

The Gambia River as a natural routeway into the West African hinterland early attracted the attention of British traders. The "Company of Adventurers of London Trading into Africa," which received its charter from King James I in 1618, later in the century (1664) built Fort James on an island some 17 miles from the mouth of the river. In the wars with France in the eighteenth century the Fort changed hands several times and was finally destroyed. The Treaty of Paris in 1814 recognized British sovereignty over the banks of the Gambia River, although there was no longer a British post in the area. After the abolition of slave trading by the British Parliament in 1807, the British navy had used Gorée as a base against slave carriers in the Gambia. The restoration of that islet to France by the Treaty of 1814 led Britain to select the site where Bathurst now stands (Figure 14.9). In 1816 the chief of neighboring Kombo ceded an island—little more than a low, uninhabited sand bank—on the south bank of the river, where the mouth is only 2 miles wide. Renamed St. Mary's Island, a military post was established in 1819 following a traders' settlement in 1816. Linked with the mainland by a line of sand banks, bordered on the south by a large area of mangrove swamp, well sheltered from Atlantic storms, it was an excellent defensive site for the original purpose but a poor one for the location of a

Figure 14.9   The site of Bathurst at the mouth of the Gambia River. (After H. R. Jarrett.)

capital from which to develop an extensive colony. Because the island is liable to flooding, especially in the low ground between two original higher parts, the drainage problem (until the mid-fifties there were insanitary open sewers) has never been fully solved. An adequate water supply remained an additional problem until 1951. As usual with African rivers, there was a bar at the entrance to the intricate channel, now dredged to 26 feet at high water. Although Bathurst harbor is sheltered, it had only shallow-water wharves, and vessels of more than 2000 tons had to load and offload by lighter. A deep-water wharf was provided in 1952.

Technically only St. Mary's Island and certain other islands and settlements—a total area of 96 square miles—constitute the colony, the remainder of Gambia being a protectorate—in all 4101 square miles. This British protectorate takes the form of a long narrow strip on either side of the river, at most only 20 miles in total width, though extending more than 200 miles eastward into the interior. Under the new constitution of 1962—a prelude to independence—the distinction will virtually disappear. A century and a half of effective British control has resulted in considerable differentiation from the surrounding French territory in which the Gambia forms an enclave. The former local differentiation into the Upper River, Middle River, and Lower River has a justification geographically. The *Upper River* is a region of light sandy soils devoted especially to the cultivation of peanuts as a cash crop and millets (especially coos or kous) for food. Peanuts constitute over 95 per cent of the exports of the Gambia, and in the Upper River the pressure on land resources is such that food is brought in; only small tracts by the river are liable to flood, and these too usually have sandy peanut soils. The *Middle River* has tracts of alluvium liable to river floods along the Gambia (known as *banto faros*) flanked by sandstone terraces yielding sandy soils. The flood lands have been reclaimed by building "bunds" or banks of mud and reeds, and the fields so formed are cultivated year after year for rice by the women. The men work the higher ground by the usual African system of bush fallowing, with an emphasis on peanuts. In the *Lower River* there is the same distinction into the low-lying areas liable to flood and the uplands. Here, however, the flooding is by brackish water; there are extensive mangrove swamps (Figure 14.10), and the utilization of the banto faros depends upon the breeding of a rice which can withstand brackish water.

Detailed land-use surveys, with published colored maps on the scale of 1:10,000, have shown a remarkable shift in cultivation between 1947 and 1957. As the reclaimed mangrove swamp lands become more fully used, there is a tendency to abandon the higher land.

The whole protectorate has a population of about a quarter of a million, and it has remained a somewhat backward area. There are roads, but most

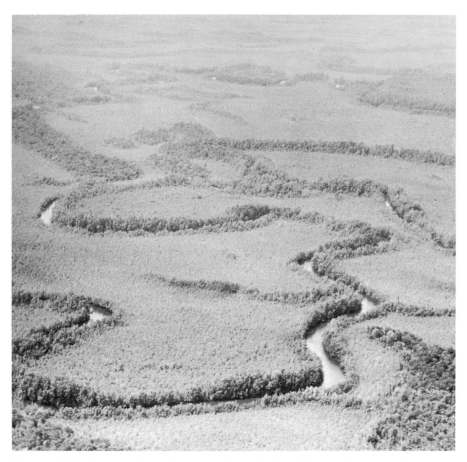

Figure 14.10 Air view of typical mangrove forests. Niger delta—the larger growth along the margins of the delta streams is characteristic. (Copyright Aircraft Operating Company of Africa.)

of the movement of produce and people is by river, though the ferry services are inadequate. Georgetown may be described as the head of ocean navigation, but river steamers can reach the eastern boundary with Senegal throughout the year and in the high-water season even beyond. The river serves as an outlet for a small area of the hinterland (Figure 14.11).

As one of the underdeveloped areas of Africa, the Gambia called for special consideration after World War II. It became famous on account of the Field Working Party for scientific study and infamous for the expensive, abortive Poultry Scheme, designed to assist the smallholders to produce poultry and eggs for sale. The latter failed through the prevalence of the disease known as "fowl pest" and cost the British taxpayers $2,500,000.

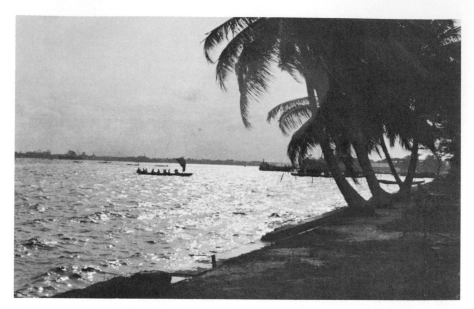

Figure 14.11   A typical West African lagoon. These stretches of inland water are invaluable where the surf-bound coast is dangerous. This is the lagoon at Lagos. (Copyright L. Dudley Stamp.)

Portuguese Guinea

The Portuguese were early among the European explorers of the coasts of West Africa and claim to have discovered what is now Portuguese Guinea as early as 1446. Sovereignty was claimed by the Kings of Portugal from 1462 onwards. In 1669 a station was established on the Corubal, and by 1690 Bissau, or Bissao, was a flourishing slave port. The territory was separated from the governorship of the Cape Verde Islands only in 1879, and in 1886 a long series of disputes with France was ended by a boundary settlement. By this settlement Portuguese Guinea is entirely surrounded, except on the seaward side, by former French territory—Senegal to the north, Guinea to the south.

Although the area is 13,944 square miles and the total population over half a million (U.N. estimate, mid-1960, 571,000), Portuguese Guinea remains one of the least developed parts of West Africa. The coastline is here extremely intricate. The coastal plain devolves into a succession of low peninsulas and innumerable islands between which lie a maze of channels. The deep estuaries of the Cacheu, Mansôa, Geba (with its tributary the Corubal), and Cacine afford access considerable distances inland. Though less than in Sierra Leone, the rainfall is high, and mangrove swamps give place inland to dense forest and then savanna. Some of the delta lands are covered with rice fields; bananas and oil palms are grown on the slightly drier lands, giving place to peanuts in the interior. There are few cattle, but some sheep and goats of low quality.

The Portuguese are a mere handful, mainly officials. Such trade as there is—with export of peanuts, rice, wax, palm oil, and hides—is mainly in the hands of Lebanese or French, with the chief port at the capital, Bissau. This port is on a fertile island and can be reached even at low tide by vessels drawing 36 feet through the Geba Canal; it has deep-water wharves. Both Cacheu and Bolama can be reached by comparatively large vessels. The main disadvantages of the coastal strip are the poor drainage and the bad health reputation.

Most of the people are Mandingos or Fulani, little touched by either Mohammedanism or Christianity, who are of course agriculturalists and pastoralists.

Sierra Leone

The West African coast from Portuguese Guinea to Cape Palmas in southern Liberia trends almost directly from northwest to southeast and thus at right angles to the rain-bearing airstreams of the wet season. In the typical wet month of July, Sierra Leone and Liberia its neighbor receive the full force, and nearly everywhere the rainfall in that one month exceeds 15 inches. Both countries belong, therefore, to the wet forested regions of West Africa, with evergreen forests of equatorial type forming the natural vegetation cover over the greater part of the whole. On the coastal belt of Sierra Leone some 150 inches of rain falls in the rainy season from May to October. Rightly or wrongly this excessive rainfall was long regarded as particularly unhealthy for white people, and it was Sierra Leone in particular which gained the name of the "white man's grave." In the interior the rainfall decreases, and orchard bush or savanna is reached.

Like Portuguese and Republican Guinea, Sierra Leone has a much-broken coastline and a series of rivers draining direct from the interior highlands to the coast, with estuaries sometimes affording good natural harbors. By far the best of these is the mouth of the Rokel, with Freetown nestling under its protecting headland called The Peak, perhaps the finest natural harbor of the whole coast.

Although the inland boundary of Sierra Leone does not correspond strictly with the water parting, in general rivers rise either within its territory or only just over the border. A short distance farther inland, over the mountains which continue the Futa Jallon southeastward, the water drains northeastward into the headstreams of the Niger. In contrast to the Gambia or Nigeria, no great river gives access to the far interior.

The history of Sierra Leone has been briefly recounted in Chapter 2. If the British in early days took an active part in the African slave trade, they have every reason to be proud of their pioneer work for its abolition. Settlement was begun in Sierra Leone in 1787 with 400 runaway African slaves who were waifs in London, and for those rescued from slaveships. Though the first settlement failed, it was followed by others, and Free Town (later Freetown) was refounded in 1794. Behind Freetown is a mountainous peninsula some 25 miles long; it was the roaring of the winds in the mountains which gave rise to the Portuguese name meaning "Lion Mountain." The history of Sierra Leone repeats many features common to the West African coast. For a long time British interests were restricted to the coast. It was not until 1896, more than a hundred years after the foundation of Freetown, that a British protectorate was proclaimed over the hinterland where about 2 million people, in tribes under their own chiefs, live on 27,669 square miles. Sierra Leone had a Legislative Council as early as 1863, but not until 1924 was there direct representation of the protectorate. In 1958 a democratically elected House of Representatives came into existence; on April 27, 1961, Sierra Leone became independent and was later elected a member of the U.N. It remains a member of the British Commonwealth.

Sierre Leone falls naturally into a number of tracts roughly parallel to the coast.

The coastal belt is one of swamps. They are built up to a large extent by eroded soil from the uplands. They develop into mangrove-covered swamps or *Raphia* swamps covered to a few inches by high spring tides and heavily flooded by fresh water during the rains. Back from the coast they may be flooded only by fresh water. More than half a million acres of reclaimable swamp exist; only 10 per cent are at present cultivated. Indeed, a large proportion of the rice which is the staple food grain of Sierra Leone is upland rice grown in the interior. Much of the land actually used is along the lower reaches of the Great and Little Scarcies rivers. These potential ricelands could undoubtedly relieve the pressure on the existing food-producing lands and provide a surplus for export, but the necessary land reclamation is difficult and expensive.

Behind the coastal belt is one of undulating ground where shifting cultivation has caused the destruction of much of the original high forest. Here forest products include palm oil and palm kernels, providing up to a quarter of the total value of the country's exports. Though the solid rocks of Sierra Leone away from the coastal plain are mainly granite and gneisses, there is usually a thick covering of laterite which hinders the discovery of minerals. Some of the lateritic deposits are sufficiently rich in iron to have provided the basis of an African smelting and blacksmith industry, but the iron ore deposits which have been opened up are hematites near Marampa, to which place a 50-mile railway was completed from Pepel 15 miles upstream from Freetown and on the northern side of the estuary. Chromite is mined near

Hangha on the railway. Diamonds, the leading export, are very important near Sefadu and on several rivers.

Inland the country rises as a much-dissected plateau towards the Futa Jallon highland (Figure 14.12). In the east are forest reserves in high forest country. Elsewhere are clearings growing cassava, yams, and upland and swamp rice. In the north is sparsely populated orchard bush country supporting 25 persons or less per square mile in contrast to Sierra Leone's average of about 70 (a high figure for tropical Africa).

The focus of the whole country remains Freetown. The hills rising high above the African town stimulated the growth of a European quarter reached at first by street cars, later by motor roads. The importance of modern transport is well illustrated in Sierra Leone. A government railway of 2 feet, 6 inches gauge runs from Freetown to Pendembu near the Liberian border (227 miles), with a branch line leaving it at Bauya northward to Makeni (83 miles). Roughly 50 miles is the economic limit for human porterage, and so

Figure 14.12   The western edge of the northern Nigerian plateau, showing the sharp drop to the coastal plain. (Copyright Aerofilms Library.)

the development of commerce, notably the oil palm belt, is virtually restricted to the lands opened up by the now extensive road system as it was earlier to a belt on either side of the railway. Unfortunately, maintenance costs on roads are high, and in view of the very heavy rainfall bridges need to be numerous and able to withstand swollen streams. In the years following the end of World War II many ferries were replaced by bridges built with the help of the Economic Cooperation Administration (E.C.A.).

Freetown is a much-used port of call and is also served by the airport at Lungi on the opposite side of the estuary. Fourah Bay College at Freetown is proud of the fact that it is the oldest university college in Africa south of the Sahara, founded in 1827 and affiliated with the University of Durham.

Liberia

The story of the establishment of Liberia—"Free land"—is well known and has been briefly outlined in Chapter 2. The high hopes which the American Colonization Society entertained in 1821 when they selected the present site of Monrovia as the new African home for freed American Negro slaves were not to be realized quickly. In the first place the American Negroes had lived in contact with Western civilization; they were just as alien to the untamed African jungle as a white settler might be. Although after the establishment of the first settlement others sprang up along the coast, they were under the aegis of the American Society, usually with white governors, and relied on American aid for their continued existence. Apart from the "independent African State of Maryland" which had been established at Cape Palmas in 1833, there were by 1847 only about 3000 Americo-Liberians. In that year the Society suggested that the settlers headed by an octoroon from Virginia, Joseph Jenkins Roberts, should devise a constitution on American lines. This was done, and the constitution of the Republic has remained closely modeled on that of the United States. The Liberian flag even follows the parent model, horizontal stripes of five white and six red with a blue field on the upper corner next to the flagstaff. On that blue field there remains the original one single star. Independence was declared in 1847, and Roberts held office as first president until 1856. Maryland was absorbed the following year.

But Liberia stagnated. There were doubtless some Americo-Liberians, who, having been slaves themselves, were inclined to look upon the new country as constituting their turn and to regard the existing inhabitants as creatures of a lower order, if not to be slaves at least to be ruled over as menials. On the whole, however, it is probably true to say that Liberia wished to develop on national lines and to cooperate with the native-born Liberian tribes, but that the latter had no desire for cooperation. And so, after a hundred years, the Liberian government exercised authority over a narrow strip of coast and was ignored 20 miles inland. In 1925 it was estimated that there were only 25,000 Americo-Liberians, more than half of whom lived in the capital, while the hinterland remained the least-known region in all tropical Africa and one where government control was nominal or nonexistent. This is despite the vigorous forward policy initiated by President Barclay in 1904 of offering concessions to American and European interests and of permitting their advisers and technicians full access to the country. The turning point was really 1925 when a large land grant for rubber planting was made to the Firestone Company. This was followed by something of a "boom" when a number of estates were laid out and big houses were built of timber imported from America.

With a coastline of about 350 miles Liberia has a total area of 43,000 square miles, roughly the same as the State of Pennsylvania (Figure 14.13).

Figure 14.13   Liberia, showing main trade routes and physiographic regions. (1) Coastal plain. (2) Rolling hills, 100 to 300 feet elevation. (3) Hills rising steeply to 600 feet or more. (4) Dissected plateau, average elevation 900 feet. (5) Mountainous country. (From G. W. Harley, *Geog. Rev.*, 1939. Courtesy of the *Geographical Review*. American Geographical Society.)

No census has ever been taken, and the population is variously estimated between 1 and 2½ million. Apart from the Americo-Liberians some 60,000 of
the coast Negroes have been in comparatively close contact with Western influences. Of the six main groups inhabiting the rest of the country the
Mandingos are Moslems, but the Gissi, Gola, Kpwesi, Kru, and Graboes
may be called pagans, except where they have been reached by Christian
missions. The Kru of the coast—indeed the southeastern coast is called the
Kru coast—are great seamen and are employed on ships trading to West
Africa. Indeed all the coastal tribes like the water and make great use of
it. They build their villages near high water mark and make extensive use of
dugout canoes in the tidal estuaries. Some of their canoes (the Accra type)
are fitted with sails and are thoroughly seaworthy. Only those who can
handle a boat with skill would dare the work of handling cargoes by surf-
boat. Except at Monrovia and one of the river mouths which can be entered
by small steamers, coastwise shipping depends on these surfboats just as elsewhere on the West African coast. Some of the coastal people have penetrated
into the interior by river and settled on the banks, but, broadly speaking, behind the coastal belt live people whose only contact with the sea is to come
at certain seasons to fish and take back home the smoked fish. Some such
tribes, the De for example, have actually reserved narrow corridors to the
sea. Inland are people who have never seen the sea, and who avoid the
rivers, which they fear and dislike. Many are essentially hill people living in
rough country. Their fear of water is not unconnected with the activities in
days not very far past of secret societies, the "water people," "human crocodiles," and the like who sought victims for human sacrifice and cannibalistic
rites by working under water with gourds of air over their heads, or traveling
in canoes covered with crocodile skin.

　　With certain exceptions Liberia is still a land the bulk of which is accessible only by trails.[7] Although a low rounded hilltop near a stream is a
favorite site for a settlement, the higher hilltops are avoided, being considered sacred or the abode of supernatural beings. The trails tend to go
straight from village to village, over rather than around the shoulders of hills
and, avoiding the river valleys, tend to be ridge roads. Most of the rivers of
Liberia are streams rising in the interior and following roughly parallel
courses to the coast, so that trails from the interior to the coast have relatively
few streams to cross. Where a crossing is needed, elaborate swing bridges are
constructed of vines woven into nets and suspended by long vine cables from
trees on the two banks. Despite handrails the use of one of these bridges is
a nerve-racking experience for the uninitiated. Bridges are sacred. Constructed
only by special guilds of men working in secret, they may not be seen

　　　[7] G. W. Harley, "Roads and Trails in Liberia," *Geog. Rev.,* **XXIX,** 1939, 447–460.

by women or children until complete. The trails from the interior to the coast cross zones of very different character and hence with different products, and the trails were essentially trade routes along which moved in days past slaves, wild rubber, and pepper to the coasts, kola nuts to the north.

But this Liberia of the past has changed considerably. The Firestone plantations brought a road into the interior as well as a demand for labor and for payment by money with which hut taxes could be paid. Theoretically the old trails could be used by bicycles and even motor bicycles, but many had previously never known a wheel. Presented with the fact of a vehicular road, the Liberian tribesmen soon realized its value; little or no compulsion was needed to persuade workers to help with road construction which went on (usually along old trails) under the direction of a local official.

Many writers have referred to what they describe as Liberia's "colonial system." By this was meant the old contention among Americo-Liberians that a very sharp line existed between them and the aborigines whose function should be to pay hut taxes and to contribute foodstuffs and cheap labor to the national economy. The aborigines regarded the Americo-Liberians as intruders of foreign origin, often in council referred to them as "Americans," and regarded the future of the country as being one of self-determination in which the Americo-Liberians would be excluded. However, two factors have here intervened. In 1944 President W. V. S. Tubman initiated a policy designed to secure equality of citizenship throughout the country. In the second place the ties between Liberia and the United States have become increasingly close. During World War II an American force was established in Liberia (later withdrawn), a large and efficient airport was constructed and maintained at Roberts Field, the construction of a commercial deep-water port at Monrovia by the United States Navy was begun, a health mission was maintained, and a road was undertaken from Monrovia into French Guinea. On their part, the Liberians granted a concession to an American company to work rich iron ore at Bomi Hill about 40 miles north of Monrovia, and a mineral line was built to bring out the ore. On January 1, 1944, the Liberian dollar was raised to parity with the United States dollar. In November 1944 an economic mission under Professor Earl Parker Hanson started work in the western and central provinces. The leader of the mission has given a very valuable account of the conditions existing at that time.[8]

Liberia can readily be divided, as shown in Figure 14.13, into five belts parallel to the coast. The first (1 on Figure 14.13) is the coastal plain with rivers and lagoons navigable for small boats where clearings in the forest yield a few palm products and citrus fruits can be grown. Behind this is a belt (2) of rolling hills, 100 to 300 feet above sea level, adapted to rubber plantations where

[8] E. P. Hanson, "An Economic Survey of the Western Province of Liberia," *Geog. Rev.*, XXXVII, 1947, 53–69.

the forest can be cleared. The narrow belt marked 3 on Figure 14.13 is the main rise to the inevitable African plateau—hills rising steeply to 600 feet or more. Beyond this lies a dissected plateau (4) at an average elevation of 900 feet which has a low density of population (much under five and most under fifteen persons per square mile according to Hanson's calculations in the Western Province) but has much commercial forest and is the home of the kola tree. The interior (5) is mountainous country with elevations up to 3000 feet in the northwest, 4000 feet in the center and even reaching, in Mt. Nimba on the frontier, 6500 feet. Like the remainder of Liberia this country too is forested.

At the mission station at Ganta (see Figure 14.13) Harley has described the climate with care. The year begins with the dry month of January, with the harmattan blowing. This wind continues till about mid-February; it then reduces the temperature by promoting evaporation of residual moisture. Some rains then arrive, but it is not until about mid-March that the ground has been sufficiently softened for a heavy fall to be followed by a flight of termites. This is taken as a sign for bush cutting and the planting of cassava on the uplands, rice in the swamps. The harvest of rice—of which at least thirty-five varieties are known—begins in July, main crop in August, late varieties in December. In July and August the harvest is helped by a decrease in rain, the "little dries." October and November have heavy dews and are best for growing vegetables, cotton, and tobacco.

Rice may be called the staple food of Liberia. Not enough is produced, however, for the town population of the coast, and the Firestone Company imports thousands of tons. Hanson's mission secured the cooperation of Liberian government agriculturalists and reports how readily the people in the Kpoh Valley copied ideas demonstrated to them—use of fertilizers, compost heaps, new crops such as wheat, cabbages, and corn, insecticides. In particular they appreciated the long-suffering donkey as a beast of burden. This gives a glimpse of Liberian possibilities at a time when 90 per cent of the exports came from the Firestone rubber plantations with gold making up most of the remainder. Development moved apace. The free port of Monrovia was opened on July 26, 1948, the road to the Bomi iron ore mines with a fine bridge over the St. Paul River was completed in November 1949. The same period saw the road completed from Monrovia to N'zérékoré in French Guinea; a motor boat service on the St. Paul River from Monrovia to White Plains came into operation, as well as regular coastal services. The Roberts Field airport came to be used regularly by at least three international services. Apart from the 3 million tons of iron ore from the Bomi Hills worked by the American-owned Liberia Mining Company, the National Iron Ore Company started exporting in December 1961; there are also German interests at work in the Bong Hills northeast of Monrovia. Iron ore from Mt.

Nimba has necessitated a new port at Buchanan, southeast of Monrovia. Exports of iron ore now equal those of rubber in value, and there have been great improvements in the port of Monrovia. The Liberian government derives a considerable revenue from registration fees for ships. In 1961 nearly 11 million tons of shipping were flying the Liberian flag as a "flag of convenience."

Railroad construction began with the iron ore line to the Bomi Hills in 1951 (later extended) and was followed by a line from Nimba to Bassa. From every point of view Liberia is on the threshold of great developments. Diamonds may prove an important source of wealth.

Ghana, formerly the Gold Coast

Despite the absence of good natural harbors and the dangerous surf which pounds everlastingly along the sandy shores (Figure 14.14), the Gold Coast exhibited a combination of geographical factors which rendered it particularly attractive in the eyes of the early European explorers and traders. It is here, east of Cape Three Points, that the coast departs from its normal West African direction and trends west-southwest to east-northeast. The rain-bearing winds of the rainy season, coming from the southwest, thus

Figure 14.14 Fishermen on the coast of Ghana. (Copyright Ghana Trade Center, New York.)

blow almost parallel to the coast. In contrast to the totals exceeding 120 inches of the Sierra Leone and Liberian coasts, the seasonal fall drops to less than 60 inches, over a long stretch to less than 40 inches—at Accra to less than 30—and at Lomé on the eastern border it is only 31. Instead of a coastline of mangrove swamp backed by lofty evergreen forests, the savanna zone reaches the coast. To the coast came Africans with gold dust; along the coast were occasional headlands offering defensible sites for forts or fortified trading posts.

The Portuguese were the first to establish permanent stations, starting in Elmina in 1481. In the seventeenth century the Dutch ousted the Portuguese but had to share with the British. Denmark and Brandenburg (now part of Germany) were there too. The abolition of slave trading in 1807 caused the British to reduce their forts from twelve to four, and even those would have been given up had they not served a useful purpose—by the irony of fate—as bases for the British navy *against* slaving. An early attempt at government taking a hand in trading was unsuccessful, but a handful of merchant traders refused to leave the coast. George Maclean, their leader, was probably the first man to adopt indirect rule, encouraging the chiefs to apply their own laws to the orderly control of their territories, provided they were "in harmony with civilized ideas of justice."

When the British government realized the determination of those interested in the Gold Coast to remain they reluctantly appointed a governor, and in 1850 a charter established a separate government from that of Sierra Leone, of which the Gold Coast had been nominally a dependency. Even then the object of the British government was ultimately to withdraw. But there was no turning back. The great legend of Queen Victoria as the mighty mother protector was growing. In 1844 the Fanti tribes had voluntarily made a bond renouncing human sacrifice and agreeing that all cases of murder and robbery should be tried by British officers according to British law. So in 1865 a Report to the British House of Commons advised against any extension of sovereignty but stated: ". . . it is not possible to withdraw the British government wholly or immediately from the West African coast." But the little British territory could not remain static. The Fanti tribes threatened the remaining Dutch ports, and in 1871 the Dutch asked the British to take them over—at the price of the few stores they contained. So the British took on a war, the Ashanti war of 1873. By this time the French had been active. Their main objective had been to consolidate their interest in the Ivory Coast and its hinterland and to prevent the British in Sierra Leone from linking up with the Gold Coast. Germany secured the long narrow strip running inland of Togoland adjoining the Gold Coast on the east simply by hoisting the German flag at Baguida, Lomé, and Porto-Segouro in 1884, and notifying Britain that a protectorate had been established.

Thus the British colony of the Gold Coast (capital Accra) was defined by the actions of France and Germany. It was not until 1901 that Britain finally settled a protectorate over Ashanti (capital Kumasi), the Northern Territories having been delimited in 1897. Part of Togoland was placed under British mandate after World War I and under trusteeship in 1946. The Gold Coast in that same year became the first African dependency to secure a legislature with a majority of elected members (18 against 12), Ashanti and the Northern Territories being specifically represented. The subsequent story leading to independence within the Commonwealth in 1957, has already been told.

The rapid recent political growth is closely bound up with economic development, which in turn is closely bound up with cocoa. It was an African worker returning from Fernando Po in 1879 who brought half a dozen cocoa beans and planted them on his farm. There were later importations, and in 1891 there was the first recorded export of 80 pounds. The cultivation of cocoa spread rapidly through the Gold Coast Colony, and in 1898 was introduced into Ashanti, where it spread with equal rapidity throughout all parts of the country having suitable physical conditions. Within a few decades the Gold Coast as a whole was producing between 200,000 and 300,000 tons, two-thirds of the world's total output. It is not commonly realized that cocoa is grown entirely on African farms by Africans. It is not a plantation crop as is commonly believed. The European's part has been in buying the crop and also in helping with research, control of pests and diseases, provision of best seed and fertilizers, and, where needed, government supervision. The cocoa is bought by the great international cocoa firms through the Marketing Board. Yet the swollen shoot disease (see Figure 14.15), which assumed alarming proportions in the nineteen-forties, threatened the whole industry and with it the economy of the country. Happily science found the answer.

Cocoa has made Ghana rich, but it has brought problems. As a source of wealth the government encouraged planting, but in Ashanti the Confederacy Council (then the supreme African authority) wisely showed itself afraid of a single-crop economy. Every third chocolate, from every candy box in the world, comes from Ghana. In fancy we may visualize running from the chocolate boxes everywhere in the world a constant river of money that seeps and percolates into the humblest homes of the country, and brings a standard of living scarcely known elsewhere in tropical Africa—bicycles, radios, clothes, and homes. It is easy for a government to see in cocoa a crop readily salable and the country's most efficient dollar earner. The problem of the supply of food can surely be left to look after itself. But what of the severe fluctuations in world prices? Is it not possible that for this or other reasons the African may one day face hunger if he forgets his traditional farming?

The success of cocoa production brought increased population, especially

Figure 14.15 Adult mealybugs magnified many times. These are the cause of the dreaded swollen shoot disease of cocoa. (Courtesy of Pest Control Limited.)

to Ashanti, by immigration from the Northern Region (formerly Northern Territories) and from the former French West Africa. The population of Ashanti jumped from 406,000 in 1921 to 578,000 in 1931, 824,000 in 1948. Thus the pressure on the 24,379 square miles increased from 17 to 34 per square mile in that period—which, if not unduly high, involved much adjustment. Urbanization is also most marked; Kumasi jumped from 35,800 in 1931 to 78,500 in 1948 and to 190,400 in 1960. Mining centers trebled. The towns have to be fed by food imported from other areas; many even of the cocoa villages no longer have enough land to grow their own food. The pressure on the land has involved destruction of much forest. Runoff of rain-water is increased, soil erosion encouraged, protection from the drying harmful harmattan lost.[9]

The total area of modern Ghana is 92,100 square miles, with a 1948 census population of 4,111,680, which by 1960 had jumped to 6,690,730. The

[9] These and other problems are discussed by R. W. Steel, "Some Geographical Problems of Land Use in British West Africa," *Trans. Institute of British Geographers* (*1948*), No. 14, 1949.

whole is roughly rectangular, having a coastline of 270 miles and an extent from north to south of 300.

In its relief Ghana repeats the usual West Coast features. There is a coastal plain, though in the center this gives place to higher ground with cliffs. Behind lies an undulating upland rising gradually to the wedge-shaped Ashanti plateau with its exposures of ancient crystalline rocks. From the crest of this upland short streams drain southward straight to the coast, but northward from the crest the land falls again to the broad valley plain of the Volta and its tributaries. Two-thirds of the whole country lies in the basin of the Volta, the main stream of which, the Black Volta, rises far to the north-west in the Republic of Haute-Volta to which it gives its name.

Although not ranking with the Niger or the Congo, the Volta is one of Africa's major rivers; and though the river is of small use for navigation, a gorge course on the lower Volta offers possibilities of large power development. The great Volta River Project had been discussed seriously since about 1950. It envisaged a great dam at Akosombo rivaling in size Boulder Dam. Construction on this was started in 1962. It will create a vast lake giving water access to much remote country, providing fisheries for much needed protein. Hydroelectric power will be distributed to much of the country, including an aluminum smelter to be built at the new port of Tema. The cost, without the smelter, is of the order of $200 million. The dam was finished in 1964.

Both the relief and the climate prevent Ghana from exhibiting the simple zonation of environmental conditions parallel to the coast seen in other parts of West Africa. It does, however, fall into a number of well-marked climatic-vegetation regions, each with characteristic human response. In the extreme southwest, west of Cape Three Points, is a coastal plain enjoying almost equatorial rainfall and temperatures where swamp rice can be grown. Its focal point is Axim.

Inland in the southwest is undulating country covered naturally with evergreen forest. This yields cabinet woods of the mahogany, ebony, and teak types exported from Takoradi. This country and its extension eastward form the oil-palm belt. The production of kernels and oil has, however, greatly diminished in face of the greater attraction of cocoa cultivation.

Over the plateau of crystalline rocks which makes up a large part of the west, the rainfall is sufficiently heavy and well distributed through the year for the natural vegetation to be that of a dense equatorial forest. Here are the words of a Fanti whose home is at Sekondi:[10] "I have walked mile after mile through narrow meandering paths bounded on either side by great forest lands, primeval forests in whose depths are the farms and cocoa plan-

[10] Joseph S. Annan, "The Gold Coast Colony," *Scottish Geog. Mag.,* **LIX,** 1943, 55–59. For a detailed survey of a cocoa area, see *Geog. Jour.,* **CX,** 1948, 155–160.

tations of the African farmers and cocoa planters ... only here and there could I see streaks of sunlight penetrating through the branches and the leaves to lighten our paths ... in these forests the most prominent tree is the silk-cotton, which rises like a column to a height of over 100 feet and measures 8 to 10 feet in diameter. ... The forest is the home of wild animals ... the elephant has been almost exterminated by ivory hunters ... the forest growth is gradually being cleared in order that the land may be reclaimed for agricultural purposes and also for the building of new townships."

This word picture conveys the essential idea that the great cocoa region is still one of untidy African farms (averaging only about 3 acres in extent), largely hidden by forest—untidy but thus escaping the evils of soil erosion. But here conservation of appropriate areas of forest is vital to maintain an essential resource, maintain even flow of water, and afford a protection against the drying harmattan. The preservation of the native fauna is another worldwide problem.

The areas of densest production of cocoa are around Kumasi. Though head porterage is still used, the development of cocoa production has depended largely on a growing network of roads and a considerable mileage of railways. It is the presence of mineral deposits, however, which necessitated the construction of railways. Northward the cocoa-equatorial forest area gives place to forest where leaf fall in the hot season is marked; this is the region of kola nuts. Northward the forest merges gradually into savanna.

Gold is often second in value to cocoa among exports. Gold-bearing conglomerates are widely distributed, and the gold is both panned from streams—as it has been since long before the Gold Coast earned its name— and mined. The chief workings lie along the Takoradi-Kumasi line and its branch to Prestea. Diamonds with stones of industrial quality were first found in quantity in 1919 in the Birrim Valley, reached by the Central Region Railway. The industry here has some advantage over an industry depending on stones of gem quality; the industrial demand is steadier. Large deposits of manganese ore have been found and are worked opencast at Nsuta near Tarkwa junction. Ghana ranks as a leading world exporter of this metal vital in the steel industry. Bauxite is worked at Awaso, having there been reached by a branch line; the opening up of other deposits awaits the completion of hydroelectric power works.

Brong-Ahafo, the Northern and Upper Regions, are savanna, relatively sparsely populated but with some production of shea nuts, from which shea butter is produced.

For long the chief outlet of the Gold Coast was Accra, an open roadstead where all goods had to be taken to and from the shore by surfboats while the ocean-going vessels rode at anchor in the heavy swell. Despite the con-

Figure 14.16 Takoradi Harbor, Ghana. An entirely artificial, well-equipped modern harbor, to be contrasted with the lagoon harbors of Lagos and Abidjan and the open roadstead of Accra before the construction of Tema. (Copyright Aircraft Operating Company of Africa.)

summate skill with which these surfboats were handled—I once watched a grand piano successfully lowered on to two surfboats lashed together—delay, damage, and expensive handling were inevitable. The western railway reached the coast at Sekondi, which was also an open roadstead, until the construction and completion in 1928 of a fine harbor at Takoradi (Figure 14.16) a few miles away led to the abandonment of Sekondi. Takoradi is a deep-water harbor protected by long breakwaters built of local gneiss. It has commodious wharves, so that most trade from western Ghana goes to the port—cocoa, manganese ore, gold, bauxite, and timber. The other old roadstead ports along the coasts not served by railway—Axim, Cape Coast, Saltpond, and Winneba—are now of little significance. The whole position has been changed by the opening in 1961 of a second deep-water port, at Tema, a few miles east of Accra. It is designed to serve the whole Volta basin; already a fine road bridge spans the Volta a few miles to the north and provides ready access to the old Togoland. At the same time Accra is being transformed into a modern city, already with a population of 326,000 in 1960.

Kumasi has grown to be a focal point of Ghanaian communications, of railways and roads. Two roads from Kumasi reach the northern borders of the country, one in the west, the other through the heart of the Northern Region and continuing to Ouagadougou in Upper Volta.

The economic and political advancement of Ghana is matched by a lead in education. The University College of the Gold Coast has become the University of Ghana, with a fine campus near Accra. In contrast, the Old Danish fort of Christiansborg—a white castle crowning a sea cliff at Accra—is now used as the President's residence.

Nigeria (Federation of Nigeria)

Nigeria is the largest and most populous of the Commonwealth countries in Africa. Its area, approximately 339,170 square miles, makes the country comparable in size to Texas and Arizona together, or six times the area of New England (Figure 14.17). The population of about 35 million, although giving a density of only about 100 per square mile, is distributed in such a way that locally Nigeria faces serious problems of overpopulation, at least with the existing system of cultivation. Pressure on the land has in turn led in the south to such a shortening of the period of rest in the system of shifting cultivation as to induce serious soil erosion, in the north to such over-stocking as also to encourage soil erosion.

Historical development. Nigeria, although roughly the basin of the lower Niger, had little claim to be considered as a unit until its recent emergence as one of the new independent African states. It resulted from the almost fortuitous association of diverse territories under one British administration after Northern and Southern Nigeria were joined together in 1914. The federal structure of the new state, with Northern, Eastern, and Western Regions to a considerable extent autonomous, and a federal capital at Lagos, reflects the contrast between the Moslem Hausa and Fulani of the northern savannas with the Christian or pagan peoples of the southern forest lands. The country lies, it should be noted, between the equatorial latitudes of 4° North and 13° North.

Under the name of the Oil Rivers (from the association with palm oil) the channels of the Niger delta had been known for 300 years to European traders before H. L. Lander in 1830 proved their connection with the Niger. Wilberforce, who headed the antislavery movement in Britain, was succeeded in the eighteen-thirties by Dr. J. F. Buxton, who argued that naval or military force would never crush the slave trade but that profit from legitimate trade must be offered to the African chiefs in lieu of what they might lose by the suppression of the slave trade. A Niger expedition was organized in 1841–1842 to establish trading posts, but the climate proved fatal to nearly all concerned. Later attempts to establish permanent trading stations likewise failed.

Farther west, Lagos had long been a headquarters of the slave trade. The British enthroned there in 1851 an antislaving king, but he did not prove strong enough for the task. It was his son who, in 1861, ceded Lagos to Britain, and

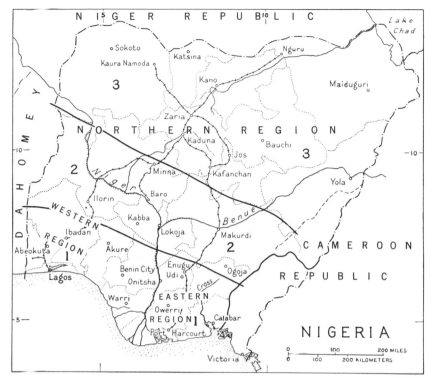

Figure 14.17   Map of Nigeria, showing three agricultural belts. (1) Southern Belt of shifting cultivation: yams, cassava, maize, oil palms, and cocoa. (2) Middle Belt of orchard bush. (3) Northern Belt of open savanna merging into scrub, with cultivation of guinea corn, millet, peanuts, and cotton; cattle and goats.

so Lagos became an antislaving base. In the meantime British trading interests established firmer holds in the Niger delta and were consolidated into the United Africa Company in 1879. When West Africa was debated at the Berlin Conference of 1884–1885, British interests in the Niger coastlands were established and by the agreement of 1886 delimited from French Dahomey to the west and German Kamerun to the east.

British trading interests received a charter from the crown and became the Royal Niger Company in 1886, with extensive powers. Lagos remained a British colony and protectorate. The Royal Niger Company established stations on the Niger and Benue until its advance brought the British into contact with the powerful Moslem emirates of the north, especially of Kano and Sokoto. Because there were differences to be settled with France, in 1899 the company's charter and governing powers were withdrawn and its sphere of operations reorganized into the Protectorates of Northern and Southern Nigeria. In the succeeding years Lugard, as High Commissioner of the Protectorate of Northern Nigeria, slowly and steadily forced the emirs to abandon slavery and accept Western ideas of law and order.

In Southern Nigeria there were pagan kingdoms where a rule of fear yielded slowly to the system of indirect rule under Britain. In 1906 Lagos was combined with Southern Nigeria, and in 1914 they were united with Northern Nigeria to form the Colony and Protectorate of Nigeria with Lagos as the seat of government. There followed a period of steady development in which the building of railways played an important part, later the building of roads. The enormous importance of modern transport in African development has been repeatedly emphasized in this book. Nigeria affords many examples. The prosperity of the southern coastlands has long depended largely upon palm oil, and the oil-palm belt can be reached to a large extent by navigable channels of the delta. But the production of tin ore from the Jos Plateau, which permitted Nigerian output to reach a fifth or a quarter of the world's total (now six per cent), would not have been possible without the provision of rail access. The same is true of the coal deposits at Enugu.

The autocratic pagan kingdoms of Southern Nigeria with their colorful and picturesquely styled chiefs felt the full force of the political movements which reached their peak in the years following World War II. Large numbers of West Africans served in the armed forces in many theatres of war (including Burma) and came back critical of much in their homeland. Serious rioting took place in several places such as Abeokuta and Benin. The ruler of the former, the Alake of Abeokuta, went into exile, to return amid scenes of triumphal splendor some two years later. Again Western concepts of democracy came into conflict with the traditional African tribal organization.

In general terms throughout this book considerable emphasis has been laid on the sameness of conditions throughout tropical Africa. Although there are important differences between the major regions—such as West Africa and East Africa—and divergencies which increase under the varied European influences, naturally some parts stand out from others in social, economic, or political development. It is in this regard that Nigeria, despite the diversity of its parts, is outstanding. Nowhere have the Moslem emirates retained their distinctive character so well as in the north of Nigeria; nowhere have the erstwhile pagan, now largely Christian, Negro kingdoms retained the individuality and the pageantry that they have among the Yoruba of the south. A description of the ancient city of Benin in 1951 referred to the pageantry whereby a new local chief in traditional garb of starched white linen skirt, coral necklet, anklets, and wristlets, supported by a young man on whose shoulders he rested his arms, preceded by sword bearer and followed by a band, received confirmation of his office from the Oba or King of Benin. The sprawling palace of the King, partly of mud and partly of sheet iron or brick, was still lit only by an occasional hurricane lamp, yet the Oba spoke English perfectly and made frequent visits to England. His son was educated at Cambridge University. Benin is the city which has produced some remarkable carving and brass work over several centuries.

The return from exile of the Alake of Abeokuta was the occasion for a thankgiving service in the Church of St. Peter which lasted for three hours. The chiefs wore elaborate brocaded silk or satin robes and crowns. With attendant court officials they greeted one another in dignified ceremony before listening to a sermon lasting more than an hour and delivered in Yoruba by an African bishop.

Clearly it would be difficult to devise one single pattern of modern democracy. The solution was the recognition of Northern, Eastern, and Western Regions linked in the Federation which came into existence in 1954. The former rulers have fitted well into the changed scene serving as governors and ministers.

The physical background. These human contrasts between north and south in Nigeria do but reflect the climatic conditions, which have resulted in a series of climatic-vegetation-agricultural zones roughly parallel to the coast. Before, however, the railroads and later motor roads came to link north and south, the Niger and its great navigable tributary, the Benue, played their part. Broadly, the coastal swamps of the Niger delta give place inland to high plains in the Yoruba country and to the Udi Plateau reaching 1000 feet above sea level. In the lower Niger-Benue basin Cretaceous and Tertiary sediments obscure the ancient crystalline rocks, and the coal seams in the Cretaceous sandstones of Enugu are economically significant. It is north of the Niger-Benue that the Jos Plateau of crystallines averages 4000 and has tin ores of great importance. Northward the plateau descends by steps to the Chad basin. The eastern margins of the country are marked by a great line of disturbance, with volcanic rocks culminating in the huge pile of Cameroon Mountain, since 1961 included in the Cameroon Republic.

Climatically, the almost equatorial belt of the south enjoys in places over 100 inches of rain (Figure 14.18), with a double maximum (April–July and September–October) and a very equable temperature ranging throughout the year only a few degrees on either side of 80°F. Northward the amount of rain decreases, the length of the dry season increases (reaching as much as 9 months), there is a single rainfall maximum but the total fall varies greatly from year to year, and the daily and annual ranges of temperature increase. In the coastal belt some very heavy rainfalls are recorded, 150 inches over much of the delta and up to 400 inches over the border on Cameroon Mountain. Storms of hurricane force tend to occur at the beginning and the end of the rains.

Mangrove forests cover large areas of the delta and coastlands, the trees ranging from 5 to 60 feet in height (Figure 14.19). Inland is the equatorial

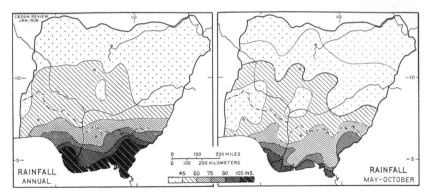

Figure 14.18 Rainfall maps of Nigeria. (From L. D. Stamp, *Geog. Rev.*, 1938. Courtesy of the *Geographical Review*, American Geographical Society.)

rainforest with its great buttressed lofty trees, some of which yield timber of mahogany type. This is the oil-palm belt, and it is the Guinea oil palm, wild or cultivated, which still provides a third of Nigeria's exports. The rainforest is a belt of poor sandy soils, badly leached in the east, and affords ample proof that the luxuriant forest growth is no criterion of soil fertility. How much of the forest is "primeval" is an interesting problem. Traces of human settlement under the longest trees when felled have demonstrated that much

Figure 14.19 Natural vegetation of Nigeria. (1) Fresh-water and salt-water swamp forest. (2) Equatorial-type rainforest. (3) Deciduous forest. (4) Savanna. (5) Thorn scrub. (From L. D. Stamp, *Geog. Rev.*, 1938. Courtesy of the *Geographical Review*, American Geographical Society.) Figures 14.8 and 14.9 show the old boundaries in the southeast.

is in fact second growth. Some African plantations of Hevea rubber have been established in Benin and Calabar. The succeeding "monsoon" or deciduous forest belt yields mahogany and bamboo but is more significant as the home of the kola nut. The great heart of Nigeria is savanna land with acacia, *Terminalia,* and baobab, and this gives place northward to thorn forest and scrub.

Agriculture. Agricultural belts follow those of natural vegetation. Gradually subsistence farming is giving place to farming where subsistence crops are combined with one or more cash crops. In the coastal and wet belts common crops in the temporary forest clearings (often with basin cultivation, described on page 94), include yams (Figure 14.20), cassava, maize, sugar cane, plantains, bananas, and oil palm. Cocoa cultivation is very important in the west, but it is difficult to dry the beans before they become moldy.

In the intermediate forest areas cultivation is similar, with kola nuts as a cash crop. Over the savanna or plateau areas the agricultural Hausas practicing permanent or shifting cultivation cultivate millet or guinea corn, peanuts, cassava, tobacco, and cotton, together with shea nuts. On the irrigated lands around Sokoto rice is grown. The Hausas share the land with the pastoral Fulani, with their 10 million cattle and many sheep and goats. Local varieties of cotton have long been cultivated, but improved types, with staples up to

Figure 14.20   Yam stacks in a village of the Cross River District, Southeast Nigeria. (Copyright C. Daryll Forde.)

one inch, as well as American long-stapled cottons, have become general along the Lagos-Kano railway line. Zaria is a leading center. But the great cash crop of the north is the peanut. The introduction of light steel plows to replace the traditional hoe was found to induce soil erosion and was abandoned.

The minerals of Nigeria include the only worked coal fields of West Africa—the discovery of a British geologist—at Enugu, now the capital of the Eastern Region, on the eastern railway to Port Harcourt. This same railway, after crossing the Benue by a great bridge at Makurdi, gives off a branch which taps the tin ore fields centering on Jos. After years of intensive search, oil and natural gas are being obtained in the delta region.

Towns and communications. The Niger is navigable by flat-bottomed steamers all the year round from the sea to near the Kaduna confluence (460 miles), and in the high-water season (July to October) as far as the railroad crossing at Jebba. The Benue is navigable for 470 miles above its confluence with the Niger to Garua on the Cameroon side of the frontier. The Cross River is of great local value in reaching the palm-oil belt and has an oil-exporting port at Calabar. Behind the coastal sand spits navigable waterways connect the Lagos lagoon with the Niger delta.

Lagos, the federal capital is partly situated on an island in a lagoon reached over a dredged bar from the ocean (Figure 14.21). Although Lagos has deep-water wharves, most of the trade is handled at the well-equipped railway wharves of Apapa on the mainland. Thence the main line runs inland through the large, sprawling old Yoruba capital Ibadan, one of the largest cities (600,000 in 1960) of tropical Africa, the seat of a university, and now the administrative center of the Western Region (Figure 14.22). The line reaches and crosses the Niger at Jebba; beyond, the administrative industrial center of Kaduna (chosen as a healthy site) has largely replaced Zaria, especially since it became the capital of the Northern Region (Figure 14.23). It is at Kaduna that the eastern line to Port Harcourt (now Nigeria's second port) on the Bonny River joins the main line. Reference has been made elsewhere to the way in which in Nigeria railway and mineral development went hand in hand. Later motor roads have played an increasingly important part, and air transport is important both internally and internationally. A particularly fascinating example of a major center surviving and adapting itself to change is afforded by Kano, which accordingly merits special study.

Kano. The walled cities which are the capitals of the Moslem kingdoms or emirates of Northern Nigeria and neighboring states are among the most fascinating features of West Africa. An excellent example is offered by Kano, though many others might be chosen—Sokoto or Katsina, for instance. Kano is fundamentally as it was when studied and described by Dr. Derwent

Figure 14.21   The site of Lagos.

Whittlesey.[11] It is the center of one of the major pockets of dense population in West Africa. In the area immediately tributary to the city within a radius of 30 to 40 miles live more than a million people, within the administrative division more than double that number. The *umland* or tributary area is well tilled: there are hamlets every half mile and about forty walled towns. The population of Kano City was recorded in the 1946 census as nearly 100,000 (130,000 in 1960) but these numbers are greatly increased at harvest time.

[11] "Kano: A Sudanese Metropolis," *Geog. Rev.,* **XXVII,** 1937, 177–199. Compare Sokoto.

Figure 14.22   A general view of Ibadan from Mapo Hall. (A Shell Photograph.)

Kano well deserves the title of "metropolis" as there is a constant stream of buyers and sellers into and out of the city; as many as 25,000 may pass inward through the gates in the wall during the day.

In contrast to most of Africa the Kano umland is continuously cultivated. The soils, derived from underlying granite, are light and easily worked and benefit greatly from manuring. The Hausa cultivators pay the nomadic Fulani who own all the cattle in the neighborhood to pasture their herds on the stubble fields during the dry season and thus to benefit the land by animal and human manure and "treading." The soil is enriched also by the manure of the sheep, goats, and pack animals—especially asses and mules—which are kept by the farmers. The light land of the Kano area has also benefited greatly from the increased cultivation of peanuts, which, though they require other manures, add nitrogenous material made from atmospheric nitrogen to the soil. The field crops raised in the rainy half of the year are chiefly Guinea corn (*Sorghum vulgare*), spiked millet (*Pennisetum spicatum*), and peanuts, with smaller proportions of cotton, manioc, sweet potatoes, and sesame. Where water can be obtained throughout the year from well or stream (by shadoof), gardens are found with onions, tomatoes, sugar cane, tobacco, peppers, and indigo.

For more than a thousand years Kano has been a trading center, and for a long time the focus of Hausaland. It may have been sited because of a locally usable deposit of iron ore; the city was long famed for the skill of the smiths and metal workers. Within the mud walls which enclose an area of some 9 square miles is still much open land, intended to supply food in case of siege. The mud houses are characteristic; modern dwellings faced with concrete usually follow traditional styles. There is an aristocratic section of the town where the Emir's palace is a walled city within a city. When my wife and I were received by the Emir (Figure 14.24) and entertained at tea within the thick-walled, color-washed adobe palace, some rooms were furnished in Western style, notwithstanding the charming decoration afforded by colored china plates and saucers or fragments let into the arched roofs and walls (Figure 14.25). The Emir's ministers, the city ward headman, and rich merchants have houses in the neighborhood, and many rural headmen keep a "town house" in Kano (Figure 14.26). In the main part of the town are quarters devoted to cotton spinning, weaving, dyeing (with local vegetable dyes prepared in pits) and tailoring. Another leading industry is tanning of leather (goats, cattle, sheep, camels, and asses all supply hides and skins, with goats easily leading), some tanning materials being derived from the seeds of a local acacia. Kano has a main market, well stocked, and many smaller ones, including one which before the British entry in 1903 was the slave market.

Outside the city walls is the township established by the British, with

Figure 14.23   The courts of justice, Kaduna. (Federal Nigerian Information Service.)

Figure 14.24   The late Emir of Kano, who became minister without portfolio in the federal parliament. (Federal Nigerian Information Service.)

government buildings, a European residential quarter, and two African towns where many of the immigrants into the area reside. Though no longer the railhead, Kano has a large transshipping trade from camel caravans to the railway. The large trade in peanuts, cotton, and skins is outward; the inward trade includes kola nuts from the south as well as a large range of imported goods.

Kano has become a great international and local airport as well as a focus of an increasing number of all-weather roads. The old city has been equipped with electricity, it has a good water supply, and some improvement has been made in sanitation. Its walls have tended to disintegrate; its old narrow gates have been widened to admit automobiles and the now widely used buses. Nevertheless, Kano retains much of its medieval charm.

Kano has been chosen as an example of a walled capital of an ancient Hausa state. There are others equally worthy of detailed study; a good example is Katsina.

Nigerian problems.[12] Despite the diversity between north and south and the artificial character of its boundaries, Nigeria in achieving independence has remained politically united. Perhaps it is the country in tropical Africa nearest to the Western concept of a nation involving the federation of peoples of different speech and religion. In this the development of communications has played a major part, and the varied economic basis is important. Peanuts, palm kernels, palm oil, cocoa, and tin ore (Figure 14.27) all represent more than 10 per cent of exports. Other exports include hides and cotton. The possession of West Africa's only coal mines and oil fields is a valuable asset. Both Lagos and Port Harcourt serve a large hinterland; the older ports of Burutu, Warri, and Sapele never did this.

But there is keen rivalry among the three regions which may lead to some duplication of effort. Not only are there three administrations—or four if one includes Lagos—as well as the federal, but each region has established, for example, such expensive items as a separate university. Indeed, five universities exist or are planned. The census population of 1963 announced February 24, 1964 was 55,653,821 (North, 29.8; East, 12.4; West, 10.3; mid-west, 2.5; Lagos 0.7 m.)

[12] See especially J. S. Coleman, *Nigeria—Background to Nationalism,* Berkeley University of California, 1958.

Figure 14.25   Decorated vaulting inside a house in the Kano area. This was in the home of a wealthy young man; the designs were executed in bright colors. Often decorated plates, saucers and fragments of china are let into the mud-cement. (Copyright L. Dudley Stamp.)

Former French West Africa (Afrique Occidentale Française)

The total area of the former French West Africa has been calculated at 4,675,700 square kilometers, or 1,815,768 square miles, with a total population estimated in 1949 at about 16½ million. The alterations of administrative boundaries after World War II included the creation of the new territory of Upper Volta and the incorporation of the former *circonscription* of Dakar and dependencies into Senegal, so that direct comparison with earlier statistics is difficult. A large part of the Sahara desert—at least three-quarters of a million square miles—lay in French West Africa, in Mauritania, French Sudan (now Mali Republic), and Niger. The administrative divisions as constituted after World War II were as follows:

	Area, square miles	Population (1949)	Population (1960)
Senegal (with Dakar)	81,050	1,992,000	2,597,000
French Guinea	108,400	2,180,000	2,726,900
Ivory Coast	129,800	2,065,000	3,115,100
Upper Volta	122,900	3,069,000	4,004,000
Dahomey	44,650	1,505,000	2,003,000
French Sudan	461,300	3,177,000	4,307,000
Mauritania	364,000	518,000	727,000
Niger	494,700	2,029,000	2,803,000
Total	1,806,800	16,535,000	22,283,000

Each is now an independent republic, and even the association with the French Community is nominal. Former French Guinea became quite independent and outside the French *Communauté* in 1958.

It should be noted that the trusteeship territory of Togoland did not form part of French West Africa and is now the independent republic of Togo.

Historical background. French interest in West Africa really began in 1483 when Louis XI sent an expedition to Cape Verde in search of a remedy for the leprosy from which he died before the expedition returned. Although French vessels anchored off the site of Saint-Louis in 1558, the first French Company (the Norman Company) to receive a charter to trade with Senegal and the Gambia was founded in 1624, a few years after the British had established themselves on the Gambia. Within the next few years three French companies were granted rights by Richelieu extending from Cape Verde to the mouth of the Congo. In 1635 the first Christian mission was established; in 1658–1659 Gorée and Saint-Louis were founded. Although the French companies were established for purposes of trade, they soon became interested in territorial accessions, and the Compagnie du Sénégal (the successor of the Norman Company) undertook to provide 2000 slaves annually to the French possessions in America.

In 1698 the Frenchman André Brue built a fortified post on the Senegal

Figure 14.26 A typical merchant's town house in Kano. Notice the flat roof and elaborate decoration. (Copyright L. Dudley Stamp.)

400 miles from the coast, the first attempt by a European to establish a permanent station away from the coast. The century which followed was one of constant strife between British and French; it was the Treaty of Paris in 1814 which marked the end of the struggle. At that time France was the only European power with any claims to possessions inland. France kept her possessions as they were in 1792—Arguin, Portendik, Saint-Louis, Gorée and its dependencies, Cape Verde, Rufisque, Portudal, and Joal. The British retained only trading rights.

Although the Revolutionary Convention of 1794 abolished the status of slavery in the dominion of France, slavery was not finally abolished throughout the Empire until 1848. But the concept of French citizenship grew gradually, and the French tried to reorganize the economy of Senegal on the basis of agriculture. The turning point was the beginning of the export of peanuts in 1840, and French development was concentrated in Senegal, based on Saint-Louis.

In 1845 the French possessions were divided into two governments:

Figure 14.27   Old and new methods of tin working in Nigeria. In the upper picture the tin-bearing earth is being dug by hand and the heavy baskets or basins carried by women. In the lower picture the same type of ground is being worked by hydraulic sluicing, with a minimum of labor. But the modern method has the disadvantage of affording little employment. (Copyright R. J. Harrison-Church.)

Figure 14.28   A "pagan" village and lands, Northern Nigeria. (Copyright Aerofilms Library.)

Figure 14.29   The Jebba railway bridge over the River Niger. (Copyright Aerofilms Library.)

Senegal based on Saint-Louis and Rivières du Sud based on Gorée. In 1847 the French created a corps of African cavalry (Spahis); in 1848 the first Senegalese *Tirailleurs* were enlisted from freed slaves. The French military tradition was thus introduced very early into Africa.

A little later the French clashed with El Hadj Omar who had set up a Moslem state over a large area to the southwest of Timbuktu. French development at this time owes much to General Faidherbe, who was appointed governor of Senegal in 1854. He established schools, banks, and a survey organization, and he was the real founder of Dakar, where a military port was set up in 1857 and the first jetty built in 1863.

French interests in West Africa were well established at the time of the Berlin Conference in 1885. The same year France recognized German claims to Togoland, and boundary agreements with Portugal, Britain, Liberia, and Spain followed gradually. Until the German occupation Togoland, with a seaboard of about 30 miles and a depth of 300, had not existed as a unit, and it status as a German colony from 1885 to 1914 was typical of the entirely artificial units created by European powers in Africa. On the outbreak of World War I Togoland fell to British and French forces in the first month. Later the division of land between Britain and France was accepted by the League of Nations and the United Nations.

Senegal was thus the earliest area of French penetration into West Africa. France's rights in French Guinea were recognized by Britain in 1882, and Conakry was occupied in 1887. In the Ivory Coast the French had a factory at Grand Bassam at an early stage—lasting until 1707—and treaties with local chiefs were revived in 1842. The French were later concerned to maintain an access from the coast to the Upper Niger basin. In Dahomey they obtained rights to establish a trading post as early as 1669 at Ouidah, but it was not till 1851 that a treaty of friendship was concluded with the King of Dahomey. Porto Novo accepted the protection of France in 1863.

Consolidation of French West Africa came with the establishment of a central government in 1895, when the Governor of Senegal became Governor-General with his capital at St. Louis. The capital was moved to Dakar in 1904, and Dakar, described below, continued to grow in political and economic importance. The emergence of the independant African states in 1960 reduced Dakar in status to the capital of Senegal, but it continues to serve in several ways as a focal point of French-speaking West Africa.

The peoples of former French West Africa. The people fall into the two main groups—the Islamized peoples of the north and the Negroes of the south. But northern religions, organizations, and languages have invaded the south, and Negro blood has penetrated far into the north. The lands are not neatly parceled out into tribal areas, but broadly the peoples of the north are Moslems of Arab, Berber, and Fulani stock, the Negroes of the south are Christians or Animists. The Negro villages usually comprise "clans," each of families descended from a common stock, and there was no intermarriage between members of the same clan under French administration.

Each territory was divided into "cercles" under a "commandant du cercle," who was often virtual ruler of his province. He appointed the village chief (after consultation with the village elders) and the canton chief, supervising a group of villages.

Senegal (République du Sénégal)

Historically Senegal was the bridgehead for French penetration into West Africa. Here the French established St. Louis on a remarkable island site (obviously for defensive purposes) near the mouth of the Senegal River, an important highway into the interior. Although Dakar replaced St. Louis as the capital of the Federation and chief port, and the railway inland from Dakar to Kayes on the Senegal (and then to Bamako on the navigable Upper Niger) supplanted the old Senegal River highway, St. Louis remains a considerable town. It has spread from its congested sandbank island to the main sandspit (the "Langue de Barbarie") facing the Atlantic Ocean. A long road bridge spans the Senegal River to the railhead at Sor, whence a line runs to Dakar. St. Louis, like Bathurst in the Gambia (and to some extent Lagos), is a good example of a town site well suited to its original function as a European trading outpost but not permitting expansion to meet modern conditions.

Senegal lies in the Sudan savanna, the "Sahelian Zone" of French writers, where the dominant vegetation is a sparse grass brush with spiny bushes. Much lies within the basin of that important navigable highway, the Senegal River. Floods permit the cultivation of millet and guinea corn in the river valleys, and along the coast between St. Louis and Dakar there is a line of oases behind the coastal sand dunes. Elsewhere settlement and cultivation are restricted to the more fertile pockets where water is available; it is the peanut which has made the fortune of Senegal. Commercially cultivation is important only where the crop land can be reached by river, rail, or road. At the head of the estuary of the Saloum is the rapidly growing port and town of Kaolack, linked by a branch line with the Dakar-Niger railway. The river Gambia, navigable through the British strip to the border, also taps peanut country. The story is always the same—the dependence of economic development on modern transport.

Unlike so many of the political divisions of West Africa, Senegal lies mainly in one vegetation zone. The exception is the southern part, lying between the Gambia and Portuguese territory, which is drained by the Casamance and falls in the wetter zone. That area is less well developed.

Dakar.[13] Dakar is unique among the settlements of tropical Africa, and as such merits special attention. When it replaced St. Louis as the capital of French West Africa and seat of the governor-general, it became, despite its situation near the sea level well within the tropics—it is less than 15 degrees from the equator—a European city. This is true both because the European residential center with its tall apartment houses, its shops, cafés, and hotels (run by Europeans) is unlike anything else in tropical Africa and because large numbers of French and other Europeans settled there, to all appearance permanently. There were schools for their children, bathing beaches and yachting facilities for their outdoor recreation, cinemas and dance halls for indoor. The congested site on the peninsula (Figure 14.30), cut off by the African town, led to a closely knit city, but the suburbs, now mixed African and European, have spread beyond the airport to the Atlantic beaches (Figure 14.31). The vast increase in sea and air traffic has concentrated much business in Dakar. With a magnificent natural harbor protected by Cape Manuel and extensively improved, the site is unmatched in West Africa, and the isolated rocky site supports Dakar's claim to be considered an "African Gibraltar."

The Cape Verde Peninsula behind which Dakar shelters owes its origin to sheets of recent volcanic lava, partly covered with sand dunes. West Africa affords many examples of the importance of such geological "accidents"; Freetown is another.

It has been argued that, although Dakar is well within the tropics, the local climatic conditions link it with midlatitude rather than lowland tropical conditions. It is from Dakar or Cape Verde northward that the cool Canaries current with up-welling cold bottom waters tempers the air temperatures, and there are pleasant sea breezes, especially from November to February. The January average is 73°F. (with a mean of daily minima and maxima from 64°F. to 82°F.). There is no doubt that immediately to the *south* of Dakar the humidity becomes higher throughout the year, and the tempering effect of breezes off the sea is less where the Canaries current does not exist.

In the sheltered bay of Dakar is the tiny island of Gorée, so important in the history of French expansion in Africa but no longer of any significance.

Mauritania (République Islamique de Mauritanie)[14]

As already noted in the previous chapter, Mauritania is an essentially Saharan state; only its long historical association with French West Africa warrants a second mention here. The comment in the first edition of this book was, "Its southern boundary is the Senegal River, and insofar as the

[13] Derwent Whittlesey, "Dakar and Other Cape Verde Settlements," *Geog. Rev.,* **XXXI,** 1941, 609–638. "Dakar Revisited," *Geog. Rev.,* **XXXVIII,** 1948, 626–632.
[14] See R. J. Harrison–Church, *Focus,* November 1961.

Figure 14.30   Dakar, Gorée, and Cape Verde in 1946–1947. (1) European city. (2) African city. (3) African market. (4) African village. (5) Sanitary zone. (6) Military reservation. (7) Airfield. (8) Factory district. (9) Tank farm. (10) Main roads. (11) Railroad. (From Derwent Whittlesey, *Geog. Rev.* 1948. Courtesy of the *Geographical Review*, American Geographical Society.)

Since Whittlesey carried out his study and this map was prepared, Dakar has expanded greatly to the west and north. Large blocks of apartments now face the Atlantic both north and south of Cape Verde, and it is no longer correct to consider as separate a "European city."

Figure 14.31   Modern African housing in Dakar. A blown-up balloon forms the "frame" over which the cement is poured. The result is a beehive-shaped home not unlike a traditional African pattern. (Copyright R. J. Harrison-Church.)

territory has any trade it is tributary to or lies in the hinterland of St. Louis. There is an African population along the Senegal in the south, but most of the half million people scattered over a third of a million square miles are nomadic Moorish Moslems who bring into St. Louis the gum and salt or cattle and skins which the country produces. Through Mauritania, linking eventually Dakar and St. Louis with Morocco and Algeria, runs the Mauritania Road—more difficult and less important, however, than other trans-Saharan motor routes."

But that was ten years ago. Now Mauritania, an independent republic, is is on the threshold of great developments. One of the richest iron ore deposits in the world, at Fort Gouraud near the Mauritania Road, is to be opened up, and a railway (following a tortuous course to avoid running across the Spanish territory of Spanish Sahara) is being constructed from Port Etienne. Also on the road, halfway from Fort Gouraud to St. Louis, are copper deposits at Akjoujt, and where the road reaches the Atlantic the settlement of Nouakchott is being developed as the capital.

Mali (République du Mali)

For a short time the territory of the French Sudan (Soudan français) on achieving independence became known as the République du Soudan, an unfortunate clash in terminology with the Republic of the Sudan, previously the Anglo–Egyptian Sudan. Following the example of Ghana, the people chose to revive the name of one of the great African empires of the past, in roughly the same area (see pages 271–273), and the country became known as Mali, with its capital at Bamako, with an international airport. The former rail link between Dakar and Bamako was severed in 1960 when the railroad was dynamited at the boundary.

Mali comprises essentially, though the boundaries do not coincide, the basin of the Upper and Middle Niger from above Bamako, past Ségou and Timbuktu (Tombouctou of French maps) to below Gao. These towns are the main centers, and Mali thus includes the great bend of the Niger, the heartlands of the old Mandingo and Songhai Empires. For the most part the region is one of uniform and feeble relief. In the east and south the Archean peneplain is dominant, and its monotonous surface is varied only rarely by small eruptive masses. Horizontal sandstones, resting on the peneplain, form a large plateau depressed in the center and with other broad valleys occupied by the Senegal, Niger, and Black Volta. The sandstone plateau has a marked edge 1000 to 1500 feet in height—even reaching 3000 in the Hombori mountains—forming a great semicircle. Erosion has left flat-topped mesas such as the Manding plateau near Bamako. The sandstones are often covered, especially along the Niger, by flat stretches of alluvium, and toward the Sahara are stretches of fixed sand dunes.

The inland Niger delta.[15] Not only is this area of very great interest in itself, but it also affords a practical example of what can be achieved, albeit at high cost, in economic development with irrigation of a large flat area, and so points the way to possible developments in other parts of the continent. Below Ségou the River Niger once flowed into a large inland lake. When this dried up, the Niger split into a number of branches and meandered over the old lake floor, successive courses being abandoned because of silting. In 1941 the French completed a great barrage at the head of the delta at Sansanding (Figure 14.32), with the object of raising the river level 5 meters

[15] R. J. Harrison-Church, "Irrigation in the Inland Niger Delta of the French Sudan," *Geog. Jour.* **CXVII**, 1951, 218–220.

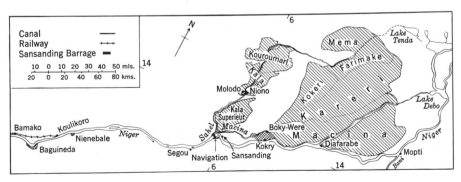

Figure 14.32   The inland Niger delta.

Figure 14.33   Large-scale mechanized cultivation, inland Niger delta. (Courtesy Office du Niger.)

(16 feet). The water could then be conducted through old channels, recut or deepened as required, to flood the lower lands (the area known as Macina) near the Niger for rice cultivation and also to irrigate the drier area of the Sahel for cotton, rice, and sorghum. The old lake silts afford good black soils with a high humus content. The plan was eventually to benefit 2¼ million acres. The sluice gates were not available until 1947, and the area immediately irrigated was about 50,000 acres. The scheme includes the eventual settlement of 200,000 or 250,000 African colonists, each to work 8 to 13 acres. With their families this would represent a million people. By 1961 there were about 27,000 colonists with their families settled on 100,000 acres (Figure 14.33). On arrival each settler is provided with a hut, garden, three head of cattle, a plow, and a well. They market through a cooperative and purchase further equipment through the same channel. What may be called a pilot scheme on a smaller scale (about 5,500 colonists and families) was carried out higher up the Niger at Sotuba near Bamako.

Upper Volta (République de Haute-Volta)

In 1919 the colony of Upper Volta was carved out of the old colony of Upper Senegal and Niger, but later, in 1932, the colony was suppressed, its territory being divided between the Ivory Coast, Sudan, and Niger. Then, in 1947, the separate division was re-established as a territory, with an area of about 123,000 square miles and a population of about 4 million. It became a member of the French Community in 1958 and an independent republic in 1960.

This country lies in the same latitude as the populous parts of Northern Nigeria. The French made great efforts to counteract the disadvantages of its inland situation. There are numerous but not very good roads which focus on the two chief centers of Bobo-Dioulasso and Ouagadougou (sometimes anglicized as Wagadugu), the capital. Both are served by air. The railway from the greatly improved port of Abidjan to Bobo-Dioulasso was extended to Ouagadougou in 1954.

Most of the country is a flat, poor savanna land with numerous cattle, sheep, goats, horses, and donkeys. Shea butter is produced, and cultivated crops include corn, millet, rice, beans, peanuts, and manioc. Exports include cattle and peanuts.

Niger (République du Niger)

The vast Republic of the Niger, with nearly 3 million people, lies mainly to the north of the Federation of Nigeria and stretches roughly from the Niger in the west to Lake Chad in the east. The north is desert; the southern strip has sufficient vegetation to support large numbers of cattle, sheep, and goats with smaller numbers of asses, camels, and horses. The main difficulty of the country is scarcity of surface water. Indeed only four areas have sufficient water to permit settlement: the western districts watered by the Niger and its tributaries; the parts of the southern zone where the water table can be reached by wells and the water is potable; the area near Lake Chad; and the wadis of the Aïr massif in the north.

Dried or drying lakes yield salt and sodium sulphate (the latter in quantity for export near the Komadugu River in the east), and there is a demand for both in Nigeria. The Hausa cultivate millet, peanuts, beans, and manioc, with cotton and locally rice near the rivers.

A focal point is Niamey, the capital, on the Niger. Zinder, north of Kano in Nigeria and linked with it by road, is another center, from which the trans-Saharan Hoggar road passes northward through Aïr and the towns of Agades and Tamanrasset (see page 261).

The vast open savannas of Niger abound in game and form a favorite area for big game hunters—for lions, elephants, buffaloes, and various antelope.

Ivory Coast (République de Côte d'Ivoire)

The capital of this republic of 130,000 square miles is the thriving town of Abidjan on the northern side of a large lagoon (Figure 14.34). As an example of French enterprise in Africa, Abidjan rivals Dakar both in interest and in importance. The whole orientation of the area was changed with the completion of the ship canal through the obstructing sandbar and the opening to traffic of the deep-water wharves in July 1950 (Figure 14.35).

Figure 14.34   The site of Abidjan.

Prior to that time Grand-Bassam at the mouth of the Comoé River and where the lagoon is connected with the sea served as an inadequate roadstead port. Later a port was established at Port-Bouet (Petit-Bassam), where deep water (*Trou sans fond*—the "deep without bottom") approaches the coast, but the situation was obviously open and exposed. From the wharf at Port-Bouet a rail link was thrown across the lagoon to Abidjan. In the meantime the former administrative center of Bingerville had been gradually abandoned in favor of Abidjan. With the completion of the canal from the lagoon to the *Trou sans fond,* Grand-Bassam, Port-Bouet, and Bingerville have all become ghost towns. From Abidjan the railway is the great highway to the interior. In the 716 miles to Ouagadougou it cuts through roughly the same zones as exist in Ghana to the east, except that the coastal zone has the heavy rainfall of the Axim area of Ghana and is naturally covered with an equatorial type of forest.

This equatorial forest belt yields mahogany, and there is some production of palm oil, cocoa (first introduced 1904–1908), bananas, and coffee. Inland in the savanna country there is a small production of cotton, but cattle, peanuts, and millets form the mainstay of the subsistence economy.

Though diamonds are being increasingly won, minerals play a smaller part in the country's economy than in neighboring Ghana.

The republic has, however, a range of agricultural products corresponding to the vegetation zones and comparable with those of its neighbor Ghana. Its indigenous farmers are prosperous and the whole country has an air of well-being and progressiveness.

Dahomey (République du Dahomey)

Dahomey lies between the Republic of Togo (former German Togoland) on the west and Nigeria on the east. With an area of 45,000 square miles and a population of some 1½ million, its coastline is only about 70 miles long. From the old port of Grand-Popo through the chief port Cotonu (with an iron pier) a railway runs along the coast to the capital, Porto-Novo, a few miles away, and thence a short distance inland. The main line inland leaves this coastal railroad and serves the southern half of the country.

Naturally the vegetation and agricultural zones link with those of Nigeria and of Togo and Ghana. The forest zone of the south furnishes palm oil and

Figure 14.35   **The Vridi Canal at Abidjan. This canal connects the lagoon with the open sea and has permitted Abidjan to develop as a modern ocean port.**

kernels—the chief products of the country—but coffee and cotton have been successfully introduced farther north as commercial crops. Roads now render accessible the northern parts of the country.

Guinea (République de Guinée)

In the referendum of September 28, 1958, Guinea voted for complete severance from France and was proclaimed an independent republic four days later. The Republic of Guinea stretches from the coast between Portuguese Guinea and Sierra Leone inland to the headwaters basin of the Niger. The capital and chief port, Conakry, sheltered by the Iles de Los which were ceded by Britain to France in 1904, is itself on an island linked by a bridge with the mainland. Thence a railway runs through the territory to Kouroussa on the Niger, below which point the great river is navigable. Conakry is free from the sandbars which are a curse of so many African ports.

Guinea in its 108,000 square miles comprises several very different regions. The coastal plain, 30 to 50 miles wide, is a very wet region inhabited by the Susu (Soussou). Cultivated plants include the oil palm, and there are banana plantations. Inland are rolling plateaus which form a foothill zone to the Futa Jallon. These are inhabited by the cattle-rearing Fulani, living in villages of round huts surrounded by fruit trees. Crossing the Futa Jallon, (Fouta Djallon on French maps), a considerable stretch of which lies more than 3000 feet above sea level, the land slopes toward the north, draining to the Senegal, or northeast, to the Niger. This part of Guinea is linked naturally with neighboring parts of Mali—savanna country with peanuts and sesame. An important center and terminus of the rail from Conakry is Kankan. Finally, the southeast of Guinea is a forested region, much dissected and extremely difficult of access, lying behind Sierra Leone and Liberia, which cut it off from the sea. It is now, however, penetrated by roads from Kankan as well as being linked by road with the Liberian port of Monrovia. Guinea now has a large output of iron ore from the Kaloum peninsula, bauxite from the Los islands and elsewhere, alumina from the Fria factory, and diamonds from the Macenta district.

With nearly 3 million people and a wide range of natural resources, Guinea has the prerequisites for development as a powerful state. By leaving the French Union in 1958 Guinea was at first somewhat isolated, but Ghana offered help by suggesting linkage, in the ideal of a United States of Africa, joined by Mali later, in 1960. They agreed as a first step to coordinate their diplomatic representations and their economic and monetary policies.

Togo (République Togolaise)

Togoland surrendered unconditionally to British and French forces in August 1914, shortly after the outbreak of World War I. It was ruled under mandate from the League of Nations (approved 1922) until December 14, 1946, when the United Nations agreed on the terms of the trusteeship. Of the total area of 33,700 square miles of the former German territory, the French were given the control of 21,893 square miles, including the whole of the coast. Lomé, on the coast, with some 30,000 people, was the seat of administration; the total population of French Togoland was about 1 million.

Togo is entirely an artificial unit—even more so than its neighbors. Its people resemble those of neighboring lands, Ghana and Dahomey. Its geographical divisions are those of its neighbors. There is a lagoon coast, somewhat arid as in Ghana, succeeded inland by a terrace some 200 to 300 feet above sea level, which gives place to a marshy but fertile depression (with oil palms, bananas, maize, and cocoa). Northward is the zone favorable to cotton, before the country of the Fulani and Hausa is reached. There are railways totalling 266 miles running inland from Lomé, which has a wharf handling the export of cocoa, cotton, coffee, palm oil and palm kernels, shea, peanuts, and copra. Production of phosphate is now important.

Under the mandate and trusteeship systems Togoland could not become an integral part of French West Africa, and so when, in the 1958–1960 period, the French territories became republics within the French Community, Togo became an independent republic on its own.

Togo illustrates the way in which African peoples remain divided by political frontiers. The Ewe people, for example, have occupied the same area continuously since the sixteenth century. But half of them found themselves in French Togoland, about two-fifths in British Togoland, and the remainder in southern Ghana. Somewhat similarly placed are the Dagomba, who lived partly in British Togoland, partly in the northern part of Ghana. Yet so far have modern political concepts replaced old tribal ties that when the independent republic of Togo was formed, the former British Togoland had already in 1956 elected to join Ghana, and the division remains.

BIBLIOGRAPHY

Changes following World War II have been so rapid and important in West Africa that most older accounts are completely out of date, except where they refer to geographical conditions undergoing little change.

The accounts in the *Géographie universelle* must be read with this in mind. For the British territories *Annual Reports* on each colony were formerly issued by the British Colonial Office, and these contain extensive geographical accounts.

Since the first edition of this book was published, West Africa has been well served by the publication of Dr. R. J. Harrison-Church's *West Africa* (London: Longmans, 1957, 3rd Edition, 1961; New York: John Wiley & Sons) affording a comprehensive survey, including much original field work as well as summaries of all work to date, and especially the studies of French geographers. The development of West African universities with strong departments of geography is reflected in a number of detailed works such as E. A. Boateng, *A Geography of Ghana* (London: Cambridge University Press, 1959), H. P. White and D. J. Varley, *The Geography of Ghana* (London: Longmans, 1959), K. M. Buchanan and J. C. Pugh, *Land and People in Nigeria* (London: University of London Press, 1955).

Several numbers of *Focus* have been devoted to West African countries: Sierra Leone (December 1957), Ghana (April 1959), and Mauritania (November 1961).

R. J. Harrison-Church, *Environment and Policies in West Africa* (New York: Van Nostrand, 1963) deals with the geographical background of recent political changes and alignments.

CHAPTER FIFTEEN

The Sudan[1]

The word Sudan is used in several different senses. Literally it is the plural of the Arabic word *suda,* meaning black; hence the Sudan is properly the land of the blacks. It has long been and is still frequently applied to the whole belt of country stretching approximately from the Atlantic Ocean in the west to the Abyssinian Mountains in the east, with the great Sahara Desert on the north and the hot, wet forest belt of the West African coastlands and Equatorial Africa on the south. In this sense it is essentially the belt of grassland, usually with scattered trees, constituting what is more frequently called the savanna country. The greater part of the west and center of the belt lies in former French territory. In the west are the Republics of Mali and Niger, which are considered in Chapter 14. In the center the Chad Republic was formerly a part of French Equatorial Africa.

A very important part of the belt lies in the east. In this chapter we are concerned both with the eastern Sudan as a geographical unit and with the political division of Africa known until 1951 as the Anglo-Egyptian Sudan. As this name implies, the Anglo-Egyptian Sudan was under the joint control of Egypt and Britain as a condominium from 1898 effectively to 1951, and nominally to 1955. The present Republic of the Sudan has a huge area, only a little under a million square miles, the closest calculation available giving a total of 967,500. The population according to the 1955–1956 Census was 10,262,536, nearly 95 per cent Sudanese, the remainder largely nomads of Arab or Berber stock. The Sudan became an independent self-governing republic on January 1, 1956.

[1] In the complete rewriting of this chapter which has been necessary because of the wide-ranging character of recent changes, I have been very greatly assisted by Dr. J. H. G. Lebon, until 1961 Professor of Geography at the University of Khartoum.

The geographical limits of the Republic of the Sudan

The Sudanese Republic stretches from the heart of the great desert in the north, where the boundary with Egypt is for the most part a straight line drawn across wastes of sand, to the borders of equatorial forest lands in the south (Figure 15.1.). In broad terms it coincides roughly with the basin of the Central and Upper Nile, but excluding the sources of both the White and the Blue Niles. Thus the Sudan as a whole, like Egypt, draws its life blood, the

Figure 15.1   The relief and provinces of the Sudan. All land more than 600 feet above sea level is stippled.

water of the great rivers, from territories beyond its control. The waters of the White Nile come from the plateau lands of Uganda, Kenya, Tanganyika, and even to a small extent from the Congolese Republic. The source of the waters of the still more important Blue Nile, which below Khartoum supplies three-fifths of the total volume of Nile water, is among the mountains of Ethiopia.

It might be theoretically possible to divert the whole of Nile waters reaching the Sudan for purposes of irrigating lands in that country, in which case Egypt might virtually cease to exist. In Chapter 3 of this book, emphasis was laid upon the natural division of Africa into river basins and how existing political boundaries cut across the natural water partings or watersheds, with little regard for the ever more obvious fact that the future prosperity and development of the African continent must be based upon unified control of the waters in each of the great river basins. The unity of the Nile basin became a political slogan of certain sections of the Egyptians, culminating in October 1951 when the Egyptians abrogated the treaties with Britain and declared Farouk King of Egypt and the Sudan. The inhabitants of the Sudan are radically—though comprising different groups—entirely distinct from the people of Egypt. They left no doubt that they wished independence and not union with Egypt.

The regions and peoples of the Sudan

In broad general terms the Sudan consists of a succession of belts of country stretching from east to west, that is, from the margins of neighboring countries, Chad in the west to the Red Sea or the borders of Ethiopia on the east (Figure 15.2). Following a course from south to north, and therefore cutting across these zones at right angles, is the White Nile, entering Sudanese territory from Uganda as the Bahr-el-Jebel in the extreme south. It will be convenient to consider these belts of country from the north, that is from the Egyptian border, to the south.

The desert belt. The frontier between Egypt and the Sudan crosses the Nile some distance below the Second Cataract, which itself is just above the Sudanese town and railhead of Wadi Halfa. To the west lie the great sandy stretches of the Libyan Desert, to the east the almost equally arid wastes of the Nubian Desert, extending to the rugged Red Sea hills and the shores of the Red Sea.

In the west and center this desert belt extends southward roughly as far as Khartoum, approximately in latitude 15° North. Through this desert belt the united Nile passes in its course, making a huge S-shaped bend. The Libyan Desert, to the west, is uninhabited, but to the east, near the Nile, there are a few desert nomads, Berbers, who give place toward the Red Sea to Hamites, known as the Beja. The Beja are wiry people with a great mop of

Figure 15.2   The vegetation belts of the Sudan.

curly hair which has given them the name of "Fuzzy-Wuzzies"—so well
known to those who call at Port Sudan. They possess camels, mainly, and
some sheep and goats, which become more numerous in the south. Both
desert feed and water are scarce; when the rains fail, animals die, and the
Beja suffer great hardships.

The Nile valley which passes through this desert belt may be described
as an attenuated version of the Nile valley in Egypt below Wadi Halfa. The
Egyptian cultivators, the fellaheen, are not found south of the Egyptian
border. Their place is taken by Nubians, who in Egypt were found side by
side with the Egyptian cultivators between the Egyptian border and Aswan,
but who have now been evacuated from their villages before flooding by the
High Dam project. In the Sudan they have established a chain of little agricultural villages on both banks of the Nile as far south as Korti. Upstream

from Korti these little villages are occupied by sedentary Arabic-speaking tribes.

Cultivation is carried out by using the Persian wheel, or *saqia,* to raise water from the river, also by the shadoof, the Archimedean screw, and, though to a relatively small extent, basin irrigation from the Nile floods. In the last twenty years these traditional methods of irrigation have been largely displaced by diesel-engined pumps. Small towns, such as Dongola, Karima, Abu Hamed, Berber, and Shendi are markets. Because there are few oases in the desert belt outside those associated with the Nile, little cultivation exists away from the river.

The stretch of the Nile between Khartoum and Wadi Halfa, being interrupted by cataracts, is not used for through navigation; however, the sections between the cataracts are still used by sailing craft (feluccas), and there is a river steamer service between Karima and Dongola. The railroad from Wadi Halfa to Khartoum deserts the valley itself and cuts across the Nubian Desert between Wadi Halfa and Abu Hamed. At Atbara is the junction from which another main line cuts across the desert and the Red Sea hills to the important port of Port Sudan on the Red Sea. It is natural that Atbara should have become a "railway town" with extensive locomotive and carriage repair shops. It is at Atbara that the river of the same name draining from the northern hills of Ethiopia joins the Nile.

The semidesert or steppe belt. Between latitudes 14° and 15° the desert belt gives place gradually to one where vegetation, though sparse, becomes slightly more abundant. The number of people increases, and life becomes richer and more varied. North of El Obeid, now reached by rail from Sennar and Khartoum, are numerous nomadic Arab tribes. They have camels and flocks of sheep and goats. They follow the movement of the sun during the dry season, and then return toward the north during the rains between June and October. Herding is much helped by shallow ponds or "hafirs," some now being excavated by machinery. Between the Blue Nile and the Atbara are tribes who own very large flocks of sheep.

It will be seen that in this semidesert belt there is no permanent agriculture, so that the well-cultivated Gezira, that famous triangular area between the White and Blue Niles before their union, depends for its prosperity entirely on the great irrigation scheme described below.

The savanna belt. South of latitude 15° summer rainfall increases, vegetation becomes more rich, one passes into the grassland with trees, or savanna, and agriculture becomes general.

The Nile seems to have provided a line of communication through this country in such a way that northern and southern influences have intermingled. So it is by no means uncommon to see side by side the little square hut of hard mud, so characteristic of the Nile valley through its desert stretches,

Figure 15.3 Villagers collecting "tears" of gum from *Acacia senegal* bushes. Gum arabic is the second export of the Sudan. (Courtesy Sudan Government.)

and the round hut with conical roof made of straw or grass and typical of the people of the savanna lands of so much of tropical Africa. Here the people are a mixture of Hamites and Negroes.

In the typical savanna country the people combine cultivation of millet, peanuts, and sesamum. In the dry months they collect gum arabic. Gum ranks second to cotton among the exports of the Sudan. The acacia trees or bushes are cut with small incisions, from which "tears" of gum are later collected (Figure 15.3). There are also transhumant cattle-owning tribes (Baggara), who move toward the Bahr-el-Arab and Sobat in the dry season; these people market live cattle and hides. To translate the words of Professor Maurette, "Nothing is more mixed than the population of these steppes and of these savannas, vast spaces without natural limits between the desert of the north and the forest or marshes of the south. There was the southern limit of the advance of Arab tribes and of the Nubians. The first Nilotics appear with the people known as the Shilluk. But above all, from Darfur as the region of the Blue Nile the Sudanese tribes are numerous."

These open savannas have for very long periods been a line or belt of communication from east to west. As the people on the fringes of Negro Africa became converted to the Moslem religion, there followed the necessity of the pilgrimage to Mecca. Pilgrims who pass along the routeways do not always return, but sometimes remain to settle and form colonies among the indigenous peoples. In later times disturbed conditions in the Sudan led to much movement along this belt, and in still more recent times the movement of laborers, perhaps remaining to become settlers, has been equally marked. The study of migration, past and present, along this belt is one of fascinating interest, if of extreme complexity.

A traveller by road in 1951 expressed the position in the following words: "Two hundred miles south of Khartoum we left the turbanned, long-robed Moslems behind and came into a different world, one of primitive people, who spoke no Arabic and for the most part wore no clothes. They carried spears, no longer for fighting, but for prodding their animals. Dura is their main food." (He should have added milk and blood.)

The southern clay plain. The southern part of the Sudan is a huge shallow basin situated essentially on the great African plateau surface of crystalline rocks, through which meanders sluggishly the upper White Nile, or Bahr-el-Jebel, after it leaves the Uganda border. As already described, it is joined by the Bar-el-Ghazal and the numerous tributaries which flow down from the watershed which lies between the Congo basin and the Nile basin. In the heart of the basin is a marshy area known as El Sudd, from which the great masses of floating vegetation find their way into the river courses and into the Nile itself (Figure 15.4).

In addition to permanent swamps there are much larger areas which are inundated every rainy season but dry out between December and May.

In the Sudd Region there are immense numbers of fish in the shallow pools which attract vast flocks of fishing birds. The people of the region

Figure 15.4 A fishing village in the Sudd Region of the Sudan. (Courtesy Sudan government.)

spear the fish in the early months of the year when many have been trapped in natural ponds by the fall of the flood waters. They are dried and can then be used throughout the year. But mainly the population, known as the Nilotics or Nilotes, are cattle-keeping. They seek areas above the flood waters between June and October. As the floods recede they seek moist pastures near the rivers, called *toiches.*

The margins of the basin, including much of that province of Sudan known as Equatoria, are remote regions where the negroid peoples practice their shifting cultivation on the old soils of a plateau 2,000 to 3,000 feet above sea level. This is a vast area, and the population is sparse. There is considerable truth in the assertion that the Sudan from the point of view of its human geography consists of two utterly different and contrasted parts —the Islamized north and the part-Christian, part-pagan south.

The history of the Sudan

Such in brief outline is the geographical background of the Sudan. Because of past British interests in the Sudan I propose to use the brief historical account given by a Frenchman as an objective view of one having no reason to side with any particular group. The following is an approximate translation of the account given by Dr. Fernand Maurette in the *Géographie universelle,* published in 1938, the year after the death of the author.

From the nineteenth century B.C. Egyptian Pharaohs had an interest in "Nubia." An inscription of 1879 B.C. found 40 miles south of Wadi Halfa forbids "Negroes" to pass farther down the Nile. From this time onward all the masters of the moment in the east tried, whether from the north or from the east, from the Mediterranean or the Red Sea, to put their hands on the country which was the source of precious materials—ivory, ostrich feathers, gums, and, above all, slaves. In the time of the Emperor Julian the Roman power advanced as far as Ethiopia. The Coptic form of Christianity established itself at Soba, near Khartoum, and at (Old) Dongola, the foundation of which dates from this time. In A.D. 641 the Arab government of Egypt invaded Nubia, took (Old) Dongola, and demanded from the Nubian chiefs an annual tribute of slaves; the treaty was observed for the next 500 years. In 1169 the Turkish Sultan, Saladin, famous champion of Islam, founded in Egypt a dynasty whose raids into the Sudan were numerous. Then there were Arab sultans from the Yemen who, coming by the Red Sea and landing at Suakin, advanced as far as the Nile and to Darfur, which they Islamized, thus cutting off for a long time the Christians of the north from those of Ethiopia. Islamized and Arabic-speaking tribes also came from the northwest. After them and concurrently in the sixteenth century, the Islamized Negroes living between the Blue and White Niles, the Fung, founded a vast empire, with Sennar as its capital, which stretched from Ethiopia to Dongola.

They systematically exterminated Christianity from all the low country lying below the Ethiopian massif. The Ottoman Turks themselves advanced from the other direction as far as Dongola. From the sixteenth century up to the time of Mohammed Ali the Kingdoms of Darfur and Sennar and the Turkish power divided the country among them; but they were concerned mainly with that lucrative trade, the supply of slaves to the Lower Nile or to the Red Sea.

In 1822 Mohammed Ali established an Egyptian government in northern Sudan. His son, Ismail Pasha, obtained from the Turkish Sultan the right to establish himself at Suakin and Massawa. The whole of the eastern Sudan was in the hands of the ruler of Egypt. The temporary unification resulted in a sort of nationalism and an increase of trade (in slaves, ivory, ostrich feathers, and gum), but this was the time when the antislavery campaign reached its peak in Europe. Ismail, who needed Europe's support, was forced to accept a policy of reform. From 1869 to 1880 three European governors were named by him to the Sudan (Equatoria Province): Samuel Baker, then Gordon, then Emin Pasha (see Chapter 2). They suppressed the slave trade between Khartoum and Uganda. Economically, however, there was nothing to replace the profit, immoral and illicit but lucrative, and this spelt ruination for the country.

The revolt of the Mahdi, which began in 1881 and which was an explosion of Mohammedan fanaticism, undoubtedly gained strength by exploiting the discontent of the impoverished Sudanese chiefs. In four years, from 1881 to 1885, Mahdism conquered the whole Sudan. General Gordon, who had returned as governor-general, was killed at Khartoum in 1885. The British, in partial control of Egypt since 1882, kept only the Red Sea ports. For eleven years, until 1896, the country remained in the hands of the Dervishes or Mahdists. The commerce in slaves began again, although it was hindered by the Anglo-Egyptian occupation of the ports. This occupation was, besides, the base for a pincer movement for encircling the Dervishes. From 1885 the Berlin Conference had declared war by the whole of Europe on the slave trade.

In Uganda in 1893 a British company had given place to a government protectorate. In 1891 an Anglo-Italian treaty fixed the frontiers of Eritrea. Against the Dervishes, thus concerned, an expedition under the command of Kitchener was sent in 1896 (from Egypt). It finished in 1898 with the complete conquest of the Sudan by Anglo-Egyptian forces.

So it was that the Anglo-Egyptian Sudan, as its name implied, came under the governments jointly of Egypt and Britain. The treaty of 1898 laid down that the flags of the two countries should fly side by side; that the governor-general of the Sudan should be named by the Khedive, like the governor of Egypt, on the recommendation of the British government.

Figure 15.5   A general view of Port Sudan, showing the fine, spacious harbor.

This arrangement was, says Maurette, ". . . a sort of mandate, without the letter, and which lacked only the control of the League of Nations." The British government guaranteed also to the Egyptian government the defense of the southern frontier of Egypt and guaranteed to Egypt such volume of waters of the Nile as was necessary to the country. It was this question of the Nile water which was partly the basis of the Anglo-Egyptian Treaty of 1898 and the subsequent development of irrigation in the Sudan.

A treaty between Britain and Ethiopia in 1902 guaranteed the interests of Great Britain and Egypt as far as the waters of the Blue Nile were concerned, and the tripartite agreement between Britain, France, and Italy in 1906 extended a similar arrangement. A new agreement with Ethiopia in 1933 went into technical details in that it dealt with the construction of a dam at the exit from Lake Tana in Ethiopia, thus covering one of the points of a great plan for the control of the waters of the Nile which had been prepared after a long enquiry by the great British hydrologist, Sir William Garstin. The Garstin plan had five essential parts.

The first part of the plan was to preserve part of the waters of the White Nile for the period of drought following the flooding of the Blue Nile, and for this purpose a dam was to be constructed at Jebel Aulia, some 29 miles above Khartoum. In the second place, in order to secure this regular volume of water, a large canal was to be constructed through the Sudd Region. In the third place a dam at the exit from Lake Tana was to be constructed to maintain reserve water for the flooding of the Blue Nile and to regulate its contribution for perennial irrigation. These three parts of the plan concerned not only the Sudan but Egypt also, and the third required the agreement of Ethiopia.

The parts of the plan which concerned only the Sudan were the first to be carried out. The one outside the Nile proper was the irrigation of the deltaic plains of Gash (below Kassala) and of the Baraka around Tokar near the Red Sea. From 1929 the canals constructed resulted in the perennial irrigation and cultivation of 45,000 acres at Gash and 55,000 acres at the Baraka. The much larger scheme was the construction of a gigantic dam at Sennar across the Blue Nile for the purpose of irrigating part of the Plain of Gezira between the two Niles. The dam was finished in 1925 and the canal works by 1929, but continual expansion and development have taken place since.

Economic development of the Sudan

The economic development and present economy of the Sudan rest upon two bases. The first is the production of traditional commodities, the second is the production of cotton, which is based essentially on the modern irrigation works.

The traditional production of the country is designed primarily for human consumption and consists mainly of cereals—wheat and barley in the valley of the Nile, millet (*dura* and *dakha*) in the remainder of the Sudan. The harvest has always been adequate for the population except locally after drought. A feature of the drier northern Sudan has long been the storage of grain in specially constructed elliptical silos in the ground known as *matmuras*. Farther south grain is stored in primitive storehouses or "elevators" above ground. There are also the products of the herds of cattle, sheep, and goats.

After cotton, the most important Sudanese product for sale outside the country is still gum arabic. The Sudan is the world's chief source of this sub-

Figure 15.6 In the streets of Port Sudan. A local tribesman bringing a load of firewood on his camel. (Copyright L. Dudley Stamp.)

Figure 15.7   Bringing in cotton to a Sudan market.

stance, of which there are two kinds, obtained from two different species of small acacia tree. With the low rainfall these trees may degenerate to mere bushes. The better gum is obtained from *Acacia verek* (*A. senegal*), the inferior but more abundant from *Acacia segal* (*A. arabica*). The greatest source of material is in the heart of the country in the Province of Kordofan, but production is also active in Darfur, Blue Nile, and Kassala Provinces.

There are inexhaustible supplies of papyrus which might be collected in the Sudd Region, and with a world shortage of paper materials this is a possibility still to be explored.

Other agricultural products include sesamum and peanuts, both of which are exported in small quantities, and some of the millet also goes to Egypt for cattle and poultry feed. In the northern desert region dates are produced, and melon seeds are important and are exported. By far the most important crop cultivated for export is cotton (Figure 15.7). Some American cotton is grown as a rain crop, notably in the Nuba Hills region of Kordofan, and also in Equatoria and the Upper Nile Provinces. This is a development which took place almost entirely after World War I.

The great development, however, is that of Egyptian varieties—sakel and types which have succeeded or replaced it—on permanently irrigated land. There are three major areas of production. The older are the inland deltas of the Gash and Baraka streams already mentioned, streams which descend from the mountains of northern Ethiopia and disappear in fan-shaped silt plains. But the great area is that of the Gezira, irrigated by the Sennar Dam and its canal streams, and where the area under cotton has steadily increased to reach over 200,000 acres in the years following World War II and nearly half a million acres by 1962, thanks especially to the Manaqil extension (1958-1962). Much of the Egyptian type of cotton is also grown on state and privately owned pump schemes drawing water from the Blue and White Niles.

The development of the Gezira irrigation area is a fascinating story. It is the supreme example in Africa of a successful cooperative scheme between a European management and African cultivators settled in an orderly way on the reclaimed land. Until it was nationalized in 1950, the Gezira scheme was run on a unique system of triple partnership—between the government, the two concession companies, and the Sudanese tenant cultivators. It was in fact the largest peasant agricultural cooperative in the British Commonwealth and probably in the world, covering close to a million acres along the banks of the Blue Nile. The land is now the main cotton-producing area of the Sudan. It is irrigated by free flow from the Sennar Dam. Before the construction of this dam the Gezira, a name which applied to the doab between the White and Blue Niles, was a flat clay plain with a precarious rainfall on which cultivators grew an uncertain crop of *dura* (millet). They lived in scattered villages, usually on the higher ground, and embanked small fields in an endeavor to conserve moisture. When the irrigation scheme was decided upon, the land was surveyed and the owners' titles registered. The government then rented the land from the owners or purchased that required for permanent works, about a quarter of the whole.

The railway reached Sennar in 1910; the great Sennar Dam, built by the government but delayed by World War I, was completed in 1925. Two companies, Sudan Plantations Syndicate Limited and Kassala Cotton Company Limited, were given concessions (which expired in 1950) to carry out subsidiary works and generally to manage the land and market the crops. The third partner, the Sudanese cultivators, grew their crops under guidance as well as providing labor and sharing in profits of the whole scheme. Although cotton is the cash crop, the crops are carefully rotated to provide millet (*dura*) for food and a leguminous fodder, *lubia* (*Dolichos lablab*), for working bulls and other livestock. These food crops occupy together considerably more land than the cotton. Of all profits on the sale of cotton 40 per cent goes to the tenant cultivators, the remainder being shared by the government and the companies. From a few acres in 1912 the area under cotton approached an average of a quarter of a million acres in 1940-1950. Of the tenants about 20 per cent are also the owners of the land; 60 per cent are local peoples. Other tenants come from countries to the west, especially Moslem pilgrims to or from Mecca who have stopped to obtain work and funds and sometimes to settle.

The history of the Sudan Plantations Syndicate Limited is interesting. In 1904 the American philanthropist Leigh Hunt obtained an option over about 11,000 acres along the Nile at Zeidab, but his plan to settle American Negroes there proved a failure. An English company took over his option, and it was this company which made a new agreement with the government in 1907, changed its title slightly and took over the management of the Gezira lands. It is an example of successful private enterprise cooperating with and approved by the government, but with a minimum of government interference.

With the nationalization of the scheme and under an independent Sudan, progress has continued. The urban focus is Wad Medani, now a considerable town of 50,000 and capital of the Blue Nile Province. The controlling authority is the Sudan Gezira Board.

Transportation and communications in the Sudan

It may be said that the million square miles of the Sudan fall naturally into two zones. The first zone can be reached by modern means of communications, the second zone is a vast hinterland within which life remains primitive and resources relatively undeveloped, primarily because of difficulties of access. The transportation routes, excluding airways, are shown in Figure 15.8.

It will be noticed that the 3000 miles of railroad of the common African 3 feet, 6 inches gauge make the important irrigated tracts, including the Gezira together with Khartoum and the Nile valley settlements, accessible to the modern port of Port Sudan, which has replaced the old Arab port of Suakin, a few miles to the south on the Red Sea coast. Sudan is a country where there is still active railroad construction, notably to reach Nyala and Wau and open up the great southwest.

Over 2400 miles of river steamer routes exist, and apart from communication by air these provide the only permanent link between the northern and southern parts of the country. Stern-wheel steamers of shallow draft are principally employed. The cataracts of the Nile result in three separated stretches of navigable river. There is first the connection from the Sudanese railhead at Wadi Halfa, down the Nile to Shellal in Egypt just above the Aswan dam, where connection is made with the Egyptian railway system. Between the Third and Fourth Cataracts there is a short stretch where the Nile settlements are connected by river services and linked with the terminus of a branch railway at Karima. By far the most important navigation is that above Khartoum, from which steamers ply up the Nile itself to Juba, whence road motor services operate to the Uganda frontier and into Uganda as well as into the Congo.

The steamer routes up the Sobat into Ethiopia and up the Bahr-el-Ghazal are used in the high-water season only.

Figure 15.8   Transportation in the Sudan.

As in so many other parts of Africa, road transport has increased enormously in importance. In the Sudan tracks suitable for use except after rain are comparatively easily prepared in the steppe and savanna belts. But the Sudd remains an impenetrable barrier which must be skirted by road transport. The road from Khartoum to Juba is open only from December to March, when the early showers in the south turn the clay plain into a quagmire. When the heavier rains come in June, water covers the road; the grass is fired or cut in December. There are, however, all-weather roads in Equatoria and Bahr-el-Ghazal Provinces beyond the clay plains.

Very great use is made of air transport. From the important international airport of Khartoum, within 9 hours of London by jet, there are local services to all chief centers.

Khartoum, the capital, has of course become the focus of the Sudan. It is a modern town with broad streets laid out to a design of the British general Kitchener. From about April to December the heat is often intense for long periods, broken only by rainstorms with torrential and damaging downpours, frequently following sandstorms, in August and September. From January onward days are hot and sunny but nights are cold enough for Europeans to appreciate a warm coat, even if heating of houses is rare. Khartoum is the center of higher education, with the University of Khartoum, which has evolved from a collection of colleges to independent status; there is also a branch of Cairo University. Khartoum is expanding as an industrial town, especially in north Khartoum, across the Blue Nile and reached by a road and rail bridge, and with light industry in south Khartoum.

Facing Khartoum, on the other side of the White Nile, is Omdurman, also reached by a fine road bridge, which is one of the largest market towns in Africa. It became the capital and a center of caravan traffic during the Madhist period (1885–1896); it is now a center for truck traffic. Omdurman has over 120,000 inhabitants, and it also is changing rapidly, with much modern building.

The steady growth in importance of Port Sudan since its completion as a modern port in 1926 is reflected in the fact that it handles over 80 per cent of the foreign trade of the Sudan. To the casual visitor its coral gardens, seen through glass-bottomed boats, are perhaps the finest in the world to be visited thus easily.

BIBLIOGRAPHY

J. D. Tothill (Editor), *Agriculture in the Sudan,* New York, 1948. This is a veritable encyclopedia on the country.

K. M. Barbour, *The Republic of the Sudan, A Regional Geography,* London, 1961.

J. H. G. Lebon. Land Use mapping in Sudan, *Econ. Geog,* **35,** 1959, 60–70.

A. Gaitskell, *Gezira: A Story of Development in the Sudan,* London, 1959. See also *Focus,* January 1958.

CHAPTER SIXTEEN

Ethiopia and the Red Sea Margins[1]

A glance at the physical map of the African continent reveals the presence of a great knot of mountainous country stretching from the shores of the Red Sea to the northern borders of the East African plateau in the neighborhood of Lake Rudolph. This great knot of mountains forms a continuous barrier cutting off both the Nile basin of the Sudan and the Sahara Desert from the part of the African continent which projects eastward for some hundreds of miles into the Indian Ocean, and which is occupied by the country of the Somalis, actually divided politically into tiny French Somaliland and the Republic of Somalia, which since 1960 has replaced British Somaliland and Italian Somaliland (Figure 16.1).

Referring back to the rainfall map of Africa, we see at once that the mountain knot enjoys a heavy precipitation, whereas the whole of Somaliland to the east is a continuation of the desert lands stretching across Arabia on the other side of the Gulf of Aden and the Red Sea. The mountain knot coincides in general extent with the ancient Empire of Ethiopia. This is another part of Africa to which the much-used adjective "unique" can be applied.

The Ethiopian Empire

The whole area of Ethiopia (the people of Ethiopia dislike their country's being called Abyssinia) is one-third of a million square miles, the population is unknown, and, whereas official estimates place it at 18–20 million (1958) other calculations suggest about two-thirds of this figure, though the United Nations' is as high as 22 million. The Empire of Ethiopia has the status of a sovereign independent state, which has grown out of a combination of a number of kingdoms which used to recognize the King, or Negus, of Ethiopia as

[1] I am greatly indebted to Mr. Geoffrey Last and many other friends in Ethiopia for both hospitality and assistance in revising this chapter.

Figure 16.1   Ethiopia and the Eastern Horn.

their King of Kings. The smaller kingdoms, such as Tigré, Gojjam, Gondar, and Shoa, have become mere provinces, as have other parts which previously enjoyed at least some autonomy.

Haile Selassie I, who was born in 1891, was crowned king in 1928, proclaimed and crowned emperor in 1930.

It should first be made clear that Ethiopia is an empire and not a simple kingdom. The most important race in Ethiopia is the Amhara, who number about two million and who inhabit the Central Ethiopian Highlands. They were converted to Christianity in the early days of the Christian era and, until recently, maintained close contact with the Egyptian Coptic Christians. In fact, the Abuna, or Metropolitan Archbishop of Ethiopia, had always been an Egyptian Copt appointed and consecrated by the Coptic Patriarch of Alexandria. The church is very strong in the country, the clergy numerous, the church holding large possessions of land. It was a natural consequence of recent events that Ethiopia should seek a greater degree of independence in this as in other directions. In January 1951, an Ethiopian became archbishop of the country.

To the north of the area which forms the homeland of the Amhara are the Tigréans, closely akin and also Coptic Christians. Both these races are probably of mixed Hamitic and Semitic origin. The most numerous of the people of Ethiopia are, however, the Gallas, constituting about half the entire population. They are a pastoral people of Hamitic origin, some of whom are Christian, some Moslem, some pagan. The Empire also includes Nilotic tribes in the southwest, Falashas of Jewish origin north of Lake Tana, and numerous tribes either of Somalis or allied to the Somalis in the plateau country of the southeast of the Empire. Various Negro peoples live in the southwest, bordering the Sudan. As in East Africa, an Arab and Indian commercial element is found in the towns.

The importance of appreciating the racial complex within the Ethiopian Empire is great because of the widespread belief in America and Europe that Ethiopia is the supreme example of an African country where the people have determined their own destiny.

Between Ethiopia, which nowhere reaches the seaboard, and the southern coasts of the Red Sea lies Eritrea, which was part of the pre-1939 Italian African Empire. The people of Eritrea, who number more than 1 million, consist of Coptic Christians living on the plateau areas and Moslems, with few exceptions, on the lowlands of the western province and the Red Sea littoral. Italians settled at Assab in 1869, and Eritrea became Italy's first colony in 1889. When the time came to decide the future of the country, from which the Italians were driven by British Commonwealth forces in 1941, there was clearly opportunity for a difference of opinion as to whether Ethiopia should be allowed to extend its empire over the whole of this country, on the grounds of uniting together all the Coptic Christians, despite the alien character of the coastal Moslem population. By virtue of the decision made by the United Nations it was agreed that Eritrea should be federated with Ethiopia—that is, should enjoy partial autonomy—by 1952.

With regard to its physical setting, if Ethiopia is examined in some greater detail, it will be seen that the western half includes most of the lofty mountain area, where large tracts exceed 10,000 feet above sea level. This extensive mountainous western half is bounded by a great fault scarp overlooking the rift valley previously described. The rift valley in fact forms a great trench southeast of the capital, Addis Ababa, occupied by a succession of lakes, but northward it broadens out into the lowlands abutting Eritrea and the Red Sea; a considerable area is below sea level. To the east of the rift valley trench in the south of the country there are other lofty mountains, but the country passes thence into a plateau, eventually fading into the lower elevation of the Somaliland desert plains. The highly mountainous character of western Ethiopia is a direct result of an immense number of volcanic lava flows poured out in old fissure eruptions one above the other. They give rise to huge plateau areas, often more than 10,000 feet above sea level and with some points reaching over 13,000 feet. Hail may lie on the higher parts and look like snow, but there is doubt whether snow actually falls even on the highest parts, since precipitation is monsoonal and comes in the hot season. This mountain massif enjoys a heavy rainfall, coming at the time of the Indian monsoon. The rainy season is thus in the mountains the rainy season of India, June to October. This mountainous heart of Ethiopia is a land of abundant rainfall, of swiftly running mountain streams carving their way through deep and tortuous gorges, many of them eventually finding their way to the Blue Nile or to other Nile tributaries, the Sobat in the south, the Atbara in the north. The western rift valley edge is the main water parting of the country. Eastward the water drains toward the Somali deserts.

In the sparsely inhabited but well-watered mountain land the chief industries are pastoral and agricultural. Cattle, sheep, and goats are numerous, the horses of the country small and hardy, donkeys sturdy and well adapted as baggage animals; mules are also available as pack animals. The immense range of environmental conditions (Figure 16.2) has meant that Ethiopia is just as able to produce cotton and coffee as sugar cane and cereals like millet, wheat, and barley.

From the point of view of agricultural production the Ethiopian highlands may in fact be divided into three zones. The lowest, called *Kolla*, comprising the lower slopes of the plateau itself and the deeper valleys up to 5000 or 6000 feet, is forested with a vegetation of tropical character, for here frost is unknown. Here may be found rubber vines, ebony trees, and bananas with coffee, which grows wild in abundance in the higher parts, date palms in the drier. There could be an enormous output of coffee of the Mocha type of Arabia from this zone.

Above the Kolla is the *Woina Dega,* or wine highlands, extending up to 8000 or 9000 feet, a healthy tract with numerous trees, where such Mediterranean fruits as the orange, fig, and apricot as well as the vine will flourish, where cereals can be grown and cattle and sheep are reared in large numbers.

Above the *Woina Dega* rises the *Dega* proper, extending from about 8000 to 14,000 feet. The degas are actually equivalent to Alpine pastures of open grassland with bushes, but there such cereals as wheat and barley can be cultivated, and there is abundance of pasture for cattle and sheep.

In the arid regions gum arabic and gum tragacanth are collected, and also those aromatic substances so prized by the people of former days, frankincense and myrrh. Beeswax too is obtained, from the honeycombs of wild bees.

Figure 16.2 Climatic regions.

I	Ethiopian (monsoon)	Humid climates
II	Equatorial	Humid climates
III	Sudan	Humid climates
IV	Dry Sudan type	

V	Sahelian type (dry Sudan)	
VI	Somali type	Desert climates
VII	Eritrean winter rain	Desert climates
VIII	Saharan	Desert climates

In Ethiopia there is obviously the possibility of vast mineral wealth, of gold and silver, known to exist, of the more mundane metals such as iron, or of resources like marble, mica, rock salt, coal, sulphur, and potash. The discovery of oil on the Red Sea littoral of Egypt, and later in such enormous quantities on the Arabian coasts of the Persian Gulf, naturally suggests possibilities in unknown Ethiopia.

Ethiopia has been described as the Switzerland of Africa, a description more apt of the mountainous western half of the country than the unkind designation of its arid northeastern plains in Danakil as the "hell-hole of creation."[2] Mountain Ethiopia shares some of its features with other mountain lands—its great scenic beauty (Figure 16.3), its invigorating mountain air, and its sturdy, independent peoples organized on a feudal clan basis, the clans long accustomed to fight, raid, and pillage one another. A description of mountain Ethiopia today reads not unlike one of Highland Scotland a few centuries ago. One day it may well become a Mecca for tourists, a jewel in the great deserts protected by forbidding escarpments. Ethiopia boasts an ancient civilization. Its people, proud, intelligent, and clever, face the bewildering modern world as a young nation.

Around the great mountain heart of Ethiopia proper are wastes of rock and sand where existence in an environment of heat and drought is possible only when wells are known whose life-giving waters enable the desert nomads to keep alive their camels, donkeys, and mules or their herds of wiry goats, lop-eared sheep, and big-horned gaunt cattle. Wild and domestic animals alike live precariously on the scrub vegetation under the eyes of the ever-watchful vultures. Captain Angus Buchanan, who led a body of Abyssinians re-entering Ethiopia from the direction of Khartoum shortly after the Emperor had followed the same route on his restoration in 1941, counted 9 dead camels in a 25-minute march. His party had 400 camels, but in the defile on this route entering Ethiopia every package they carried had to be man-handled to the summit, a task which took three days.[3] He records that on reaching the top of the pass at an altitude between 6000 and 7000 feet, ". . . we could hardly realize the beauty of the wonderland before our eyes . . . we had passed abruptly from the African desert to a green-clad paradise of wooded hills and placid cultivated valleys." This country of Gojjam south of Lake Tana is well populated. There are groups of small round huts of baked clay and thatched roofs, the people owning small areas of arable land similar to Scottish crofts, plowing with wooden plows, and growing wheat, barley, and oats. In the gardens fenced with thorn bushes are numerous vegetables. Despite the climate the children who tend the sheep,

[2] L. M. Nesbitt, *Hell-Hole of Creation: The Exploration of Abyssinian Danakil,* New York, 1935.

[3] "Some Impressions of Abyssinia," *Scottish Geog. Mag.,* **LIX,** 1943, 24–27.

Figure 16.3 Ethiopia—view of the Blue Nile, flowing out of Lake Tana. (Courtesy of United Nations.)

goats, and cattle on the hillsides go naked. Much meat is eaten, raw or served highly seasoned with pepper; goats and sheep are milked, and a home-brewed beer or rough wine helps the diet. The mark of a grown man, tall, lean, and wearing a draped cotton *shama* over the shoulders, is the possession of a rifle and a well-polished cartridge belt to be worn around the waist. Though the men do the heavy work, most of the domestic chores fall as elsewhere in Africa to the voluminously clothed women. In Ethiopia, however, the women exercise considerable authority and are far from shy or unassertive. Here and there, as in Debra Markos, the former capital of Gojjam, are walled forts, and the rifles carried are not for show but demonstrate the continued existence of tribal and personal feuds. As a result, rifle fire is by no means an unusual sound even in Addis Ababa.

Addis Ababa is an attractively sited town on a plain sweeping upward to escarpments on north, west, and south. There are many steep, narrow, winding streets, and some excellent modern buildings on broad modern avenues stand side by side with shacks—of the old mud walls or rusting tin—just as finely paved streets, lined with eucalypts, fade into muddy byways. Loose sheep and horses wander about jostling with horse buggies or modern automobiles.

Recent developments

Overpopulated Italy's colony in North Africa, Libya, her colony along the Red Sea in Eritrea, and the large area of Italian Somaliland were all virtually desert. But the establishment of Italy in both Etritrea and Somalia not unnaturally brought Ethiopia into the sphere of Italian interests. At a time when the Negus of Ethiopia was consolidating his hold over the surrounding peoples from bases in Amhara, Tigré, and Shoa in the period of 1880–1900, the Italians were consolidating their position on the Red Sea coast, and the French were already in possession of Jibuti (Djibouti), which they had annexed in 1884. An Italian force, invading from the Red Sea coast, was annihilated by the Ethiopians at Aduwa in 1896. Undoubtedly the resounding defeat rankled in the minds of Italians for many years. Although the three European powers concerned, Britain, France, and Italy, reached an agreement with Ethiopia in 1906 confirming the independence of the Ethiopian ruler and acknowledging his right over the territories he had conquered in consolidating the Empire, the Italians accepted this settlement with the memory of the past defeats still in mind.

It was in 1936 that Benito Mussolini, the Italian dictator, felt himself sufficiently strong and independent of adverse European opinion to invade Ethiopia and to annex it to the Italian Empire. The Emperor fled to Britain and there lived in exile until, with the outbreak of World War II, British Imperial troops drove the Italians from Ethiopia and gave the country back to the control of Haile Selassie, who re-entered his capital, Addis Ababa, in 1941.

In the brief five years that the Italians occupied Ethiopia they carried out some remarkable work in road building and left Ethiopia with a legacy of motor roads which have since proved of great value. Previously the only other modern means of entry into the country had been the French-constructed and French-owned railway from the port of Djibouti in French Somaliland to the Ethiopian capital of Addis Ababa. This railway was constructed between 1897 and 1926 on a meter gauge, but two trains a week in each direction were sufficient to cater for the meager traffic over the 500 miles. The Italian roads, now greatly extended by the Imperial Highway Authority, are extensively used, but elsewhere mules and camels remain the principal means of transportation in extremely difficult country.

It was not until 1947 that the country was linked with the outside world by wireless telegraph. The easiest way today of reaching Addis Ababa is by the efficient Ethiopian Airways. Other outlets for Ethiopian trade are westwards to Gambela on the Sobat River, from which steamers run in the high water season to Khartoum; to Berbera mainly through the Harar district of the northeast; or to the Red Sea ports, now Ethiopia's own ports, of Massawa and Assab. It is interesting that many Italian technicians remain in Ethiopia and are helping in the modernization of the country.

Almost the only town of any size in Ethiopia is Addis Ababa, with one-third of a million people. It stands in the highland zone at 8000 feet, so that the three hottest months (before the rains break as in India) are March, April, and May, but they average only a little above 60°F. In winter nights temperatures drop to 40°F. and even below, but the average is 58°F. for the coldest month. These figures of small range compare closely with the figures for Nairobi. In contrast to the old walled cities Addis Ababa is modern. It was deliberately selected as a site for his capital by the Negus Menelik II only towards the end of the nineteenth century and has benefitted greatly from the introduction of Australian eucalypts—supplying large quantities of firewood from the surrounding hills.

Harar, the ancient walled city and center of the coffee district, is the starting point for caravans to the coast. It is a Moslem stronghold and the former commercial capital, with a large Arab and Indian population. The old city is on a plateau; a new city has grown up at a lower level on the railway.

Eritrea consists of two regions. The first is the narrow coastal plain, backed in the north by the wall-like fault scarp of the Ethiopian highlands and in the south by the uplands of Danakil. The second region, the highlands, drains westward to the Nile plain. The population is mostly nomadic, engaged in the occupations of animal rearing and the collection of gums and resins. The Italians sought to develop irrigation agriculture, especially for cotton and food grains in the coastal plain. In the highlands agriculture is possible only in a few more favorably watered parts.

Most of the trade passes through Massawa, the largest port, and Assab, and it will be interesting to see how far these ports will serve to help an increase in the foreign trade of Ethiopia now that they come within the Empire. A railway runs from Massawa to Asmara, the administrative center, and thence to Agordat. From the latter there are roads southward and to the Sudan frontier. Asmara is a progressive modern town with an international airport and is situated near the plateau edge overlooking the rift valley plains.

French Somaliland (Côte Française des Somalis)

The small French overseas territory on the Somali coast has little economic importance apart from the port of Djibouti, which replaced the original

French port of Obock, acquired in 1867, when Djibouti was chosen as the terminus for the railway to Addis Ababa. French Somaliland would seem to occupy an important strategic position at the narrow entrance to the Red Sea through the Straits of Bab-el-Mandeb. Actually in the straits there are several small islands. The chief—Perim—is British but too small to continue to serve as a naval base, a function carried out by the fortified British possession of Aden on the Arabian coast. Aden has the advantage of a magnificent natural harbor, which possible rivals have not.

Somalia

Somalia became an independent republic on July 1, 1960, when the British Somaliland Protectorate and the Italian trusteeship territory of Somalia merged. The area is about 245,000 square miles and the population, almost entirely of Somalis, about 1,870,000. The capital is Mogadiscio (Mogadistin) with a population of about 100,000. Many Somali tribesmen live in the eastern part of Ethiopia, which projects into Somalian territory and is accordingly claimed by Somalia, and there is a considerable Somali population in northern Kenya.

The former protectorate of British Somaliland, dating from 1882, consists of a narrow coastal plain only about a dozen miles wide, backed by a steep fault scarp. The highlands rise abruptly to a height between 4000 and 7000 feet, and then the surface of the plateau slopes gradually southward. The whole country is extremely arid, the population almost entirely nomadic, with a dependence upon sheep and goats and a few cattle. Some gums and resins of different kinds are collected from the bushes of the semidesert, and there is a small production of salt.

The administrative center was Hargeisa and the principal port Berbera. Berbera has long acted as an outlet for products of the Harar and the Somali plateau.

In desert and semidesert country vegetation patterns are often clearly visible from the air which are not readily visible on the ground. The commonest pattern is of course that which picks out underground water courses. Scrubby bushes which seem to have no pattern on the ground are seen from above to follow the windings of a hidden flow of water, often complete with branching tributaries. In Somaliland a curious rhythmical arrangement of vegetation in arcs has been noticed, at first sight like ripple marking on sand, but on a huge scale—apparently due to delayed runoff in slight hollows. In the same country are relatively straight water lanes simulating a gigantic plowed field. The study of these patterns has been found useful in locating water supplies.[4]

[4] W. A. Macfayden, "Vegetation Patterns in the Semi-desert Plain of British Somaliland," *Geog. Jour.*, CXVI, 1950, 199–211.

The former Italian Somaliland, later the trusteeship territory of Somaliland, consists essentially of a plateau 2000 to 3000 feet above sea level, sloping gradually eastward and presenting a series of steep scarp faces toward the coastal plain and Indian Ocean. Much is absolute desert, but from Mogadiscio (Mogadishu), a roadstead port, formerly part of the domains of the Sultan of Zanzibar, a fair road runs inland to a cultivated belt along the Webi or River Shebeli. The Juba River is navigable, and at its mouth is Kismayu.

The pastoral people of the country gain a little financial return from the collection of gums and the sale of hides of their cattle. A little cotton and sesamum oil are produced by the agriculturalists in the oasis settlements.

Italy's first concession dates from 1889, largely extended in 1901, and later by treaty with local chiefs. The Italians, who invaded British Somaliland on the outbreak of World War II in 1940, were driven out the following year, and the British took Italian Somaliland. After nine years of British administration Italy was allowed to resume control, on a trusteeship, on April 1, 1950, with the express objective of preparing the country for independence after ten years.

Socotra

Some idea of the difficulty of economic use of the arid east of Africa is illustrated from the island of Socotra, or Sokotra, lying 150 miles east of Cape Guardafui. It is a British Protectorate and has a population of perhaps 12,000 nomadic or seminomadic pastoralists. Though the flat-topped island is a familiar sight to the many thousands who travel by ship to India every year, the island cannot be reached by any regular steamship, nor is it even served by air.

BIBLIOGRAPHY

See *Focus*, June 1955 (Ethiopia) and April 1956 (Somalia). For Socotra see D. Botting, *Island of the Dragon's Blood*, London, 1958.

CHAPTER SEVENTEEN

Equatorial Africa

Equatorial Africa coincides in general with the great basin of the Congo, together with a region between the Congo mouth and Cameroon Mountain drained directly to the Atlantic Ocean. Politically it thus includes for all practical purposes the whole of the great state which until June 30, 1960, was the Belgian Congo and the very large section of former French Equatorial Africa draining southward or westward. French Equatorial Africa as a whole covered an area of well over a million square miles, but we must exclude from this the 400,000 square miles which lie in the inland Lake Chad basin and belong properly to the Sudan, and which now constitute the Chad Republic, sharing many features with neighboring parts of Nigeria. The parts of former French Equatorial Africa with which we are concerned are thus the coastal regions, Gabon and the Cameroun Republic, the whole of the Congo Republic, and a large southern part of the Central African Republic.

Through the heart of the great area runs the line of the equator, but equatorial Africa in the sense generally understood does not stretch right across the continent, since to the east lie the high plateaus occupied by Tanganyika, Kenya, and Uganda, with a very markedly contrasted character. The Congo Basin is essentially an enormously broad flat basin in the great African plateau. Although there are considerable differences from one part to another over such a huge area, there are many features common to the whole drainage area of 1,600,000 square miles.

The heart of the area enjoys an equatorial climate with no dry season, and this extends to the coast of southern Cameroun. The so-called rainfall equator lies about 3 degrees north of the true equator, and along this line rainfall is well distributed throughout the year; the total reaches 60 to 80 inches. The range of temperature between day and night does not commonly exceed 10 or 15 degrees, and the difference between the mean of the hottest and coldest months is not more than 3 to 5 degrees. This is the region of the hot wet forests so closely associated with true equatorial regions.

To the north one passes into a subequatorial region of northern type, with rainfall maxima in June and September, and an appreciable dry period in December and January. Southward from the rainfall equator the southern type appears, with rainfall maxima in March and November, and a distinct or relative drought in June, July, August, and September.

Where the southern margins of the basin are reached in the Katanga, the daily temperature range has become considerable (15 to 20 degrees), and the annual as much as 15 degrees. The rainfall regime has become that of the southern tropical areas, with a rainy season from November to April.

There are fascinating local differences. Where the heights of the Cameroon mountains are reached there is a rapid rise in rainfall so that stations on a slope of the mountain itself show an average fall of 400 inches a year. Circumstances closely associated with the upwelling of cold water and offshore winds bring the arid coastal belt of South West Africa and Angola almost to equatorial latitudes in the neighborhood of the Congo mouth, where the fall is only 30 inches per year.

Equatorial forests of the evergreen type naturally occupy the heart of the basin, but give place as the land rises to a high savanna type of forest where trees lose their leaves in the dry season, though evergreen forests stretch as long tongues up the river valleys. Drier types of forest succeed towards the margins of the basin and pass naturally into the African savannas.

Along the coasts there are extensive mangrove swamps, especially north of Cape Lopez. It should be noted that the true equatorial forest is of much more limited extent than was supposed in the early days of the African explorers, who rather naturally penetrated by rivers and were unaware of the relatively open character of the ground between the main streams. How far the large areas of savanna are natural and how far they owe their existence to the long-continued system of rotation cultivation practiced by the widespread though not very numerous African peoples belonging to various primitive tribes is an open question. What strikes one in flying over the more populated parts of the Congo basin is the amount of forest which has been destroyed and the numerous areas either under cultivation or recently deserted. It is doubtful how much of the high forest is original; even in the depths of the forest evidences of former human settlements are frequent. Unfortunately when the land is cleared of forest the soil is very rapidly leached by the heavy rainfall and recovery takes a long time.

In the early days of European penetration equatorial Africa was chiefly of interest as a source of slaves. Later under white influence the tapping of native trees and the collection of palm oil from the wild oil palms attained large proportions, and so too did the trade in ivory, one of the few commodities whose value enabled it to stand the high cost of transport by human porters from the heart of the forest to the rivers, or the coast. Overtapping or ruthless destruction of the rubber-bearing trees killed that trade. It became more profitable to grow oil palms in accessible plantations. Some of the more accessible parts of equatorial Africa have come to make an appreciable contribution to world commerce, with plantation rubber, plantation palm oil, cocoa, and coffee. Though valuable timbers, mostly heavy wood of the mahogany type, have been worked, the great variety of trees in the equatorial forests makes the working of any one type difficult.

It is true to say that today vast areas of equatorial Africa still remain almost completely untouched by European contacts.

Three main ethnic groups are to be found in equatorial Africa. There are the pygmy tribes, who still live a semi-nomadic existence in the western part of the equatorial belt. They do not mix, though they are in friendly relationship with their Bantu neighbors. Some of the tribes have achieved a special notoriety in school textbooks in the English language from their habit of building temporary shelters among the branches of trees, away from the danger of floods and certain wild animals. Some of them do still depend to a considerable extent on animals which they can kill for food, or on fruits and roots which they gather, but the majority practice some form of agriculture.

In the north of the region are people of Negro-Hamitic stock, forming a distinctive group of agriculturalists. They are people who were formerly cannibals. Over the remainder of equatorial Africa the people are Bantus. They live for the most part in straggling villages, often of great size. These Bantu peoples for some centuries before European penetration had established and organized extensive empires. Indeed, the Congo derives its name from the Congo Empire, which covered much of this area in the fifteenth century when the first Portuguese discoveries were made.

The whole of equatorial Africa has good reason to remember its contacts with white civilization with very mixed feelings. It has been estimated that from the French area alone some 12 million slaves must have been obtained in the course of 300 years, and the number exported from farther south by the Portuguese was probably greatly in excess of this number.

It was Stanley who said that the Congo, without railroads, is not worth a penny. It is still true that any form of development depends upon the provision of access by river, supplemented by rail, latterly by road and, for specialized purposes, by air.

Flowing as it does through the heart of equatorial Africa, the great Congo is a more constant stream than the Nile or the Zambezi (Figure 17.1). The tributaries from the south, such as the Kasai, have two periods of low water and two of high in the year, but the tributaries from the north such as the Ubangi have a single maximum. Consequently the regime on the main river varies from place to place; at Stanley Pool the river is at its lowest in July

Figure 17.1   General physical map of the Congo basin.

and August. The emphasis, however, should be on the relative constancy of the flow. Below Stanley Falls the river is unimpeded by rapids for a thousand miles to Stanley Pool. The central navigable channel is never less than 10 feet deep, though the river with its shallows and islands is often 8 or 10 miles wide. It should be realized that the Congo, with its enormous basin and huge volume, is probably the largest undeveloped source of hydroelectric power in the whole world. One must remember too that the river in about 220 miles descends nearly 900 feet in a series of thirty-two rapids, known collectively as the Livingstone Falls, from Leopoldville to Matadi. What a dream for a water engineer!

The Congo Republic (République du Congo), formerly the Belgian Congo

The Congo Republic, capital Léopoldville, to be distinguished from the Congo Republic, capital Brazzaville, is estimated to cover 902,082 square miles (Figure 17.2). This vast area is nearly eighty times the size of Belgium (11,775 square miles), formerly the mother country of the colony.

The Congo Independent State was set up in 1885 by Leopold II, King of

Figure 17.2 Countries at the mouth of the Congo.

the Belgians, and for more than 30 years was virtually the personal property of the king. It was only in 1907 that it was annexed by Belgium. The boundaries were defined by declarations dating from 1885 and by successive treaties with the powers interested in neighboring lands. An interesting adjustment took place as late as 1927 when Portugal exchanged 3 square kilometers—a little over a square mile—near Matadi in the Congo estuary for 3500 square kilometers in the extreme southwest.

Although the eventual independence of the Belgian Congo had been envisaged and it would have been difficult for Belgium to maintain a colonial status for the region when adjoining territories of French Equatorial Africa had already become independent, the declaration of independence on June 30, 1960 was premature. The departure of the Belgian administrators, teachers, and doctors on the day of independence left no effective organization behind, and neither of the two rival African leaders, Kassavubu and Lumumba, succeeded in establishing his authority. Personal, tribal, and regional rivalries flared up; the rich Katanga province broke away, and Lumumba called upon both the United Nations and the U.S.S.R. for intervention and help. The Secretary General of the United Nations sent out a military force of 20,000 (mainly African and Asian troops) but was himself tragically killed in an air disaster while visiting the area; Lumumba was murdered by tribesmen. There have been mutinies, massacres by rival groups, massacres of European missionaries, and a precarious semblance of law and order in a few centers maintained by United Nations troops. The present is obscure, the future uncertain; the description which follows must be read as applying mainly to the period of the Belgian regime.

Though the Congo Republic lies almost entirely within the Congo basin, it is much less extensive than the basin. Only over a few stretches does the political frontier coincide with the water parting. The whole vast area has but a tiny though immensely important coastline on the Atlantic—the deltaic lands of the river north of the main stream, hemmed in between Portuguese territory to south (Angola) and north (Cabinda, which is administered as part of Angola).

For some 1500 miles the main river, and then its great tributary the Ubangi (Oubangui), and then the Bomu (which flows into the Ubangi) form the boundary with former French Equatorial Africa, now the Republics of Gabon, Congo, and Central Africa. In the extreme northeast the water parting between the Congo basin and the Bahr-el-Ghazal basin of the Nile is the frontier with the Republic of the Sudan, and in the extreme south the water parting with the Zambezi is in part the frontier with Northern Rhodesia. In the east the Congo stretches to Lake Tanganyika.

In general terms the Congo basin is a shallow depression on the surface of the great African plateau; most of the heart of the republic is less than 1600 feet above sea level. The geological structure is essentially simple (Figure 17.3). The basin is geologically very ancient. Recent alluvium borders the main river and stretches around Lake Leopold II; older alluvium—once the bed of a great lake—occupies the lower core of the basin. These give place on the higher ground to vast stretches of soft sandstone known as the Loubilache (Lubilash) Beds. Older than these are the famous Koundeloungou (Kundelungu) Beds, more localized in distribution. These are the oldest sedimentary rocks found resting on the ancient crystalline massif. They are probably Permian-Triassic in age and have been folded, not very severely, by the movements responsible for the folded mountains of the Cape in the extreme southwest of Africa. These beds include limestone, shales, and sandstones, but the adjective "famous" refers particularly to the basement beds with great boulders scratched by ice. It would seem that at this period the whole of the heart of Africa was covered by great ice sheets, and it is held by many geologists that either the North or the South Pole of the earth was then over the heart of Africa.

Apart from the actual or potential value of the younger rocks as providing the material for agricultural soils, economic interest centers on the ancient crystalline rocks and mineralized ancient sediments. In the Katanga district in the extreme south on the Congo-Zambezi divide is one of the richest mineral-bearing tracts in the world.

For long the population of the Belgian Congo was a matter for surmise, but according to the census of December 31, 1951, the African population numbered 11,593,494 and the white population 69,204, of whom 75 per cent were Belgian. The United Nations *Demographic Yearbook* gave a tentative

Figure 17.3   Outline geological map of the Congo basin.

estimate of 14,150,000 for mid-1960. Thus the overall population density is only about 15 per square mile, in actuality very irregularly distributed. There are some pygmies in the forests and Nilotics in the northeast, but the bulk of the Africans are Bantu with some Sudanese. Most are fetishists; some 4000 missionaries (80 per cent Catholics) before the present chaos were scattered through the country. On the basis of the 1941 census, Pierre Gourou prepared a detailed population-density map, published in color as one of the sheets of the *Atlas général du Congo* by the *Institut colonial belge* on the scale of 1:5,000,000. He used the 1047 administrative divisions known as *circonscriptions indigènes,* and apart from groups of forest pygmies who may have escaped enumeration the map may be accepted as an accurate representation of the facts. It shows some very remarkable contrasts in population density. Some 10 per cent of the whole Congo is truthfully a "forest desert" with fewer than 0.3 person per square kilometer—less than 1 person per square mile—and three-quarters of the whole Congo has less than 12 to 13 persons per square mile. By way of contrast most of Rwanda and Burundi have a density exceeding 125, and in the Congo itself Gourou finds an east-west belt roughly 5 degrees south of the equator, including Kikwit and Luluabourg, of relatively dense population, and a less pronounced one north of the equator. Surprisingly, Elisabethville is an "island" of population in a sparsely inhabited area. The heavy population of Rwanda and Burundi is in line with that of neighboring Uganda and is closely related to elevation. The highlands are healthy because of the deleterious effect of height on the mosquitoes and flies which carry malaria and sleeping sickness. Local factors which influence the number and variety of these disease carriers are responsible, Gourou believes, for local population growth, and he instances the good health record of Coquilhatville right on the equator with the poorer record of Elisabethville, nearly 12 degrees south. Gourou believes the freedom of Coquilhatville from malaria is connected with the character of local waters which, draining from laterized surfaces, have a high content of aluminum hydroxide in solution. He believes that the well-populated belt south of the equator coincides with a belt where the forest, though of equatorial type, is sufficiently dry in some years to be burnt but where the fires do not become so intense as to damage the soil. Gourou's map affords an interesting example of a factual survey used as a starting point for an analysis of the influence of geographical factors.

The Congo was divided by the Belgians for purposes of administration into six provinces, each of which included several districts. The provinces and the chief towns are Katanga (Elisabethville), Léopoldville (Léopoldville), Equator (Coquilhatville), Eastern (Stanleyville), Kivu (Bukavu) and Kasaï (Luluabourg). The capital was changed in 1927 from Boma to Léopoldville. Boma and Banana are now of little importance, but Léopoldville, with its adjoining river port of Kinshasa, has become a great modern city (Figure 17.4). The same is true of Matadi, the chief ocean port, with its extension known as Fuca Fuca and the associated oil port of Ango Ango, from which a pipeline takes fuel to Léopoldville for Congo river steamers (see Figure 17.5).

The modern history of the Belgian Congo falls into several marked stages. When Stanley in 1877 came from the east and solved the problem of the Congo itself, the whole territory had long been in the hands of scattered tribes, sometimes grouped into ephemeral and ill-defined Negro empires. It had been a reservoir of slaves going latterly eastward by Arab slave traders to the Indian Ocean, previously to the west and so eventually to America. Stanley found, in Europe, one man able to understand the importance of his discoveries: Leopold II of Belgium. He thought out a comprehensive scheme of transport development to open up the whole basin, first

Figure 17.4   Air View of Léopoldville, capital of the Congo. A good example of an imaginative layout of a modern city in the heart of equatorial Africa. The River Congo is seen in the background. (Wide World Photos.)

a portage railroad from Léopoldville to Matadi on the estuary, second a combined rail-river route to the Katanga, which he secured, and third a direct rail to the Atlantic. All of these were eventually constructed. It was Leopold who had established in 1876 at the Brussels meeting of the International Geographical Union a Commission for the Exploration of Central Africa. After several expeditions Leopold established the *Association internationale du Congo*. This Association, under the active presidency of Leopold, rapidly followed political and economic rather than scientific aims, and, despite French and Portuguese objections, was "recognized" by the United States and Germany in 1884. Leopold granted numerous concessions to companies and, although the slave trade had ceased, there followed a period of exploitation in the companies' efforts to obtain, in particular, ivory and wild rubber. Gradually stories of harsh treatment of Africans came out, but the stories were found to be exaggerated for political reasons.

In 1900 four-fifths by value of all the exports from Leopold's domain were represented by wild rubber from vines such as *Funtumia elastica*. But Leopold, being a farsighted as well as an ambitious man, had secured control over a part of the plateau to the extreme southeast of the Congo basin known as the Katanga (Figure 17.6). This he secured in 1892 at a time when local chiefs were considering asking Britain for protection. The mining period may be said to date from 1906, when the Katanga copper deposits began to be exploited, though there was but a small output until after 1911. Africa, had, of course, shared with other continents the stories of fabulous wealth in minerals, but although copper, tin, iron, and even gold were brought out of the interior, the stories of the trackless forest and its perils had prevented anything approaching a "gold rush." The discovery of substantial copper deposits in the Katanga may be credited to the Belgian geologist Jules Cornet, who explored the area in 1890 to 1892. When I had the honor of studying geology under Cornet at Mons in 1919 he must have been the last of the great tradition of geologists who worked in the field in striped trousers and a tail coat and carried a black umbrella!

Vast concessions were granted by Leopold to land mining companies, notably to the *Compagnie du Katanga* (1891) and its later subsidiary the *Comité spécial du Katanga,* and these had to be recognized when the territory became a Belgian colony in 1908. Since that time the Katanga has become the focus of European activity in the Congo. Most of the mining activity is

Figure 17.5   Communications in the Congo basin.

Figure 17.6   The position of the Katanga. Railways and river routes (dotted).

in the hands of the great combine formed in 1906 (involving Belgian and British interests), known as the *Union minière du Haut Katanga.*

At first production was restricted mainly to the vicinity of Elisabethville, especially from the famous mine known as the Star of the Congo (Étoile du Congo), but later the center shifted a hundred miles north-northwest to Kambove. Rail access was first provided in 1910 from Northern Rhodesia, through which comes the coal from Wankie in Southern Rhodesia, but the completion in 1931 of the Benguela railway across Angola from Lobito Bay provided a convenient "side door" much nearer Europe. Three developments of great importance took place. One was the establishment of smelting works at Elisabethville and Jadotville so that nearly all the export is in the form of crude copper. Then, from 1925 onward, came the increasing use of coal from two fields within the Belgian Congo instead of from Wankie. The third is the growing development of hydroelectric power (Figure 17.7), first from the Cornet Falls on the upper Lufira River. In consequence of all these developments the southern Katanga has become the largest white settlement in tropical Africa apart from the Kenya highlands, and the industries are dependent on immigrant African labor drawn from many parts of the Congo as well as from Angola, Portuguese East Africa, and even farther afield.

Apart from the great copper deposits the Katanga also yields tin and zinc, as well as the greatest output of cobalt of any region in the world, and for some time, almost all the world's output of radium. Later Shinkokobwe became the world's largest production center of uranium ores for a number of crucial years.

There are other mining areas in the Congo, especially the Kilo-Moto region in the highlands northwest of Lake Albert which yields gold and the Kasai region which yields alluvial diamonds. Tin is found in northern Rwanda.

A very interesting account of the Belgian Congo as it appeared in 1948

Figure 17.7 Potential water power in the Katanga. The waters of the southern Kalulo River plunge over a wall of horizontal schists over 260 feet high. Away from the mining centers there are few people in the Katanga, and only some of the many rivers have been harnessed to provide power for the mining operations.

has been given by Professor R. L. Pendleton, whose wide experience in many parts of the tropics in southeast Asia and America gave him a natural standard of comparison.[1]

Like other recent travelers he stressed the amazing contrasts. He suggested that development in Central Africa has been by jumps rather than by slow stages; that Africans, who never used a wheel in their native culture, rapidly and unaided learned to operate railroads and river steamers and to drive automobiles and trucks; that they had no draft animals and no plows and yet soon learned to run tractors, though many of them—perhaps wisely—consider the hoe a better implement.

Not far from the huge reduction works for the mines in the Katanga are to be found primitive charcoal furnaces for the smelting of iron and copper blown by means of skins tied over wooden funnels. Pendleton drew attention to the rapidity with which the forests, by being burnt, are giving place to savanna, and where the soil, thus exposed, deteriorates almost at once. There has been the need for extended production of foodstuffs, particularly manioc, upland rice, corn (maize), and beans, for feeding the new urban and mining population. The Europeans seem still unable to appreciate that north temperate methods of soil management and crop production cannot be applied in the new environments in which they find themselves.

Pendleton called attention to the not altogether happy changes taking place among the African peoples. Formerly villages were essentially communal minded, sharing what they had; the men cleared the land and did the hunting, the women planted, tended, and harvested the crops and prepared the food. Where a husband prospered he usually bought a second wife so as to have more labor for more food production. Where a young man in a community learned by some Western contact to be a better farmer, his relatives would immediately expect to share his better crops rather than copy his methods for themselves. Europeanization had resulted in the growth of individualism, the young Africans adopting European customs such as style of haircut and wearing some Western clothing. They became virtually detribalized, but with no adequate substitute for the old established order.

The Belgian administrators were fully alive to the difficulties of the position. They sought to study and understand tribal and family organization and to graft a knowledge of better agricultural methods with higher yielding and better quality crops on the traditional crop rotation. As Pendleton said, the Belgians and their associates deserve great credit.

Despite the developments in the Congo as a whole the Katanga forms a region perhaps without parallel in the world. In the heart of this busy mining area stands Elisabethville, the capital, with its magnificent skyscraper

[1]"The Belgian Congo—Impressions of a Changing Region," *Geog. Rev.,* **XXXIX**, 1949, 371-400.

blocks of offices which would be a credit to cities anywhere in the world. The layout of the modern towns is on comparable lines. Much has been written of the importance of access in Africa, and the story of the opening up of the Katanga is well known. It is now reached by the Congo routes, where road and rail have shortened former long tedious journeys. It is reached by rail from the ports of Benguela or Lobito. It is reached by the South African railway systems through the Rhodesias; and the later link by railway to Lake Tanganyika renders it accessible from that lake and hence from Dar-es-Salaam on the Indian Ocean.

It will be clear that the development of the Katanga had placed it in a very different position from the other provinces of the Katanga. It is certainly not surprising that, in the midst of chaos elsewhere, Katanga should seek to break away and establish its independence. It will be clear from the account of its mineral resources given above that the Katanga has the resources to stand alone, but without the revenue from this vital province the Congo as a whole is precariously placed.

It seems strange to think of any area of the heart of Africa as one to be used as a holiday or health resort by whites. Yet the high country, largely open grassland, around Lake Kivu and especially the remarkable modern settlement of Bukavu (Costermansville) are examples of what opportunities there are for attracting visitors even in the very heart of Africa. Ease of access by air to places like Bukavu has placed equatorial Africa within a days' journey of the cities of Europe and made such a center convenient for conferences. The present means of communication in the Congo are clearly shown in Figure 17.5 and do not require description here.

Rwanda and Burundi, formerly Ruanda-Urundi[2]

At the end of World War I Belgium, as one of the Allies, received under mandate from the League of Nations the territory of Ruanda-Urundi, a tract of some 20,900 square miles lying east of the main western rift valley, that is, east of Lake Kivu and the northern end of Lake Tanganyika. Formerly part of German East Africa, it belongs geographically to East Africa but formed administratively an integral part of the Belgian Congo after 1925— adjoining the progressive province of Kivu. It thus lies on the high plateau and adjoins southwestern Uganda on the north, forming in fact a continuation of that island of dense population in the heart of Africa. The census of 1959 showed 4,847,931 Africans belonging to three tribes, 8127 Europeans and 2869 Asiatics. The cattle-raising and agricultural Africans were organized as fully as their neighbors in Uganda and planted only enough for the season, so that there is, or was, the usual "hungry" season before the harvest. The

[2] See *Focus,* February 1963.

bean is the great food staple with peas and corn, but crop failure is an ever-present danger owing to the vagaries of the climate. The introduction by the Belgians of manioc and sweet potatoes, less dependent on the weather, did not prove immediately popular owing to the longer period taken to reach maturity.

Climatically there are five regions. First there are two long narrow belts running north and south parallel to Lake Tanganyika. This is in the tropical lowland of the rift, with about 35 inches of rain. Here is situated Usumbura, on the shores of Lake Tanganyika, now the capital of the independent Kingdom of Burundi. High-forested mountains with heavy rainfall (and a double maximum) follow to the east and form the Congo-Nile watershed. The Central Plateau with about 50 inches occupies most of the heart of the two countries, and here, in the north, is Kigali, capital of the Republic of Rwanda. Farther east is the warm, dry eastern depression. Finally the volcanic district of the northwest forms a distinct area of Rwanda (Figure 17.8).

Figure 17.8   Among the hills of central Rwanda. (Courtesy of the United Nations.)

The two countries, each a little over 10,000 square miles, became independent on July 1, 1962. Each has well over 2 million people, so the average density is about 240 per square mile. Though much of the land is fertile, soil erosion is serious, and the pressure on the land is such as to cause migration, especially to the Congo, either temporarily for work or permanently.

Former French Equatorial Africa

Afrique equatoriale française (or A.E.F.) was perhaps the least homogeneous of all the political divisions of Africa, stretching as it did from the Saharan margin around Lake Chad to the Congo River and Atlantic margins, actually as much as 5 degrees *south* of the equator. What has been said about equatorial Africa in general applies thus to the southern half only of this huge tract. Despite its vast area the whole is without the proved mineral resources of the Congo and so remains for the most part much as it has been for centuries past. French settlements on the Gabun or Gabon River date from 1839, and Libreville on the Atlantic coast was founded in 1848, as its name implies, for liberated slaves. From these settlements as bases the sphere of French influence was steadily expanded and limits defined by a series of treaties. The boundary between French Equatorial Africa and the Anglo-Egyptian Sudan was not fixed until February 1924, and the later organization into the four territories of Gabon, Middle Congo, Ubangi-Shari, and Chad dated only from 1946. With the advent to power of de Gaulle in 1958 the territories were offered the same choice as other French territories in Africa. All elected to remain associated with the French Community and, before the end of 1960, had become the four independent republics of Gabon, Congo, Central Africa, and Chad. This Congo Republic, capital Brazzaville, must not be confused with the other Congo Republic, capital Léopoldville, formerly Belgian Congo.

Gabon[3] is the smallest, most sparsely populated, but wealthiest state of the three. Its capital, Libreville, is at the same time a port, and along the long Atlantic coastline there is also Port Gentil. Although shifting cultivation, practiced by half the country's estimated 420,000 people, is the mainstay, forestry is basic to the economy. Mineral oil, first obtained in 1956 near Port Gentil, is now significant.

The Congo[4] (République du Congo), formerly the Moyen Congo, reaches the Atlantic coast. From the port of Pointe Noire a railway runs inland to the capital, Brazzaville (99,000 in 1959), which is situated on the Congo river opposite Léopoldville. The population of this largely forested state was 795,000 in 1959, giving a density of about 10 per square mile.

[3] G.P. Patten, Gabon, *Focus,* Amer. Geog Soc., October 1961.
[4] G.P. Patten, Republic of the Congo (Brazzaville), *Focus,* October 1962.

The *Central African Republic* (République Centrafricaine) is a huge tract of forest and savanna country with only 1,193,000 people in 1960 and an average density of only 6 per square mile. Indeed, much is uninhabited forest, though two-thirds of the small export trade is timber. A resource of great significance is water power. In 1959 a small oilfield near the Atlantic came into production. The capital is Bangui (78,400).

Sparse populations and huge distances render the development of these three republics very difficult. Although roads now reach the cotton-growing lands of Chad in the far north, clearly haulage costs must remain very high. Port Gentil and Libreville serve more directly as the outlets of Gabon since this, the original French colony, is largely the basin of the Ogowe (Ogooué) River and oriented towards the Atlantic.

The total population of the three republics shows an overall density of about 6 per square mile. There are huge areas virtually uninhabited. There is thus no reservoir of labor to support a plantation system such as might naturally follow the system of granting concessions to land companies, which the French started at the end of the last century. Similarly, railroad construction, road building, and other public works start with the same handicap.

Cameroun (République Fédéral du Cameroun) formerly Trusteeship Territory of the French Cameroons

As briefly noted in Chapter 2, the Germans secured a hold on the Cameroons coast in 1884. British traders and missionaries had already established settlements in the country near the present Victoria and Debundja (Figure 17.9) within sight of the great Cameroon Mountain, but Britain had declined the request of the Duala chiefs to extend a protectorate over their lands.

The Germans were quick to appreciate the value of the highland zone, and in 1901 moved their administrative headquarters from Duala to Buea (now the capital of West Cameroun) on the southeastern slopes of the mountains. On the healthy heights above the equatorial rainforest they looked to establish European settlements. In particular they set to work to study scientifically the problems of tropical agriculture and established a fine botanic garden at Victoria. Their buildings were constructed with double roofs for purposes of insulation and were built to last. At first the wealth of the country came from palm oil and rubber gathered from the forest, but they introduced plantation agriculture, notably of bananas, which were sent in large quantities from Victoria to Hamburg before World War I. The Germans pushed their territorial claims inland to Lake Chad, passing thus (like neighboring Nigeria) out of the forest through the savanna zone to the Saharan margins. They adopted over the people of the grasslands a form of indirect rule, recognizing the integrity of tribal groups.

Figure 17.9   Contrasts in Debundja, Cameroun Republic. This view shows a modern hotel, an African store, an American automobile, a British bicycle, and Africans in various stages of European dress. (Copyright R. J. Harrison-Church.)

In 1911 the French were forced to cede to Germany 100,000 square miles, giving German Kamerun direct access to the Ubangi and to the Congo, thus cutting the French equatorial empire in half. Almost as bad was the inclusion of a strip of land reaching the Atlantic only a few miles north of Libreville. This was the price of Germany's noninterference with French plans in Morocco.

Early in World War I British and French forces took the Cameroons; the French reincorporated the territory they had been forced to yield three years earlier and the remainder was divided—166,000 square miles going to France and 30,000 to Britain, including Victoria and Buea. This was recognized by the League of Nations under the mandate system, and later trusteeships under the United Nations.

To a considerable extent the French built on the economic foundations laid by the Germans. The port of Duala was progressively improved (formerly ocean vessels anchored 25 miles away); a railway was constructed to Yaunde (Yaoundè), on the plateau, which is now the federal capital and the focus of an important road system. One road goes through to Fort Lamy, the capital of the Chad Republic, crossing the upper Benue at a point from which it is navigable through Nigeria. Though the European-owned plantations advanced but little, the plantations for coffee, oil palm, and cocoa which the Germans encouraged African chiefs to establish have now a considerable output. The total population of the whole vast tract is only 3 million, and it is difficult to develop plantations without an element of compulsory labor. An important development is the aluminum smelter—largest in Africa—at Edéah.

The country became an independent republic in January 1, 1960 and in 1961 the people of the British trusteeship territory of the Southern Cameroons with the valuable port of Victoria on the Nigerian border elected to join the Cameroun Republic rather than the Nigerian Federation. On October 1, 1961, the country accordingly became the République Fédérale du Cameroun —consisting of East (former French) and West (former British) Cameroun.

Spanish Guinea

This is a small and undeveloped territory covering rather less than 11,000 square miles and with a total population of less than 220,000. These figures include the island of Fernando Po, of 778 square miles and about 40,000 people, with the town of Santa Isabel, where the governor resides. The islands of Annobón (7 square miles), Corisco (5½ square miles), Great and Little Elobey (less than a square mile) are also included in Spanish Guinea, so that the continental area, otherwise known as Río Muni from the chief settlement, has a density of only nine or ten persons per square mile.

Spanish Guinea is the sole tropical remnant of the once vast Spanish Empire. But to believe that Spain now neglects this remnant would be to harbor a very false idea. The mainland, it is true, of 10,163 square miles is, like the neighboring territory, but little developed. There are, however, large and important timber, oil palm, and coffee concessions and the Africans— besides growing their usual foodstuffs—also grow coffee and cocoa for export.

Tiny Annobón has some 1400 people and is heavily overpopulated; many seek work in fishing off Fernando Po.

Fernando Po (Fernando Póo to the Spaniards) is unique in West Africa. The volcanic line of the Cameroon mountains extends southwestward. Fernando Po is thus a collection of extinct volcanoes rising from ocean depths to heights of 6000 feet above sea level. The fine harbor of Santa Isabel is part of an old crater invaded by the sea; elsewhere on the island are volcanic peaks rising from the ash and lava plains and fascinating crater lakes. The heart is forested or grassed, with some Dutch and Swiss cattle on the grasslands. On the west, north, and east fringes of the island, up to about 2000 feet, are extensive plantations. Fine-quality cocoa is by far the most important crop and, with coffee, accounts for four-fifths of the cultivated area, the rest being occupied by African foodstuffs. Export crops are produced on plantations, some extending to about 2000 acres; these are owned and managed by Spanish settlers and companies. Europeans number between 3000 and 4000. These European plantations are but one of the contrasts with all other parts of West Africa.

Santa Isabel is essentially a Spanish town set in the tropics—fully as European as Dakar or Abidjan—in which Africans happen to live. It houses a quarter of the people of the island; its fine Spanish-type houses and public buildings suggest both prosperity and a lively interest in the island's welfare. There are excellent macadam roads, and there is even a pleasant hill station (Moka) with chalets, where conferences can be held, at 4500 feet.

The Spaniards were excluded from Africa by the Treaty of Tordesillas of 1494, and it was not till 1778 that Portugal ceded these territories and not till 1845 that Spanish occupation was really effective. The indigenous Bantu people, numbering 10,000, form an inadequate labor supply for the plantations, so that there are twice as many immigrants, especially Ibos from Nigeria. As usual in such cases, men outnumber women by three to one.

São Tomé and Príncipe

These Portuguese islands lie between Annobón and Fernando Po and form part of the same line of volcanic peaks. They constitute a province under a governor. With an area of 372 square miles, they have over 60,000 people, including a thousand Europeans and three thousand of mixed blood. São Tomè in particular is prosperous and well developed, with roads and numerous well-equipped plantations. Exports include cocoa, coffee, copra, palm oil, and cinchona. Here again, with favorable physical conditions, is proof that the Portuguese are not backward in fostering the economic development of their colonies. The soil is extremely fertile. Settlement and development on a permanent basis by the Portuguese date from 1493. The earlier prosperity was based on sugar. Labor shortage, as in Fernando Po, led to the introduction of contract labor from Angola and elsewhere, now forming the bulk of the population.

There are interesting historical survivals in many parts of Africa. A good example was the fortress of São João Batiste of Ajuda on the coast of Dahomey, claimed by Portugal and forming part of the province of São Tomé and Príncipe, until it was seized by Dahomey in August, 1961.

CHAPTER EIGHTEEN

East Africa

The physical background

Each of the great regions into which the continent of Africa naturally falls has certain points of distinctive individuality. Over so much of the continent the point of individuality is the river basin—the basin of the Nile and the basin of the Congo and to a less extent the basin of the Zambezi, for example. East Africa is different in that there the emphasis is on the unity suggested by a great continuous plateau on the surface of which, occupying a shallow depression, is that enormous stretch of shallow water, Lake Victoria. To the west is the most remarkable trough to be found on the earth's surface, the main East African rift valley, with its chain of long, narrow, deep lakes. To the east are coastal lowlands of varying widths (Figure 18.1).

The greater part of the East African plateau lies at an elevation of more than 4000 feet above sea level. Large sections in Kenya where the plateau is crossed by the equator are at an elevation of over 6000 feet. An entire modification of climatic conditions results, in such a way that under the very equator itself are lands claimed to be ideal for the settlement and development of white men nurtured in cool midlatitude lands. As elsewhere around the fringes of Africa the plateau descends to the coast by a series of steps, and as soon as lower land is reached physical conditions afforded by the terrain and the climate are utterly different. Hence the eastern half of Kenya with the port of Mombasa, or the islands of Zanzibar and Pemba off the coast, or farther south Mozambique (Portuguese East Africa) which lies almost entirely on land of lower elevations, offer marked contrasts to the regions high up on the plateau itself.

Structurally the East African plateau does not differ in any marked degree from the other parts of the African continent. There is the same complex of ancient metamorphic rocks of gneisses and schists, of ancient sandstones, and there are huge areas occupied by granite, all making up the pla-

Figure 18.1   East Africa.

teau mass. As elsewhere in Africa, the solid rocks are obscured by a varied mantle of decomposed rock and soils predominantly of a red color, a mantle sufficiently deep to hinder the discovery of those mineral riches sought by man and which occur scattered through the ancient complex. In consequence there are important mineral deposits still in course of discovery, and doubtless others to be discovered, so that East Africa affords examples of some spectacular mineral developments within recent decades, including the discovery of some of the richest diamond-bearing ground in the world.

We have discussed elsewhere the development in Africa of peneplain surfaces, that is, of surfaces which are almost plains and which in terms of years are very ancient. At a time when great mountain-building movements in other parts of the world were folding the weaker rocks to form the great mountain chains, the western Cordillera of North America, the Andes system of South America, the Alpine and Himalayan chains of Europe and Asia, and even the Atlas of northwest Africa itself, the bulk of the African continent was a great rigid block, resistant to any further folding movements. Its very rigidity, however, resulted in the development of great cracks, and along these cracks there was differential movement. In particular it would seem that in East Africa, to compensate for the great movements of compression in other parts of the world, a region of crustal tension developed. Parallel cracks developed, and long narrow blocks of country were let down between them, giving rise to rift valleys. It is possible that the rift valleys of East Africa link up into two great lines, an eastern and a western. This possibility is shown diagrammatically in Figure 18.2.

According to this scheme, based on the early interpretation of Professor J. W. Gregory (*The Rift Valleys and Geology of East Africa,* London, 1921), there is one main or eastern trough. This is occupied today by Lake Nyasa in the south, and passes almost directly northward through the heart of Tanganyika and Kenya to include the depression occupied by Lake Rudolph near the northern border of Kenya. It then passes through the heart of Ethiopia, where it is partly filled by outpourings from volcanoes, though also marked by a chain of deep lakes. It then broadens northward to be occupied by the Red Sea; and finally it terminates in the north-south trough of western Asia occupied by the Dead Sea, the Jordan valley and the Sea of Galilee.

From this main rift valley Gregory believed that a major branch passed off westward, forming the trough occupied successively by Lakes Tanganyika, Kivu, Edward, and Albert. More detailed geological investigation over the ensuing quarter of a century confirmed the existence of the great faults and the troughs, but suggested a succession of rifts rather than the continuous lines of faulting postulated by Gregory. The later more moderate view is expressed in the map, Figure 3.3.

If one draws a section across the country of the great rifts to true scale

Figure 18.2   The Rift Valley (generalized), railways, and settlement areas of East Africa.

Labels on map:
Jinja
Kampala
Kasese
Entebbe
Kisumu
Mt Kenya
Equator
Nairobi
Mwanza
Mt Kilimanjaro
Mombasa
Kigoma
Tabora
Tanga
Pemba I.
Kongwa
Zanzibar
Mpanda
Dar es Salaam
10°S
Mtwara
Blantyre

Legend:
Rift Valley ― ― ―
Fertile upland areas
Approximate edge of coast lowland ----
Chief railways ―+―+―
Miles
0   250

the rift valleys appear insignificant in that the foundering of their floors to the extent of a few thousand feet is small in comparison with the horizontal distances involved. Nevertheless, when seen on the surface of the ground they are spectacular indeed. To reach the edge of the East African rift, to see the ground falling away at one's feet and, if atmospheric conditions permit, to catch a glimpse of the mountain wall on the far side are experiences never to be forgotten.

It would be surprising indeed if such a fracturing of a large section of the earth's surface did not give rise to another of the earth's phenomena. It was associated with a great outburst of volcanic activity. Huge sheets of lava cover enormous areas in Kenya and extend southward into Tanganyika and westward into Uganda, to be continued northward by still larger areas amid the mountains of Ethiopia. These stretches of lava have in many areas broken down to form some excellent soils. More conspicuous than the sheets of lava are the gigantic individual extinct volcanoes which tower to great heights above the plateau surface. Among the outstanding giants are Mount Kenya itself, almost on the equator, and rising to heights (17,058 feet) which ensure a permanent snow capping. Southward within Tanganyika territory, Kilimanjaro rises to 19,340 feet (Figure 18.3). On the Kenya-Uganda border the notable Mt. Elgon is 14,172 feet. Near the western rift, on the western margins, the great mass once known as the Mountains of the Moon and now as Ruwenzori rises to 16,794 feet but is quite different in character, being a faulted block or horst.

Between the two great branches of the rift it would seem that the old plateau surface sagged, hence the reason for Lake Victoria, so different from the other lakes of East Africa. It is a shallow, island-fringed lake with gently shelving coastlands. Similar, though much smaller, is Lake Kyoga to the north, through which the waters from Lake Victoria drain on their way to make the White Nile. Thus the heart of the plateau forms part of the great Nile basin, that part which we have discussed in Chapter 11 as the upper or plateau course.

East Africa as a whole, however, is not dominated by river basins as are most parts of Africa. Instead an irregular network of streams join up to form rivers important locally, though ones whose names are little known outside the country, whose waters may yet be used for those smaller storage and irrigation works advocated by writers like Professor Debenham (see page 87) for the improvement of agricultural conditions over large parts of the continent.

If we turn to a consideration of climatic conditions, the coastlands, roughly from Mombasa southward, enjoy the hot, wet climate which we associate with equatorial latitudes. Mombasa, it should be noted, lies some 4 degrees south of the equator, but the hot, wet conditions extend virtually

Figure 18.3   Vegetation zones around Mount Kilimanjaro. (After *Geog. Univ.* [Figure 28]. Topography from 1/50,000 map by F. Klute [1912] and 1/300,000 map by Sprigade and Moisel [1914].)

through the whole of Portuguese East Africa. Northward from Mombasa there is a remarkable and very rapid change to the arid conditions characteristic of the northeastern deserts, so that from the 40 inches a year of Mombasa the total drops to 20 inches on the border with Somalia and, before the equator is reached, far less.

Away from the coastal strip as the plateau is ascended, the first feature of outstanding importance is the lowering of average temperatures. The most favored regions are those of central Kenya and Uganda lying under the equator; for here violent fluctuations in temperature are absent. The rainfall tends to be well distributed throughout the year, and, though periods of drought do occur, Kenya escapes the worst of those violent seasonal differences associated with the destructive storms which become more and more significant as one goes southward across the plateau through Tanganyika, and which prove such a serious deterrent to agricultural development (see page 409). As one reaches the interior lower ground around the lakes, the climate becomes again more truly equatorial. According to Maurette, the rest of the country is subject to the influences of the seasonal or permanent winds from the Indian Ocean and receives from them more or less rain according to the altitude and the exposure of each region. Local variations are often sharp. Certain regions are very wet, others much less so. In some parts great heat and evaporation combine to lower the efficiency of a precipitation which is already small. On the high plateau there may be seasons of relative cold. Nights may be chilly as a result of rapid radiation through the rarefied air.

Such are the essential features of the climate of eastern Africa which distinguish it so clearly from that of equatorial Africa. They exercise a marked influence on the river regime, on the vegetation, on the life of the indigenous peoples, and on the possibilities of agricultural development.

Historical background

The pioneer journeys of exploration by David Livingstone quickly inspired others to follow him. The early missionaries and traders into east and central Africa found the vast lands of East Africa sparsely populated by primitive peoples menaced by famine and disease, the prey of intertribal warfare and under the perpetual shadow of the slave trade. At that time the slavers were Arabs based primarily on the island of Zanzibar, whose sultan— himself of Arab descent—claimed a loose sovereignty over a great part of East Africa. Reference has already been made (Chapter 2) to the efforts of the British consul to persuade the sultan to take strong action against the slave trade and to the way his authority was undermined when Karl Peters concluded treaties with local chiefs leading to the establishment of German East Africa. In 1886 the sultan's authority was limited to a coastal strip. The mainland was divided between German and British interests defined by treaty in 1890, in which year Zanzibar became a British protectorate.

The British East Africa Company began trading in 1887, but incurred such losses that by 1893 it had to withdraw from Uganda. The British government was persuaded by F. J. D. Lugard, afterwards Lord Lugard, not to break faith with the Africans with whom the company had made agreements but to take over responsibility. This led to a protectorate over Buganda in 1894 and East Africa (later Kenya) in 1895. It was in the latter year that the railway from Mombasa inland to Uganda was begun, a vital line of communication if Uganda was to be freed of the slave traffic and opened up economically. Labor was short and had to be brought from India, but the supply was hindered by plague. Disease killed off the transport animals as well as many of the workmen themselves, while the failure of the rains in 1898 led to famine over all of Kenya. The railway did not reach Kisumu on Lake Victoria until 1901, and Kisumu remained the port of entry to Uganda for the next 25 years.

Farther south, slave trading had a strong hold, but missions were successfully established at Blantyre in 1874 and Livingstonia in 1875, followed by trading companies. In 1891 Portugal recognized British rights to the country around Lake Nyasa, and to the west lay the country where the British South Africa Company had been accorded rights in 1889. In 1891 Lewanika, paramount chief of Barotseland, asked for and received British government protection. Arab slave traders who had been encroaching from north and west were defeated in a pitched battle by Sir Harry Johnson in 1894, and the last slave train, intercepted on its way to the coast in 1898, was set free at Fort Jameson. King Lewanika was a great ruler who foresaw coming changes. He granted trading and mineral rights to the British South Africa Company and later land rights. The company in return extended railway and telegraph lines northward from South Africa. In 1924 the British government took over administration of the country, which had then come to be known as Northern Rhodesia. The further history of the territories is given later.

The peoples of East Africa

Apart from a few pockets in remote areas occupied by the primitive pygmies, the vast majority of Africans in East and Central Africa are Bantu Negroes. For centuries they had been subjected to constant pressure from the warlike nomadic Hamites from the north, brown-skinned peoples with aquiline features. The conquering Hamites intermarried with the conquered Negroes and adopted their mode of life. Some tribes, such as the Masai of Kenya and Tanganyika, are clearly half Hamites; elsewhere the Hamitic element gives rise to an aristocratic class among predominantly Bantu.

In the absence of a written language the various tribes of East Africa have gradually evolved forms of spoken speech mutually unintelligible. This, in turn, has resulted, with improved communications following European entry, in the need for a *lingua franca* and the use of Kiswahili (Swahili) for this purpose.

For many centuries the Arabs had been active traders along the East African coast, and it was they who drove the Portuguese from their last stronghold at Mombasa toward the end of the seventeenth century. In 1832 the Iman of Muscat transferred his capital to Zanzibar, and in 1861 his son established Zanzibar as a separate sultanate, with wide claims in East Africa. The administrative and legislative authority of the new (1964) government is now limited to the islands of Zanzibar and Pemba.

European settlement was one of the objectives of the British South African Company from the start, but in East Africa it came later as the attractiveness of the climate of the Kenya highlands was increasingly appreciated and the first true settlers took up land in 1902. The land which was granted to them was largely uninhabited except when, every few years, the warlike Masai drove their cattle into the pasture from which they had long before frightened away potentially permanent agriculturalists.

It was the British who brought for the building of the Mombasa-Uganda railway large numbers of indentured laborers from India. Some 6000 elected to remain, and they have been joined by many who handle much of the import and export trade and retail distribution, as well as providing artisans, craftsmen, and clerical workers. Only gradually is the African interesting himself in these spheres; as a trader he has lacked the sustained interest needed to build up a good business.

World War I, 1914 to 1918, resulted in the voluntary mobilization of every British settler and the abandonment of most of the farms and the conquest of German East Africa. That territory, renamed Tanganyika, became a mandated territory entrusted to Britain, but the uncertainty of its political future did not encourage either settlement or economic investment. However, the discovery of gold and diamonds in Kenya and Tanganyika and the development of the great copper zone in Northern Rhodesia gave new incentives; white settlements in the Kenya highlands grew, and Nairobi developed into a modern city.

References are made below to the careful work of the late Clement Gillman who showed so clearly the remarkable contrasts in population distribution which are such a feature of East Africa. There are fertile coastlands round Lake Victoria where 400 persons are crowded on each square mile; the islands of Zanzibar and Pemba support more than 250 per square mile (Figure 18.4). On the other hand, vast areas in the heart of Tanganyika are virtually uninhabited; yet they are far from being desert lands.

The peoples of East Africa too show striking contrasts. The well-organized

Figure 18.4 The distribution of population in East Africa. This shows the irregular concentrations of population.

Kingdom of Buganda, the Arab Sultanate of Zanzibar, the war-like Masai of almost legendary valor, and the pockets of primitive peoples were but some of the indications of the range of human adaptation to the environment. Superficially there are huge monotonous stretches of rolling plateau country, yet the work of the physiographer, the soil scientist and the ecologist suggests rather a complicated pattern, though one repeated again and again.

When the World Land Use Survey initiated pilot surveys of existing land use in East Africa in 1951, the great surprise when air photographs were examined was the complexity of the pattern, too detailed to show fully even on the scale of 1:50,000. This work, carried out by Mr. John Callow under my direction, emphasized the outstanding need for factual surveys—the mapping of what exists, the attempt to interpret the pattern before any future planning can be contemplated.

The question of European settlement assumes a special significance in Kenya. On the high plateau almost under the equator are about 70,000 whites (1961: an increase of 40,000 since 1948). Many are city dwellers, and 25,000 live in Nairobi alone, but there are 2000 registered landholders representing, with their families, some 8000 people. Reserved for European farmers (Figure 18.5) are 17,000 square miles, though much of this will probably be kept under forest. This area cannot be extended; it is hemmed in by the African reserves. The future of these so-called White Highlands is problematical: it is discussed more fully below.

Kenya assumed self-government in June 1963 with an African prime minister, Jomo Kenyatta, as a prelude to independence as a republic within the Commonwealth, later in the year.

Portuguese East Africa (Moçambique, anglicized as Mozambique)

Portuguese East Africa, occupying a large part of the East African coastal plain, together with the adjoining plateau here relatively low and much dissected, occupies some 300,000 square miles, with a population at the census of 1950 of 5,739,000. The country is almost bisected by the Lower Zambezi, and it forms part of the great tract discussed in Chapter 19, or the Zambezi Basin. South of the Zambezi the port of Beira serves as the modern outlet of Southern Rhodesia, while still farther south the narrow tongue of Portuguese territory which is interposed between the Transvaal and the Indian Ocean includes the port of Lourenço Marques, the natural outlet—geographically speaking—of the Witwatersrand gold field.

It is only therefore the northern half of Portuguese East Africa which begins to have affinities with the British sphere in East Africa, the main tract discussed in this chapter.

Portugese interest in the East African coast dates from the days of the early Portuguese ascendancy in the Indian trade, but for some 300 years little was done by the Portuguese to develop the African territories they claimed. In the latter part of the nineteenth century, when the boundaries with Nyasaland and the newly established Rhodesia were fixed, the Portuguese gave a 50-year concession to the Mozambique Company which did not

Figure 18.5 A white farmer's home on the Kenya Highlands. The farmhouse is not unlike a traditional English home, but local materials have been used: mud brick walls and grass thatch. (Courtesy East African Office.)

expire until 1941. Thus about one-sixth of the whole area, the part lying between the Zambezi and about latitude 22° South, was administered until that date by this Portuguese chartered company, and included the very important port of Beira.

The remainder of the territory, administered by the government, was known as the Mozambique Colony. The whole has now passed under unified state control, but the major part of the development of the country in the present century has been the result of foreign investment, notably in the two great ports and in the railway communications, including the great Zambezi Bridge, linking Beira with Nyasaland.

A large part of Portuguese East Africa south of the Zambezi lies less than 500 feet above sea level and consequently is covered by rich vegetation of the low veld which extends also into the eastern Transvaal. Portuguese territory extends far inland up the Lower Zambezi to the small frontier post of Zumbo. Zumbo is well below the great Kariba Gorge discussed in the next chapter, there is a navigable stretch below Zumbo through a somewhat narrow gorge to the Kebrabassa Falls. Here the river descends by a series of cataracts over a distance of some 50 miles to the coastal lowland, where there is a broad navigable channel from Tete, past the junction with the Shiré, to the delta. Along the lower Limpopo is good irrigated farmland.

North of the Zambezi hilly country projects much closer to the coast. Here Portuguese territory occupies the whole width between Lake Nyasa and the Indian Ocean and, overlooking Lake Nyasa, includes the Namuli Highlands, rising in places to over 6000 feet and giving Portuguese East Africa a range of climatic conditions not yet fully exploited.

Most of Portuguese East Africa is occupied by younger sedimentary rocks fringing the crystalline plateau. Mineral wealth as far as metallic minerals are concerned is thus restricted to the interior zone of crystalline rocks with which communications at present scarcely exist.

The territory has compensation in the occurrence of some useful coal deposits in the Zambezi valley near Tete.

Climatically the coastlands of Portuguese East Africa offer some interesting points. There is the southward-flowing ocean current of warm water derived from equatorial latitudes, known as the Mozambique Current. As a result the waters in the port of Mozambique are several degrees warmer than those of Mombasa 800 miles nearer the equator. Though the regime of rainfall is that of a normal trade wind type, with a rainy season (December to May) and a dry season, the coastal lands suffer from constant high humidity as well as a small temperature range, not more than 10 degrees in the year. The latter part of the hot season is not infrequently characterized by destructive cyclonic storms (see Chapter Four). As elsewhere in East Africa the rainfall decreases inland from the coast, followed by an increase as higher ground is reached and orographical rainfall results.

Broadly speaking, African subsistence agriculture is the rule throughout the country, with the exception of the regions more immediately around the major ports where food is grown for consumption in the towns and there is a small development of commercial agriculture. Thus sugar cane, supplying raw sugar to Portugal, is cultivated behind Lourenço Marques and Inhambane, in the Limpopo valley, as well as in the Zambezi valley around the great bridge at Sena and in the hinterland of Quelimane. Among other comparatively recent developments which point the way to future progress are cotton growing and fruit growing (bananas, pineapples, citrus fruits, especially in the Lourenço Marques district). The uplands and the drier areas have parts suitable for sisal, peanuts, and other oil seeds. The ubiquitous Indian corn is the mainstay of African diet. Livestock is unimportant, owing to the low-lying nature of much of the territory and the prevalence of disease.

It is clear that just as the development of Portuguese East Africa to date has depended upon the happy collaboration of the interested powers, in this case Britain and Portugal, so does the position of the country make development in isolation unthinkable. The international implications are well seen in the story of the port of Beira. It is an example of a port whose hinterland is distant and not immediate. More than 80 per cent of its total trade, exports and imports, come from or go to the Rhodesias, Nyasaland, and especially the far-off Katanga region of the Congo. The Rhodesian railways operate the line between Beira and the Rhodesian frontier at Umtali; similarly the great main line northward crossing the Zambezi by the bridge at Sena has been constructed with British capital and is operated by British interests. Somewhat similar is the position of Lourenço Marques, only 55 miles by railway from the Transvaal frontier, which handles nine-tenths of the trade of Portuguese East Africá as well as a large volume of trade with the industrial area of the Rand. British capitalists have spent many millions of dollars on the improvement of the port, and the expansion of the port has enormously stimulated the development of the surrounding agricultural lands, which have unusually rich soils and a climate favoring bananas and sugar.

By comparison the purely Portuguese East African ports, though situated where there are rich agricultural hinterlands, like Mozambique, Quelimane, and Inhambane, remain small and undeveloped. The changing fortunes consequent upon development of modern communications are well illustrated in the case of the port of Chindè, just north of the Zambezi mouth, and the river port of Chindio, both of which have been eclipsed by Beira since the construction of the railway bridge.

British East Africa

Until the mid-nineteen-fifties there was a general tendency toward closer union of the four territories of East Africa under British influence, but recent events—the independence of Tanganyika proclaimed in 1961, the diverse aims of nationalist leaders in Uganda and Kenya—has rather tended to reverse that trend. Until 1961 the British East African territories comprised the Uganda Protectorate, the Kenya Colony and Protectorate, the Tanganyika trusteeship territory (formerly German East Africa, later held under mandate from the League of Nations), and the Zanzibar Protectorate. An East African High Commission, consisting of the governors of the first three named, came into existence on January 1, 1948, to provide for the administration of services common to the three territories such as railways, posts and telegraphs, and research services.

An important step in the unification of East Africa was also made in 1948 when the East African Railways and Harbors Administration took over on a unified basis the control of the varied railways together with the ports of Mombasa (including the modern Kilindini harbor), Dar-es-Salaam, Lindi, and a number of smaller Kenya ports. The same board operates steamer services on Lakes Victoria, Kyoga, and Albert, as well as on the River Nile, and also some important road services.

If the trend is now towards separate national units, the need for coordination in such spheres as transport will remain. This is clear when one looks at the position of Uganda, entirely landlocked and dependent for its contacts with the outside world on facilities offered by its neighbors.

Uganda

On March 1, 1962, Uganda received a new constitution with full internal self-government, preparatory to full independence on October 9, 1962. Prior to that Uganda had been a British protectorate. The territories came under British influence about 1890, and for a time some parts were administered by the British East Africa Company. It was in 1894 that the British protectorate was declared over the Kingdom of Buganda and some of the adjoining territories. When the country first became known to Europeans, Buganda was already a well-organized and efficiently run African kingdom. Prior to 1962 the Province of Buganda was recognized as an African kingdom ruled by His Highness the Kabaka, assisted by three African ministers and a Lukiko, or Assembly. Similar Lukikos advised the chiefs or kings of neighboring territories. Uganda thus afforded a very interesting example of the British system in Africa of indirect administration. The principal British representative was the governor, assisted by a legislative council, eight of whose members were Africans. The governor resided at Entebbe, pleasantly situated on the shores of Lake Victoria and within a short distance of Kampala, the capital of Buganda.[1] Kampala was long the railhead of the main line through Kenya to Mombasa, the commercial center, and through the establishment of the University College (with a strong medical school) at Makerere nearby, a center for higher education in East Africa.

Makerere, with its counterparts, University Colleges in West Africa at Ibadan and Accra, like the former Gordon Memorial College at Khartoum in the Sudan, were all university colleges established as such since World War II for the development of education at a university level and for the fostering of research in British African colonial territories. In their early stages these colleges were guided in their development by a close association with the University of London, which offered advice on matters of curricula and provided external examiners to help in the maintenance of good standards of scholarship. Appointments to the academic staffs were made with the help or advice of a council with its headquarters in London. Periodic visits were paid by senior members of the University of London to African colleges, and the whole arrangement was typical of British efforts to guide African development toward self-government in educational as in political affairs. In due course Khartoum, Ibadan, and Accra all have become independent univer-

[1] Dr. E. S. Munger has made a detailed study of *Relational Patterns of Kampala, Uganda* (University of Chicago Department of Geography Research Paper 21, 1951). Among many subjects of great interest the influence of Makerere is discussed.

sities. The full title of Makerere College was the University College of East Africa at Makerere, and it was intended that in due course it should become the University of East Africa to serve not only Uganda but also Kenya, Tanganyika, and Zanzibar. As a university college it served students from all these territories, but with the granting of independence to Tanganyika in 1961 the new state not unnaturally wanted its own university (now established at Dar-es-Salaam); similarly Kenya, and hence the elevation of the Royal Technical College at Nairobi. It leaves Makerere which became an independent university in 1963, a somewhat heavy burden for a small state.

Although the total area of Uganda is only 80,000 square miles, if one excludes the tracts of inland water which lie within its boundaries, the first full census taken in August 1948 revealed a population of just under 5 million (4,993,965), which had risen to 6,523,628 at the census of 1959. This represents a very high density for Africa, of no less than 80 per square mile. On the slopes of Mount Elgon and on the shorelands of Lake Victoria the density exceeds 200. Europeans in 1959 numbered nearly 11,000, against less than 4000 in 1948; they were administrators, missionaries, educators, and engaged in trade and commerce. But by 1959 72,000 Asians, mainly Indians, had settled in the country, having been employed originally mainly on railway construction. Of the African population nearly one-third were members of the Baganda tribe from which Uganda takes its name. In the remoter areas there are still forest tribes at a very different level of development from those in the remainder of the country.

The bulk of Uganda lies on the lake plateau at an elevation of 3500 to 4000 feet, draining from Lake Victoria through Lake Kyoga into Lake Albert and so into the Nile. Thus Uganda must continue to have close association with the Sudan and Egypt in that it covers the gathering grounds of the headquarters of the White Nile. The great works at Owen Falls have been referred to elsewhere (page 193). Already Jinja has factories; with cheap electric power it seems destined to become a great industrial center.

The eastern boundary of the country is roughly the line of highlands which separates the Nile drainage from the Lake Rudolph basin. In the west Uganda includes part of the western rift valley, and here the Bunyoro Plateau overlooks the great scarps the deep trough occupied by Lake Albert. As a result of its elevation the plateau has a modified equatorial climate. Thus Entebbe at 3900 feet has a characteristically small annual range of 70° to 73°F., and over most of the plateau the rainfall, averaging between 40 and 60 inches, shows two maxima. The first is about April to May, and the second about October to December, but the intervening "dry" periods are dry in the relative sense only. Though there is considerable variability in annual fall of rain associated with variations in the strength of the air masses which converge on this part of Africa, there are not the periods of drought which are such a curse over much of Africa. And, although the rain—largely convectional—may fall during thunderstorms, sometimes with great violence, it does not do the damage that heavy falls may do on land left dry by months of drought, as happens farther south in Tanganyika.

The absence of marked seasonal rhythm makes possible cultivation throughout the year, but this type of climate does not attract European settlers as Kenya has done. Uganda has been subject from time to time to very serious epidemics of sleeping sickness and other insect-borne diseases, though it enjoys a climate conducive to great agricultural development. On the whole the natural vegetation is that of moderately open forest or a dry savanna with abundance of trees. There are large stretches of papyrus swamp and swamp forest on the lower ground around the lakes. With decreasing rainfall toward the northeast, the savanna becomes poorer. Other local variations include stretches of grassy downland, and as elsewhere in Africa the existing vegetation pattern is doubtless in major part due to human interference and shifting cultivation.

In contrast, however, to the shifting cultivation so universal in Africa, the Baganda in the populous areas have developed an intensive system of permanent garden cultivation. A large proportion of the Baganda are Christians, and the church is often a central feature of a group of homes. A modern home would probably have a corrugated iron roof, plastered walls, doors and windows, and a cement floor. The thatched kitchen is a separate building at the back, and the house is surrounded by a carefully swept yard with a shade tree or two and a few flowers. The surrounding garden consists of several parts. First there is the banana garden, tended by the wife, then plots with sweet potatoes, cassava, maize, and beans. Then there is the cotton patch, tended by the husband, who weeds the crop. The family does the harvesting about January, and the cultivator takes his sacks of cotton tied to his bicycle to the Indian-owned ginnery.

Such is the life of the people within reach of modern roads, but throughout the country the large population naturally practices subsistence agriculture, with cereals, particularly millets, cassava, and bananas occupying pride of place. The great cash crop, cultivated commonly by the Africans mainly in small plots from one-fourth acre upward, is thus cotton. The local varieties formerly grown for current use have been largely replaced since the introduction of American and Egyptian seed in 1903, so that most of the crop is now American Upland. Grown all over the country, the acreage reached 1,565,000 acres in 1959–1960, with an output averaging 65,000 tons, with a peak in 1958–1959 of 72,000. The bulk of the crop is grown for export, and it is interesting that the local ginneries are largely owned by the immigrant Indians.

Tobacco, like cotton, is an introduced crop, grown by the Africans but not primarily for their own use. Some is sold to the factories at Jinja and

Kampala; the remainder is exported. There is, however, a constantly increasing demand for cigarettes due to the high prices of the imported article and the fact that they formerly came from dollar areas.

The western highland zone in the Tororo and Ankole districts has attracted attention because of the possibilities of growing tea with good yields and coffee, of both *arabica* and *robusta* varieties. There has been a rapid growth in the development of coffee (108,000 tons in 1960), mainly produced on African small holdings though some on European-owned plantations. Indian settlers have become interested in the development of sugar cane, and sugar factories near Lake Victoria have satisfied local demands and produced a surplus for export.

Turning to livestock, Uganda faces the difficulty of large tsetse fly areas. The bulk of the cattle are of low-grade type, becoming better on the higher grasslands of Ankole, where large herds of humped big-horned cattle are the pride of the Banyankole. The country supports some millions of sheep and goats, and there is a trade in hides and skins.

The emphasis in Uganda has been upon agriculture rather than upon minerals, the exploitation of which has been hindered by the high cost of transportation to the coast. There has been a small output of tin ore, but the extension of the railway from Kampala has made possible the development of important copper deposits at Kilembe in the Ruwenzori massif. The ore is sent down to the railhead at Kasesi and thence to Jinja for smelting.

Uganda may be cited as an object lesson for other parts of Africa. It has natural advantages of soil and climate, but not without the disadvantages inherent in African conditions, such as infestation with tsetse fly. The relatively favorable natural environment is reflected in the number and the standard of living of its African population. Insofar as trade with the outside world is concerned, such advantages are of no use without modern means of transportation. Thus the modern development of Uganda began in fact with the completion of the railway through Kenya to Mombasa, though actually the first railway in Uganda ran from Jinja to Namasagali, the head of navigation on the Victoria Nile. As elsewhere in Africa, development of roads has played and is playing an enormously important part in opening up the country. With the prosperity resulting from the export trade in cotton and coffee Uganda has now thousands of miles suitable for motor traffic throughout the year, and the truck is to be found everywhere transporting agricultural produce. The airplane has brought the country within hours instead of days or weeks of its neighbors and, via Khartoum and Cairo, of Europe.

Kenya

Before becoming independent in 1963, Kenya had been a British protectorate since 1895. It was proclaimed a crown colony in 1920, when it took the title of Kenya Colony from the famous volcanic peak, almost exactly on the equator, which is its highest point. Along the coastlands are territories at that time rented from the Sultan of Zanzibar, which became the Kenya Protectorate. A treaty with Italy signed in 1924 ceded to Italy (Italian Somaliland) the whole of the Juba River and a neighboring tract of arid country, formerly in Kenya. In 1926 the area around Lake Rudolph in the northwest was transferred from Uganda Protectorate to Kenya.

The whole of Kenya now covers a land area of 219,760 square miles. As in Uganda the census taken for the first time in 1948 revealed a larger actual population than that which had previously been calculated, a total of 5,379,966. By mid-1961 this had risen to 7,290,000. The Kenya coastlands have long been under the influence of Arab traders arriving by sea, so that the population included more than 39,000 Arabs. Indians, together with Goanese, to a large extent descendants of those who were brought to work on the railways and other construction, totaled at the time of the 1948 census nearly 100,000—over 178,000 by 1961. They constitute an important and very active minority in the Kenya population. The 1948 census revealed the presence of 29,666 Europeans, a total which had risen to 66,000 by mid-1961. In contrast to the other British territories in tropical Africa, a large proportion of these Europeans were British settlers. They lived on the pleasant heights of the Kenya plateau and engaged in farming, about which more will be said later. The Africans in Kenya are mostly peoples speaking Swahili and further inland numerous tribes speaking Bantu languages.

A simple physical division of Kenya is into: (1) the coastal plains; (2) the broad plateau of the Nyika—a step up to the plateau; (3) the eastern rift valley with its bordering mountains; and (4) the lake plateau, extending to Lake Victoria and the Uganda border in the west. If one looks at the rainfall map it is clear that only the southern margin of the coastal plain receives an adequate rainfall, and this is the fertile stretch around Mombasa. Northward a very large proportion of Kenya with less than 20 inches of rainfall is arid, and much of it incapable of supporting permanent settlements. Indeed, it is not generally realized that about three-quarters of all the people in Kenya live where the rainfall is more than 30 inches a year, and that three-quarters of the whole country is very sparsely populated indeed. Most of the one-quarter of Kenya which can be considered as fully productive, either actually or potentially, is on the better-watered highlands. At the time of independence this was divided between the 11,000 square miles of European estates and the 47,000 square miles of native reserves.

On the surface of the Kenya highlands there are large stretches of volcanic rock. The varied elevation, well seen on the slopes of Mt. Kenya, gives rise to a zonation, basically climatic, reflected in the natural vegetation. The eastern rift valley as it passes through Kenya is not a simple, straight, even-floored trough, but consists rather of several distinct basins. Those in the center, like the basin of Lake Naivasha, 6100 feet above sea level, are themselves at considerable elevations. The land drops in steps to the north to Lake Rudolph, and also to the south, where Lake Magadi—a valuable source of soda salts—is at 2500 feet above sea level. Part of the irregular character of the floor of the rift is due to the occurrence of subsidiary volcanic cones.

On both sides of the rift highland masses rise to over 10,000 feet, but the associated marginal plains, such as the Kikuyu Plateau, afford some of the most valuable land in the country. On the Kenya highlands it is the cooling effect of altitude which is such an important factor, and at these high elevations there is a very considerable daily range of temperature. Especially in the drier parts of the year, cool and bracing evenings and nights are the result; the thermometer may drop as low as 35°F. at Nairobi at night, whereas daytime temperatures may reach more than 80°F. It is this absence of monotony in the daily regime which rendered the climate on the Kenya highlands, accompanied as it is with abundant sunshine, so attractive to the European settlers.

The very wide range of physical and climatic conditions in Kenya is reflected both in natural vegetation and in agriculture. The mangrove swamps of the southern coastal fringe pass northward into the semidesert vegetation of Somaliland. The greater part of the huge coastal plain is a dried scrub with scattered acacia trees and baobabs. Narrow belts of bushes of a rather dry character follow up the main river valleys. The plains of the highland are largely grass with scattered acacias, or low bush, as on the Kikuyu Plateau, on the arid red volcanic soils. The highlands, where they rise in the Aberdares and Mau Plateau, and particularly the slopes of the great volcanic piles of Kenya and Elgon, show a remarkable and very interesting vertical zonation of vegetation and are classic examples which have been extensively studied. Good savanna occupies the lake plateau draining toward Lake Victoria.

The grasslands of Kenya were long occupied by aggressive pastoral tribes, notably the Kikuyu and Masai, who had tended to force the peaceful agricultural peoples off the better lands on to the poorer. It is these grassy uplands which naturally offered the greatest attraction to Europeans, and, as in Southern Rhodesia, the European lands are strung out in a belt along the main line of the railway, with the native reserves occupying the less accessible though by no means less fertile fringing lands. The construction of the railway from Mombasa to Uganda, as we have already seen, was part of Britain's great campaign to suppress the slave trade. It made possible the development both of the Kenya highlands and of Uganda as a whole. The whole system is meter gauge, and gradually the main line has been extended and branch lines constructed to tap such important areas as Lake Magadi and the Mt. Kenya slopes.

Figure 18.6   Tea cultivation near Kericho in Kenya. (Courtesy East African Tourist and Travel Association.)

The main agricultural production for export comes from the lands of the European farmers. Among the chief plantation crops are coffee, sisal, and tea, but the extensive farms are devoted to cereals, especially corn and wheat, with a little barley and oats. Kenya produces the major part of the world's pyrethrum, still important despite the development of D.D.T. The successful growing of coffee is almost entirely confined to areas of the rift, but it has proved rather an uncertain crop even on the good red volcanic soils in the Nairobi area. Very little is grown by Africans, despite encouragement. The sisal industry is particularly suited to large-scale production because there is a considerable period before it yields, and expensive machinery is needed for its preparation for the market. There is, however, a considerable production by Africans. Maize remains the great foodstuff for Kenya Africans, and the smaller quantities on European farms are grown as cattle food. Wheat has increased, but is grown almost entirely by Europeans. Hybrid seed evolved in the experimental stations has proved very suitable for special local conditions, and an export has been developed.

Tea is a crop of the wetter parts of the country at about 7000 feet in the Kericho area and the Limuru area about 17 miles west of Nairobi. Fruit is another recent development. Wattle bark and wattle extract form a large export of African-grown produce, though small in comparison with Natal's. Perhaps the most intensive African cultivation is in the Nyanza district, which though higher than the coastal plain was not attractive to European settlement.

What is the future of white settlement in Kenya? Although the estimated

European population in mid-1961 was 66,000—more than double the 1948 figure—the increase was mainly in the cities and represented those engaged in trade and commerce. In the early nineteen-fifties the upsurge of African nationalism produced in Kenya a very unpleasant antiforeign manifestation, known as mau-mau, with an extensive campaign of murder and pillage and much obscene ritual. Restoration of law and order proved long drawn out and difficult; worse, it left a feeling of distrust in the future when the Africans came to control their own country. The white population, mainly British, for the most part felt that Kenya was no longer a country where they could bring up their families and by permanently settling cut themselves off from the mother country. On the farms they had been in any case largely dependent on African staff. So European farms have become difficult to sell, some have been deserted, and the plight of many white farmers is a most unhappy one. Those Europeans engaged in trade and commerce in the cities are in a different position: they can pull out if need be.

Kenya now has in the more settled areas a good network of all-weather roads. Considerable development was made possible by the use of Italian prisoners during World War II, and a feature of the country is the long-distance luxury-coach services operating between all the main towns. There are, however, two towns in Kenya which overshadow all the others. Mombasa (Figure 18.8) is situated on the eastern side of the small island on a

Figure 18.7 Government Road, Nairobi, showing modern buildings. (Courtesy East African Tourist and Travel Association.)

Figure 18.8   The site of Mombasa.

coastal inlet, and with its medieval fort is the old Arab settlement. At mid-1961 39,000 Arabs still remained in Mombasa, but they are now less numerous than the 178,000 Indians, together making one-third of the total population. The island itself is intensively cultivated, and on its western or landward side is the magnificent deep-water harbor of Kilindini, probably the finest harbor on the east coast of Africa and the starting point of the railway to Nairobi and the interior.

Nairobi, the capital (over 297,000 in 1961), owes it existence to European settlement. It was originally a small railway headquarters, but has surpassed even Mombasa in population. It has become the focus of road and air communications (Figure 18.9), as well as the largest European settlement in East Africa. By charter it was constituted a city in 1950.

Kisumu, the terminus of the old main line to Lake Victoria, is the third town. Two others serve as foci for European settlers and their activities: Nakuru, in the rift valley, and Eldoret, on a fertile part of the plateau.

Tanganyika

Tanganyika, which became independent in December 1961, occupies a larger area than Kenya and Uganda combined, covering 362,000 square miles, or 342,000 excluding inland water. The coastal plain in Tanganyika is comparatively narrow, and nearly the whole of this vast tract lies on the plateau stretching from Lake Tanganyika across to the edge overlooking the

Indian Ocean, a width of 600 miles. It might be thought that Tanganyika therefore enjoyed the advantages of the higher parts of the plateau in Kenya. It stretches from 1° to 12° South and might therefore be supposed to have an excellent climate where tropical heat would be tempered by elevation. Such, however, is not the case. And although Tanganyikan development has been hindered by its uncertain political position, the natural environment is far less favorable than in Kenya to settlement and development (Figure 18.10). The plateau is less varied; there are vast, gently rolling areas. The climate is modified tropical, not equatorial—that is to say, there is a strongly marked dry season. Since the relief is less varied, over the greater part the rainfall verges on the inadequate, and there are not the pockets of really good land found in Kenya.

It is possible to distinguish four zones within the country.

The coastal lowlands. These are hot throughout the year, enjoying a rainfall between 40 and 50 inches. They may be described as pleasant in the dry season, but somewhat unhealthy during the rains. Mangrove swamps fringe much of the coast, especially around the estuaries. Behind them are groves of coconut palms, giving place inland to thorn forests.

The subcoastal belt. This lies between the coastal belt proper and the

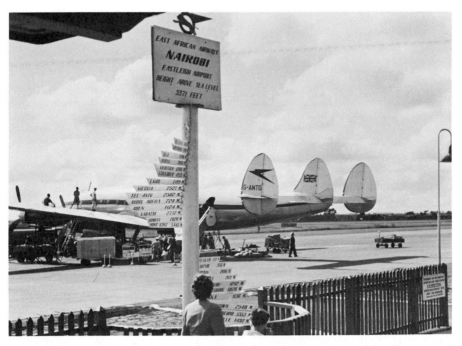

Figure 18.9   Eastleigh Airport, Nairobi, Kenya. One of the crossways of the African continent, halfway between Cairo and Durban. The well-equipped airport at Entebbe in Uganda is a strong rival. (Courtesy British Overseas Airways Corporation.)

Figure 18.10 Types of land occupation in Tanganyika. This map illustrates the huge areas uninhabited or occupied by a widely scattered population. These are largely areas without permanent surface water, or infested by tsetse fly. (From C. Gillman. *Geog. Rev.*, 1936 and 1949. Courtesy of the *Geographical Review*, American Geographical Society.)

highlands and is comparable to the hot, rather dry, Nyika belt of Kenya. Here thorn woodland with drought-resisting trees and spiny shrubs is dominant.

The main central and western plateau. Here the rainfall, though it averages 30 inches, is markedly irregular from year to year and in its incidence in the wet season. The atmosphere in the dry season is particularly dry, and a large daily range of temperature is the result. The vegetation may best be described as an open savanna or dry forest, but it often forms a great matted tangle. These are the extensive lands which promised much under large-scale mechanized clearing and cultivation and gave rise to the ill-fated groundnut or peanut scheme of the British government, described in detail below. The failure of that scheme suggests that the proper use of these vast sparsely peopled plateau areas remains an unsolved problem.

The highland zones. These have a heavier relief rainfall of over 50 inches a year, a bracing atmosphere, and considerable range of temperature. The land is clothed with luxuriant tropical forests, changing at higher levels into mountain grassland. Such lands are found in the Usambara in the extreme northeast on the slopes of Kilimanjaro and other mountains, and afford environments attractive to agricultural development.

We owe much of our scientific knowledge of Tanganyika geography to the careful studies of the late Mr. Clement Gillman, who contributed successively articles on population, vegetation, and white settlement to the *Geographical Review.*[2] His very careful population map, published as a folding plate, revealed a very remarkable state of affairs. There are areas of fairly dense population along the coastlands but especially from the neighborhood of the Kenya border and along the northern railway inland. Settlement, even in 1934, to which Gillman's map refers, had been attracted by the construc-

[2] A Population Map of Tanganyika Territory," *Geog. Rev.,* **XXVI,** 1936, 353–375; "A Vegetation Map of Tanganyika Territory," *Geog. Rev.,* **XXXIX,** 1949, 7–37; "White Colonization in East Africa," *Geog. Rev.,* **XXXII,** 1942, 585–597.

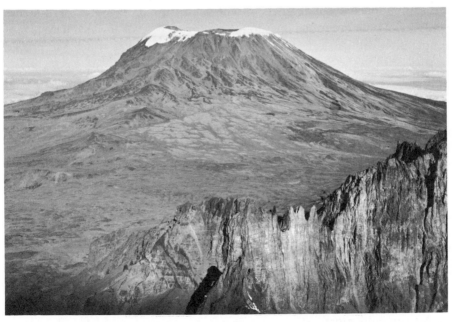

Figure 18.11   Kibo, the main peak of Kilimanjaro, and the highest point in Africa. In the foreground is Mawenzi, also part of the Kilimanjaro mass. (Copyright Aerofilms Library.)

tion of the Central Railway, and there were important clusters along the road toward the southwestern border. But the main population concentrations were actually along the borders of Lake Victoria in the north, where in places his dot system of representation breaks down and where the density actually exceeded some 400 per square mile. Vast areas of the heart of the country are shown as virtually or entirely unpopulated.

The comparatively backward development of Tanganyika may be connected to some extent with its varying political fortunes, but what are the main reasons behind this extraordinarily irregular distribution of its people? Is it the infertility of the soil, which has remained so long unattractive to agricultural settlers? Is it the depredations of warlike tribes engaged in perpetual feuds in the past? Is it the result of animal pests, or human disease? It may be suggested that the answers to these questions are not yet available. Considering the possibilities for white settlement, Gillman came to the conclusion that East Africa, more particularly Tanganyika, was not a white man's country, although there were no climatic, economic, or sociological reasons why a limited number of small owner settlers, who were prepared for a hard life, should not establish homes. He said, however, "Their problems will always be those of the precarious pioneer fringe along the margin of the world's spaces suitable for permanent settlement." And he doubted whether they would be able to survive without subsidies. He considered that settlers in large enough numbers to relieve pressure in their European homelands were quite out of the question. He expressed favor towards a system of cooperation with Africans along the line of the experience which had proved so successful in the Sudan (see page 343).

What has, in fact, been accomplished in Tanganyika? In the agricultural region of the coastal plain the products include sisal (Figures 18.12 and 18.13), coconuts, rice, and sugar cane. Around Lake Victoria rice and sugar are again cultivated, and African-grown cotton has become very important. In the scattered highland areas coffee is the most important economic crop, being produced by both African and European peoples on the Usambara highlands and the slopes of Kilimanjaro, and increasing quantities of African-grown coffee come from the highlands west of Lake Victoria. The sisal plantations—sisal being notably a crop possible on poor lands of low rainfall—are situated mainly in Tanga Province, and sisal in the years following World War II represented over half the total value of exports from the country. The industry was also the largest employer of African labor and also the most important dollar earner in the country's economy. Tea and tobacco have also been cultivated to some extent by European planters and by African cultivators.

If agricultural development has suffered serious setbacks, the mineral industry in Tanganyika has made staggering progress. An amazing find of dia-

Figures 18.12 and 18.13   Sisal industry in East Africa. Above, cutting is in progress. Below, workers are spreading drying fibers and removing blemished strands at the same time. (Courtesy East African Tourist and Travel Association.)

monds in the Shinyanga district brought diamonds into the limelight as the leading mineral product. Gold has become significant, tin and mica are being worked, and some of the indications of coal, more especially south of the central railway, may prove of importance. The lead deposits, such as Mpanda southwest of Tabora, necessitated a railway spur from the central line.

Tanganyika has not yet either a railway or a road network in any way adequate for the opening up of the country, though Dar-es-Salaam is now linked by the central railway through Tabora with both Lake Tanganyika and Lake Victoria. Dar-es-Salaam, the country's main port, lies along the north and northwest shores of an almost landlocked harbor, affording perfect protection.

Mikindani was the new port first proposed in the south to serve peanut developments, but Mtwara proved a better site. The future of both is uncertain. Prior to that, Tanga on the northern railway was the second port, serving particularly the sisal and coffee estates but with indifferent port facilities.

Zanzibar

The dominions of the Sultan of Zanzibar, until 1963 a British protectorate, comprised Zanzibar Island (640 square miles) and Pemba Island to the northeast (380 square miles), together with a small portion of the coastland of Kenya. When Zanzibar became independent in December 1963, rights to the mainland were given up. Early in 1964 a republican form of government replaced the sultanate, and in April Zanzibar was united with Tanganyika.

The port of Zanzibar lies on the sheltered western side of the island and for centuries held a dominating position in the trade of East Africa. It was a great Arab trading center, and the Arab city of the tall whitewashed houses, so familiar in Arab lands farther north, still occupies the seafront. This Arab city still offers a remarkable contrast to the small European quarter, or to the large sprawling African city, with its wattle and daub huts. Of the total population of the islands, 299,111 at the 1958 census—20 per cent—are still Arabs, and some 5 or 6 per cent (18,334) are recently immigrated Indians, into whose hands much of the trade has passed.

Before the building of the railways and the concentration of the trade of Tanganyika in the well-equipped terminal ports, the produce was brought across by small boats and transferred to larger ocean-going vessels at the port of Zanzibar. This entrepôt trade has largely disappeared, and, though Zanzibar is still an important port of call for liners, its economic interests have shifted. However, it still retains a great local coastwise trade. The climate of the islands, as so often happens, is a pleasant edition of that on the neighboring mainland, with a total rainfall of some 60 inches in Zanzibar and some 80 or 90 inches in Pemba. Though there are two rainfall maxima, one in March, April, and May, and the second in November, it is rare for a whole month to be rainless. The temperature range is small, and as a result the vegetation is the luxuriant vegetation of equatorial latitudes. In the course of centuries of long association with Indian Ocean trade, plants have been introduced into the islands from distant lands. Intensive cultivation of many crops is carried out by the inhabitants of Zanzibar, and almost every available piece of ground is made to produce something of value.

Coconut palms are numerous, large quantities of copra are exported, and the preparation of coconut oil and the manufacture of rope and matting from coir are important. But the great specialty of Zanzibar is in the production of cloves. These are actually the unopened buds of a small tree (Figure 18.14). There are some three million clove trees in large plantations, owned especially by Arabs but also found in African small holdings. It is difficult to find an adequate reason why there should have been this specialization, but it remains a fact. A serious disease that threatens the industry in Zanzibar (Figure 18.15) has resulted in a concentration on Pemba.

Figure 18.14   A healthy clove tree, Zanzibar, in full leaf. (Courtesy East African Office.)

Figure 18.15   A stricken clove plantation, Zanzibar, taken at the same date as the last picture. (Copyright Central Office of Information, London.)

If any emphasis were needed, Zanzibar offers an illuminating example of contrasts which still exist within even the area which we have here described as East Africa. A unique and fascinating small domain, with a population density of over 250 to the square mile, it offers a remarkable contrast to the vast, almost uninhabited, tracts of the neighboring mainland.

The East African groundnut scheme

No example illustrates better the difficulties which still beset any attempts to develop tropical Africa than Britain's ill-fated attempt to grow peanuts (groundnuts) on a large scale in East Africa.

Britain emerged from World War II with many acute shortages, not the least being margarine and cooking fats. It was Frank Samuel, Managing Director of the United Africa Company, itself a subsidiary of the vast Unilever concern with assets of over 500 million dollars, who visualized during a tour in 1946 the possibilities of the empty spaces of East Africa for growing peanuts, an annual crop and so one with a quick return. Britain's harassed Minister of Food seized on the idea, sent out a mission of three experts—John Wakefield, former Director of Agriculture of Tanganyika; David Martin, plantations manager of the United Africa Company; and John Rosa, banker. After nine weeks on the ground, the Wakefield Report[3] was written, soon to be accepted by the British government as a major contribution to the African population and development problem and the home food problem. This decision was reached after careful scrutiny of the report in which two strong voices, W. M. Crowther and Dunstan Skilbeck, were raised in favor of making haste slowly by pilot experiments, but the Socialist government through Minister of Food Strachey decided on full speed ahead. The United Africa Company acted as managing agents until a government corporation, the Overseas Food Corporation, could be organized and take over, which it did in March–April 1948. Meantime secondhand, heavy bush-clearing machinery was collected, especially bulldozers from American army surplus in the Philippines. Massey-Harris had already agreed to supply Canadian tractors.

The scheme was to clear 3,210,000 acres by 1953 of scrub—the dreary, useless, closely matted tangle of vegetation through which only a rhinoceros could force a way with difficulty—in "units" or farms of 30,000 acres and to secure at the end of the five years an output of 600,000 tons of peanuts. The areas chosen were:

Tanganyika Central Province (Kongwa)	450,000 acres	
Western Province (Urambo)	300,000	
Southern Province	1,650,000	
Kenya	300,000	
Northern Rhodesia	510,000	

The Central and Western Provinces were reached via the Tanganyika Central Railway from Dar-es-Salaam; the Southern Province by railway to be constructed from the new deep-water port of Mtwara near Mikindani. Advance guards of European personnel arrived at Dar-es-Salaam early in 1947; the first "cut" in the bush was actually made on April 30, 1947. Alan Wood has well described the effect on native life under the title "From Tribe to Trade Union." The chiefs cooperated in many ways, notably in securing labor, but soon their authority faded away. In the haste to get labor, a large daily ration of food (totaling 3500 calories a day, basically corn [maize], beans, meat, sugar, and oil) was issued, supplemented by cash wages

---

[3] Alan Wood, *The Groundnut Affair*, London, The Bodley Head, 1950. *A Plan for the Mechanical Production of Groundnuts in East and Central Africa*, H.M.S.O., Cmd. 7030, 1947 (The Wakefield Report). *The Future of the Overseas Food Corporation*, H.M.S.O., Cmd. 8125, 1951.

ranging from 15 shillings (2 dollars) a month upwards. Even that was too much! Prices soared, and local economies were completely upset. Although medical skill became available and was beneficial, the workers in crowded quarters missed their womenfolk and sought satisfaction elsewhere. The Dar-es-Salaam dockers organized the first trade union. There were ugly strikes. Those Africans who had served in the army seemed to have lost their mechanical skill, and, although the African quickly picked up the handling of heavy machines and could maneuver them with the best, running repairs were another matter. Soon three-quarters of all the machines were out of action.

There are many reasons which may be given for the failure of a scheme conceived in the grand manner which might have been an African T.V.A. Too much bureaucratic control was one. In January 1951 there were 1283 Europeans on the corporation staff compared with 384 on Earthmoving and Construction Limited, the company actually doing the work. The organization did not work smoothly, but primarily failure was due to lack of knowledge of the conditions (Figure 18.16). The machinery failed in its task partly perhaps because it was "secondhand," but mainly because the immensely long roots of the brush provided a tougher proposition than bush clearing in middle latitudes; the microstructure of the soil (described on page 91) defeated the disc plows; the sandy soil was "packed" by the machinery and rendered unfit for peanuts; the vagaries of the rainfall were not sufficiently appreciated. Consequently the first crops are said to have been less than the seed put in the ground.

By September 1949 it was clear the objectives could not be reached, and a revised plan for a total of 600,000 acres by 1954 was introduced, concentrating on a rotation of crops rather than peanuts. Then in January 1951 the British government was forced to abandon, in its original form, the whole project. Against an original total estimated cost of 23 million pounds, in January 1951 36 million were written off as lost, roughly 2 dollars for every man, woman, and child in Great Britain. Land already cleared was to be used for experimental purposes: four farms with about 10,000 acres under crop in Kongwa; 60,000 acres in Urambo with 13 farms. The Southern Region seems to have proved that "fully mechanized land clearing is far too costly and could be reduced by substituting hand labour," and experience suggested that cropping with peanuts, corn (maize), and millet (sorghum) should be combined with cattle grazed on grasses.

The proposals for Kenya and Northern Rhodesia were early abandoned, but permanent works of lasting value include the southern port of Mtwara, though the railway planned for extension westward to Lake Nyasa did not get far and was torn up in 1962.

The groundnut scheme reinforces Julian Huxley's words that "the most important lesson of history for Africa is to go slowly." It is an expensive

Figure 18.16   Land in southern Tanganyika cleared in preparation for peanuts. Although scrub piled in lines to form windrows has been left, should the land have been cleared in this way? (Copyright Aircraft Operating Company of Africa.)

lesson, but the day will come when with increased knowledge development will go ahead in these areas.

The Overseas Food Corporation as part of its work in East Africa set up a Scientific Department under the direction of Dr. A. H. Bunting as Chief Scientific Officer in charge of a staff of 30 or 40 scientists. His summary[4] of the work undertaken during the life of the department, 1947–1951, is a good example of the range of studies needed in tropical Africa. The soil scientists found top dressings of phosphate and nitrogen were required on all soils, but how to retain nitrogen (possibly by use of grass courses) remained unsolved. There was some evidence that a common weed played a major part in the mobilization of soil phosphate, and the retention of the weed was therefore vital. Unless there is an exact balance of nitrogen and potash, plants seem to develop abnormally; tobacco notably has a "tang" which renders it commercially of little value. It seemed that continuous cropping allowed no accumu-. lation of moisture in the soil, whereas fallowing did. Thus, following the African's system of bare fallowing, an increase of nearly 50 per cent in pea-

[4] *Nature,* **CLXVIII,** No. 4280, Nov. 10, 1951, 804–806.

nut yield resulted. Among the plants it was found that successful American types of soybean were not adapted to the equatorial equal day and night temperatures throughout the year. Sorghum needed a horny peripheral layer at maturity of the grain as a protection against storage pests; sunflowers failed to pollinate because the bees or other pollinators were too few; destructive stem borers were not affected by insecticides successful elsewhere. The *Aphis*, which carries rosette disease of peanuts, needed to have its life cycle traced before it could be controlled. Thus the scientists indicated dozens of problems to be solved before success in development could be achieved.

BIBLIOGRAPHY

Apart from the references in the text and the work of Milne and others quoted in Chapter 5, reference should be made to the various official publications of the British government, especially:

The British Territories in East and Central Africa, 1945–1950, His Majesty's Stationery Office, Cmd. 7987, 1950.

Overseas Economic Survey: British East Africa, 1948, His Majesty's Stationery Office, 1948.

Annual Reports on Kenya, Uganda and Zanzibar, His Majesty's Stationery Office.

The volume edited by J. D. Tothill, *Agriculture in Uganda* (New York, 1940), is a veritable encyclopedia on that country.

Much useful information will be found in the *East Africa Year Book and Guide,* issued by the Union Castle Steamship Company.

G. M. Hickman and W. H. G. Dickens, *The Lands and Peoples of East Africa* (London, Longmans, 1960) is a school textbook with much recent information, excellent maps, and pictures.

See also *Focus,* June 1962 (Tanganyika) and January 1964 (Uganda).

CHAPTER NINETEEN

Central Africa and
the Southern Savanna Lands

There are several reasons why separate considerations should be given to that belt of southern Africa stretching from the Atlantic shores of Portuguese Angola to the Indian Ocean along the southern part of Mozambique, or Portuguese East Africa.[1] It is a belt of Africa which lies between the equatorial forests of the Congo and the lofty plateaus of East Africa on the north and the extra-tropical white man's land of South Africa to the south (Figure 19.1). It has been pointed out repeatedly in this book that perhaps the most natural division of the continent of Africa is into river basins, but that rarely do river basins coincide with existing political divisions. In very broad general terms the area to be considered now is the basin of the great Zambezi with the addition of various peripheral tracts. In terms of political units we shall consider the great territory of Angola on the west and the huge area of central Africa occupied by Northern Rhodesia, Southern Rhodesia, and Nyasaland (now Malawi), the sphere of British influence. To round off the picture, the land below the plateau which forms the southern part of Portuguese East Africa and through which the Zambezi passes on its way to the sea is considered here rather than entirely with East Africa, where the plateau element predominates.

In the great French *Géographie universelle,* Dr. Maurette considers the whole of southern Africa together, and it is perhaps natural that the British territories of the Rhodesias and Nyasaland should be linked for purposes of study with the formerly British Union of South Africa. There are in fact some very interesting contrasts between the two, contrasts which have their roots partly in physical geography—the transition from a temperate environment to a tropical—and partly in historical geography.

---

[1] The correct spelling is Moçambique, but it is usually anglicized as Mozambique.

413

Figure 19.1   Central Africa and the Zambezi basin.

Historical geography

The story of the exploration and subsequent organization of this part of Africa has been briefly considered in Chapter 2. The Portuguese established settlements at an early date on both the Atlantic and the Pacific shores. The discovery of Angola was claimed by the Portuguese Diogo Cão in 1482, and points on the coast have been occupied continuously by the Portuguese since 1505, with the exception of the years 1641–1648, when the Portuguese were temporarily ousted by the Dutch. Comparatively little, however, was done to develop the vast area. The great drain of population from Portugal to Brazil in the sixteenth, seventeenth, and eighteenth centuries drew Portuguese attention away from Africa. As a result the boundaries of the Portuguese sphere in Angola remained loosely defined, and along the south the long-disputed frontier was not finally settled until 1926, when it was agreed that the Cunene River with the Rua Cana Falls, 406 feet high, were to be shared as far as the water was concerned equally between the governments of Angola and the Union of South Africa. On the Indian Ocean side the great Portuguese trading company, the Mozambique Company, administered the area long settled and claimed by the Portuguese until as late as 1942.

It will be recalled that the Portuguese claim to the whole of the hinterland stretching right into the heart of Central Africa and an attempt to exclude other nationals led directly to the activities of that British Rockefeller, Cecil John Rhodes. The heart of Africa in this latitude may almost be called Livingstone's land. We have noted how Dr. Livingstone, arriving in Africa as a medical missionary in 1841, proceeded at once to the mission station at Kuruman in Bechuanaland. He early discovered Lake Ngami, now in northern Bechuanaland, and the neighboring Okovango, and in 1850 reached the Upper Zambezi. His determination despite illness to follow this great river to its mouth led to his next journey, his discovery of the Victoria Falls in 1855, and his tracing the Zambezi to its mouth by the following May.

Thus it was Livingstone who brought the knowledge of this heart of Africa directly to the English-speaking peoples. It was Rhodes who brought the territories into the British sphere of commercial and political influence. Rhodes worked with amazing speed. In 1887 the Portuguese attempted to close the Zambezi basin; in 1888 Rhodes secured from the King of the Matabele exclusive rights to work minerals. Matabeleland is the core of Southern Rhodesia. In 1889 the great British South Africa Company, formed by Rhodes for the purpose of exercising these rights, set to work, and by 1891 the limits of Portuguese and British spheres of influence had been settled. Nyasaland became a British protectorate, and the huge territories, now Northern and Southern Rhodesia, were handed over to Rhodes's company.

It must not be thought that the advent of the British South Africa Company meant the advent of a period of exploitation. There is a twofold contrast continuing to this day between the Republic of South Africa on the one hand and the Rhodesias with Nyasaland on the other. In the Republic of South Africa the dominant white element is still the Afrikaans-speaking Boers; and, as we shall see in the next chapter, the effort to maintain South Africa as a white man's country involves a varying degree of racial discrimination. The British elements in South Africa have never been completely in accord with the dominant Boer view on these matters, and in the Rhodesias the development has been entirely in the hands of the British. Until the movement northwest of Boer farmers after World War II, there was only a small Afrikaans-speaking element in British central Africa. Consequently the development of the Rhodesias, although carried out to secure both agricultural and mineral products needed by European peoples, has been carried out in conjunction with a liberal policy towards the African inhabitants, and the importance of improving their standard of living, if not always stressed as fully as it might have been, has always been present.

British Central Africa

There are ancient ruins and mines in Southern Rhodesia's territory which have intrigued and still intrigue anthropologists and archeologists. The earliest inhabitants of the country, who may have been Bushmen, left behind rock carvings and colored paintings of hunting scenes on the walls of caves and rocks. Scattered through the country there are large numbers of workings from which former inhabitants gained gold, silver, copper, and iron. Though extensive, the deposits were not worked below water level, and it would seem that the workers at that time had no knowledge of how to remove water by pumping. There are several hundred elaborate stone buildings which may or may not be the work of the same mining people. Most famous of these are the ruins of Zimbabwe. Who were the builders of these great erections? Were they medieval Bantu? Were they members of peoples who have since disappeared? There are those who urge that some of the obscure references in the Old Testament are to the rulers of this great southern land. Who was the first European to reach Zimbabwe is not precisely known. It was probably the Portuguese Franciscan monk, Francis Silveira, who is believed to have reached there in 1561 and suffered martyrdom. In the three centuries which followed, before the journeys of Livingstone, the country must have been visited from time to time by missionaries and traders, but otherwise remained forgotten. Although gold was discovered in the area in 1865, the discovery did not give rise to any immediate movement, so that it was the concession granted by King Lobengula to Rhodes and his associates which really started the development of the area.

It is interesting that when the territory was proclaimed a British sphere of influence on July 20, 1888, it was known as Zambezia, thus emphasizing the association of what are now Northern and Southern Rhodesia with the Zambezi River. The pioneer column of settlers, consisting of 187 Europeans and 150 Africans, left Cecil Rhodes's farm near Kimberley on May 6, 1890. They were joined by police and guides, reached the site of the present town of Salisbury on September 12, 1890, and commenced the building of a fort. The British protectorate over Bechuanaland was declared on May 9, 1891, thus protecting the route to the new settlements.

South African farmers soon evinced an interest in the new lands, and there was never any prohibition to Boer farmers. They were dissuaded from occupying part of the country by force and were invited to take up farms, which some of them later did. The arrival of the settlers and various restrictions necessary for the preservation of peace led to some resentment by the

Matabele. In 1893 they attacked a post of the British South Africa Company, and war followed. It was brought to an end by the occupation of Lobengula's kraal near the present site of Bulawayo, which was founded on its present position in the following year, 1894.

In 1895 Northern and Southern Zambezia officially became Northern and Southern Rhodesia. The subsequent history of Southern Rhodesia includes the revolt of the Mashonas, but is closely bound up with the improvement of means of access by the coming of the railway. That from Kimberley reached Bulawayo in 1897, that from the Portuguese port of Beira reached Salisbury in 1899. The Zambezi gorge was bridged below the falls in 1904 (Figure 19.2), and one enters upon the modern phase.

The question whether Southern Rhodesia, which then had a European population between 30,000 and 40,000, should join the Union of South Africa or have a resident governor was decided by referendum in 1923. The result was for a resident governor, and on October 21, 1923, Southern Rhodesia became a self-governing colony of the British Commonwealth. Gradually the new state acquired mineral and other rights from the old South Africa Company, and Southern Rhodesia developed along modern lines.

Figure 19.2 The rail and road bridge over the Zambezi gorge below the Victoria Falls. This bridge, completed as a rail bridge in 1903, was for long the only bridge across the Zambezi linking Northern and Southern Rhodesia. (Official photograph: J. Rau.)

Referring briefly to the history of Northern Rhodesia, we see that it was not until 1911 that the separate territories of Barotseland, or Northwestern Rhodesia, and Northeastern Rhodesia joined, and it was not until 1924 that a first governor was appointed in Northern Rhodesia, taking over the administration of the country from the South Africa Company. Thus the development of Northern Rhodesia came later than that of Southern.

Though geographically Nyasaland falls within the Zambezi basin, being drained by the Shiré—that important tributary of the Zambezi—the history of Nyasaland has been somewhat different. Modern roads now make it possible to travel between Northern Rhodesia and Nyasaland, but the natural outlet of the country is along the general line of the Shiré River to the Zambezi at Chindio, and from thence down the navigable stream to the port of Chinde near its mouth. Not till the bridging of the Zambezi in 1935 did Nyasaland become part of the commercial hinterland of the port of Beira. Formerly known as the British Central Africa Protectorate, the area was renamed Nyasaland in 1907, having been transferred to the control of the British Colonial Office in 1904.

The three British territories in the heart of Africa clearly have certain common interests. An advisory and consultative body to deal with nonpolitical subjects, such as communication, health, education, and statistics, known as the Central African Council, was in due course set up. The question of the closer association of Northern and Southern Rhodesia and Nyasaland came to the fore in 1951, when active consideration was given to the possibility of forming a British Central Africa with dominion status, or its equivalent. By this time the three territories had developed along rather different lines. By virtue of its southern situation, the elevation of the great central tract of the country above 3000 feet, its well-distributed and adequate rainfall, Southern Rhodesia has become a land of white settlers predominantly of British origin, though white settlers relying to a large extent on African labor. Its chief towns, Bulawayo, Gwelo, and Salisbury, are European in concept and execution. European agricultural production maintains a dominant note, despite the existence of the important coal field at Wankie, and despite the development of the iron ore deposits for the works at Que Que.

The larger territory of Northern Rhodesia, with savanna or bush cover, nearer the equator, generally lower in elevation, has not been recognized to the same extent as a white settlers' country. But its richness in minerals, not only in the part of the country which lies along the Congo Katanga border and is part of the great copper belt of central Africa, but also in the mineral deposits still being explored and developed in other parts of the territory, has given Northern Rhodesia an importance in world economy of a different character from that of Southern Rhodesia. In some respects Northern Rhodesia has overtaken in importance its older settled neighbor to the south.

Nyasaland, the most densely peopled of the three, has but a handful of white settlers. There are very important possibilities in the development of plantation agriculture, but up to the present workers from Nyasaland have gone elsewhere for work.

Could these three territories, with their different backgrounds, form a satisfactory union? The Federation of the Rhodesias and Nyasaland was set up in 1953, and the first federal parliament met at Salisbury in 1954. Progress was not smooth; in 1963 Nyasaland withdrew and the Federation was terminated.

Southern Rhodesia

Southern Rhodesia consists of a broad belt of highland more than 4000 feet above sea level running from southwest to northeast. The northern side drains to the Zambezi, the southern to the Limpopo. The plateau is generally of rolling relief, and the 3000-foot contour may be taken as separating the healthy high veld from the low veld, where malaria is one of the disadvantages associated with climatic conditions. The natural vegetation is a savanna grassland, passing into open forests, and in the Zambezi lowlands to denser forests where Rhodesian teak and Rhodesian mahogany are obtained.

Along the eastern border between Umtali and Melsetter the elevation increases and the country is more dissected so as to become mountainous in character. This is a well-watered area, and the average rainfall between 20 and 35 inches over the bulk of the plateau renders it excellent agricultural country. It is in the south and west that irrigation becomes necessary as a precaution against drought. Soil erosion is a problem, especially owing to the heavy character of rainstorms.

On the European farms which occupy the upland belt, corn is the main crop, and cattle rearing is of great importance. Rinderpest, which seems to have broken out first in 1895, has played great havoc, but strenuous efforts have succeeded so well in curbing the disease that there are huge ranches for beef cattle, and near the main railway through Bulawayo, Gwelo, and Salisbury dairying is firmly established, with creameries at each of the large towns. With the development of cold-storage facilities there is a growing export in chilled beef, while pig and poultry rearing flourish, dependent largely on the corn crop, with associated bacon factories. The Witwatersrand and the mining districts of the Katanga offer markets which are not very far distant.

There is a general correlation between the more infertile soils and lower rainfall in Matabeleland with cattle ranching. Where better soils and more reliable rainfall permit, arable cultivation on the European farms becomes dominant. Tobacco, introduced as a commercial crop in 1910, has become of paramount importance on areas of light sandy soil overlying granite (Fig-

Figure 19.3   A crop of tobacco in Southern Rhodesia. Tobacco accounts for two-fifths of the value of the country's exports and is the leading cash crop of the white farmer settlers. (Courtesy Southern Rhodesia Government.)

ure 19.3). Cirtus fruits grow well, and there is an export of oranges as far as Europe. Other crops include cotton, peanuts, sunflowers for seeds, beans, fiber plants, and vegetables for local use. In the African belts subsistence agriculture is the general rule, with corn occupying four-fifths of the cultivated land.

The fact that the lower lands draining to the Zambezi remain seriously infested with tsetse fly deters development there.

Turning to minerals, we see that the coalfield at Wankie (Figure 19.4) with its output of 4 million tons a year is insufficient to meet all demands. Some goes northwards to the Katanga, much is consumed by the railways and the towns of Southern Rhodesia, and coke is made and supplied to the iron and steel works at Que Que, which began production in 1948, using local ores. Gold, worked from time immemorial in small scattered mines, remains an important mineral product, but the small scattered copper mines do not compare in significance with those of Northern Rhodesia. Chrome ore, now extensively worked, large reserves of asbestos, mica, and others may be taken as indications that the mineral resources of Southern Rhodesia are far from being fully exploited. Since December 1959, when the first supply of power from Kariba (see p. 426) became available, the whole situation has changed.

The railways both in Northern and Southern Rhodesia were constructed in part to permit the development of minerals. In order to avoid expensive bridging over streams they followed where possible main watersheds. They do not thus necessarily tap the richest agricultural districts; but the development of roads, marked in Southern Rhodesia as elsewhere in Africa, has to a considerable extent obviated the necessity for further railway construction.

Southern Rhodesia has attracted well over 200,000 white settlers. They are settlers in the sense that they make their permanent homes in the country. A large number are town dwellers. Roughly one-third of the population of both Salisbury and Bulawayo is white, and the larger towns have more than half the total white population of the country. When World War II ended there were about 75,000 Europeans. A large influx began, rising from 7000 in 1946 to 17,000 in 1948 and over 18,000 in 1956, dropping in later years. But the immigrants were of a different character from those of prewar years. It is recorded that in 1948 28 per cent of all new arrivals went to manufacturing industries in the towns, only 7 per cent to the farms, leaving a large proportion for administrative, distributional, and other occupations not directly productive; this general trend has been continued. At first sight it might appear that this urban growth is undesirable in a country where so much remains to be done in the open lands. Actually it enables a balanced urban-rural economy to be developed; there is not the pressure of the white farmer tending to encroach on African farmlands that there is or was in Kenya. In this heartland of Southern Rhodesia are the basic requirements of modern industry—coal, iron, metals, water power, and a good climate (see

Figure 19.4 The Wankie Colliery of Southern Rhodesia. This photograph shows the modern by-product coke ovens making coke for Southern Rhodesia's iron and steel industry. (Official photograph.)

Figure 19.5). Secondary industries such as the Gatooma textile mills and the machine-tool industry of Salisbury illustrate the current trend.

About half of the African population lives in the reserves. The remainder is employed directly or indirectly by Europeans.

Southern Rhodesia entered the iron and steel business in a substantial way when the Rhodesian Iron and Steel Commission established a plant located at Que Que near good deposits of iron ore and supplies of limestone and in direct main rail communication with the coking coals of Wankie (500 miles) and supplied with electric power from Umniati. The plant consisted of a blast furnace, an open hearth furnace, and Bessemer converters, with a capacity of 33,000 tons of finished steel. Since 1950 developments have been favored by iron ore deposits nearby at Buhera, coal deposits near Beit Bridge, and the availability of Kariba power. A certain slowing down of economic development may be linked with the political situation. As noted above, Southern Rhodesia has been self-governing since 1923 but is controlled by its white minority, those who have built up the country. On principle there is opposition from the new independent states of tropical Africa.

Northern Rhodesia

The emphasis in Northern Rhodesia is on minerals. Along the frontier at least 400 million tons of copper ore with a metallic content averaging 4 to 5 per cent have been proved, and this is only one of the mineral ores. The older mining settlement of Broken Hill with its large output of lead and silver was one of the reasons for the early extension of the railway line northward from Livingstone.

The white population, 74,000 in mid-1961 (compare 2,400,000 African), is concerned mainly with mining and other economic developments. There seems to be even on the highlands a persistent form, mild yet recurrent, of malaria affecting white settlers. It may be that they would gain the immunity from it in time which seems to be enjoyed by African inhabitants. At present modern forms of development in Northern Rhodesia are scattered, and as far as development under European influence is concerned, it is restricted to the known mineral areas and to one or two other specialized pockets of land.

The extreme south of the country in the Zambezi valley west of Livingstone is an area yielding good hardwoods—Rhodesian teak and Rhodesian mahogany. In this area Livingstone, which until 1935 was the administrative capital of Northern Rhodesia, has sawmilling establishments. The heart of Africa is still in the stage of trial and error. It was agreed that the original site of Livingstone was proving itself to be unhealthy, with the result that shortly after it ceased to be the capital the whole town was bodily moved to higher and supposedly healthier ground some miles away. The capital was shifted to Lusaka, farther north along the railway.

Figure 19.5   Developing industry in Southern Rhodesia. The first Fords roll off the assembly line, August 1961.

There are two interesting pockets of white settlements, both far removed from the railway. One is at Abercorn in the highlands south of Tanganyika, where there are government plantations, and here the outlet is via the lake and the Central Tanganyikan railway. The second is around Fort Jameson on the Nyasaland border where tobacco planting has become important. This area is linked by motor road to Blantyre in Nyasaland and thence by rail to the port of Beira.

Nyasaland (State of Malawi)

The long narrow strip of Nyasaland lies mainly to the west of Lake Nyasa, and this too is a country where development in the modern sense is still in isolated pockets. At the southern end of the country the healthy Shiré highlands have become the focus of the tea and tobacco production. The growing export trade centers on the principal town of Blantyre, though the administrative capital is at Zomba. Power development on the Shiré River would make possible great changes.

The year 1961 marked a new era in political development. In August, Hastings Banda became Prime Minister under a new constitution. But the total population is under 3 million and resources are limited. Improvement in subsistence agriculture is taking place and the encouragement of fisheries on Lake Nyasa will enhance a much needed supply of protein. From being a British protectorate, Nyasaland became independent in 1964. Its name is to be changed to the State of Malawi.

Angola

Angola, otherwise known as Portuguese West Africa, is the largest of the Portuguese colonies and stretches from the Cunene River in the south to the Congo estuary in the north. Along the coastline north of the Congo mouth is a small enclave lying between former Belgian and French territory, known as the Cabdina enclave, which is administered at a detached portion of Angola (see Figure 17.2).

The total area of Angola is a little short of half a million square miles (481,000), but the total population does not reach 5 million, so that the average density is low. Its capital, the multiracial city of Luanda, has 165,000 inhabitants, which makes it the third largest Portuguese city. Its full name is São Paulo de Luanda (or Loanda) and it was founded in 1575 and was for long the slave port for the African-Brazilian slave route. The slave trade was officially abolished in 1836.

Angola occupies a transitional position between the Congo basin to the northeast, the plateau of southern Africa to the southeast, and the coastal semideserts of the southwest. The east-west axis, along which runs the Benguela railway, is the Bié or Benguela plateau, averaging over 5000 feet and rising in places to more than 7000 feet above sea level. Along the 1000 miles of Atlantic coastline is a belt of lowland of varying width which is dry (20 inches rainfall in the north, less than 10 in the south) but surprisingly cool owing to the influence of the cool Benguela current. The average temperature for the year at Moçamedes is only 69°F. Inland the country rises, often by a series of terraces, to the plateau. Over most of the interior the rainfall is between 40 and 60 inches, with a long rainy season in the north and a shorter one in the south. On the higher parts frosts are common in the dry season. As one might expect, practically the whole of Angola is covered by various forms of savanna—a little forest along the river valleys of the north which just reaches the Congo oil-palm country.

African subsistence agriculture depends largely on corn, manioc, beans, and tobacco, with upland rice, peanuts, and even wheat on the higher parts of the plateau. Commercial agriculture depends upon transport facilities. The export of coffee (45 per cent of total exports), mainly from Luanda to America, is largely responsible for the rapid growth of that city. The north produces palm oil, sugar cane, and cocoa (Cabinda). Cotton is a natural crop of the savannas, and sisal is produced in certain drier areas. Cattle are reared extensively on the upland savannas. There is a considerable amount of coastal fishing. Both salted fish and salt itself are sent inland.

The Congo Kasai diamond fields extend into Angola, and diamonds are the second export. Manganese ore is mined along the Luanda-Malange railway; other minerals, including copper, are known to exist, and oil was discovered just south of Luanda in 1955.

Angola has a growing mileage of metalled highways, and much of the existing economic development has taken place along the four railways inland from the coast. The Luanda railway from the capital, which is also a good port, serves the coffee- and cotton-producing lands. From Porto Amboin, unfortunately with few facilities, a short line serves a rich agricultural hinterland. From the growing port of Lobito and Benguela the railway was completed right across Angola to the Congo border in 1928 and reached the Katanga in 1931. It serves the higher part of the plateau, including the city of Nova Lisboa. In the south the port of Moçamedes (Mossamedes) has another line on to the plateau, but the better port of Porto Alexandre has no railway into the interior.

Undoubtedly, Angola is a land of great potential; much must depend on political developments. The vegetation, which has been carefully described, affords a basis for a study of development possibilities.[2]

The problems of the Zambezi Basin

More and more attention is being given to the need to consider the Zambezi basin as a whole.

In Chapter 3 the Zambezi was referred to as a typical African river. In the 1700 miles of its course it flows through three distinct regions. The first is its plateau course, lying partly in Angola, partly in Northern Rhodesia, but receiving also intermittent streams from the great Okovango swamplands of northern Bechuanaland. The second part of its course is the Middle Zambezi, or Rhodesian trough, essentially the part lying below Victoria Falls where the river passes through a succession of relatively narrow valleys over waterfalls and rapids. The key to its development lies at the lower end of this course in the Kariba Gorge, where the Zambezi narrows to less than 100 yards as it cuts though a rocky barrier. Shortly below, it reaches its third course through the Mozambique plain.

Reference has been made elsewhere to the possibility of small irrigation works, using the upper headstreams of the Zambezi (Chapter Four) but the Kariba Gorge offered an ideal site for the construction of a large-scale dam. After rejecting alternative proposals for a dam on the Kafue River, work was started on the Kariba Dam in 1955, and the first stage completed in December, 1959 (Figure 19.6), when a supply of power from the first machine

[2] H. K. A. Shaw, "The Vegetation of Angola," *Jour. Ecology,* **XXXV**, 1947, 23–48.

Figure 19.6   The Kariba dam, nearing completion in August 1960. (Official photograph.)

of 100 Mw capacity became available. A final capacity of 900 Mw is planned, to be followed if needed by another station to be constructed on the Kafue River (Figure 19.7). Another project is planned for the Nkula Falls on the Shiré River to serve Nyasaland. The Kariba Lake is 175 miles long and has an average width of 12 miles. Fortunately the population which had to be moved was small, and fishing in the new lake is expected to provide a needed source of protein. As the waters rose many animals were trapped on temporary islands, and their rescue gave rise to the much-publicized "Operation Noah." An unexpected difficulty arose in the very rapid growth of a waterweed threatening to clog the power station, but biologists seem convinced that it is a temporary phenomenon. The Kariba Dam provides a new line of communication between Northern and Southern Rhodesia; power is available northward to Lusaka and southward to all the main towns of Southern Rhodesia. What has been called the "little Kariba" is the Kyle Dam, 200 feet high and 1025 feet long, completed in 1961, southeast of Fort Victoria in Southern Rhodesia.

In a survey of the whole Zambezi basin and various projects (Figure 19.8), Professor J. H. Wellington[3] drew this conclusion about the northern Kalahari: "There seems to be no other place in Africa where so much agricultural development is possible at so little cost, and the success of the French in the swamps of the upper Niger shows what planning, engineering skill and sound irrigational practice can accomplish in terrain of this character. One looks

[3] "Zambezi-Okovango Development Project," *Geog. Rev.,* **XXXIX,** 1949, 552–567.
Geog. Rev., **XXXVII,** 1947, 351–368.

Figure 19.7   The Kafue gorge. (Official photograph.)

Figure 19.8   The Zambezi-Okovango relationships and the Kariba-Kafue projects. (1) Approximate limits of the Kariba reservoir. (2) Faults bounding the Middle Zambezi. (3) Border of present and former swamps of the Okovango delta. (From F. Debenham. *Geog. Rev.* 1949. Courtesy of the *Geographical Review*, American Geographical Society.)

forward to the time when the trans-Kalahari railway will not only connect Southern Rhodesia with the west coast but will also serve a great food-producing area of two million acres, now only the playground of crocodiles, hippos, and fish hawks." The project still remains in the future.

The Bangweulu swamps of Central Africa

Although lying in the part of Northern Rhodesia outside the Zambezi basin, these great swamps were investigated by Professor Debenham,[4] who drew attention to problems common to other parts of Africa.

In the first place we have here another of the great inland deltas, a natural consequence of the plateau character of the surface of the heart of Africa. Here there have been periodic rises and falls in the level of water, and because of the accumulation of vegetation the swamp water is not level but has a pronounced gradient from northeast to southwest of some 3 inches in a mile. The swamps not only cover 3000 square miles, but also are the home of some thousands of people engaged in fishing and the growing of cassava.

Should such an area if possible be drained with the idea of adding to Africa's productive capacity and vast area of fertile alluvial soil, or would this simply destroy the important fishing industry and upset the African cultivators' careful adjustment to existing conditions? That adjustment can be only partial. Changes in water level are at once evident in drowned villages and gardens, and the now submerged Lunga Bank was once densely populated. Surely there could be no clearer proof that Africa still holds many problems for which we have no ready solution.

BIBLIOGRAPHY

In addition to references in the text, the following works will be found useful. A convenient short summary has been issued by the British government entitled *Central African Territories: Geographical, Historical and Economic Survey,* His Majesty's Stationery Office, Cmd. 8234, 1951. There is an *Official Yearbook of the Southern Rhodesian Government* published at Salisbury, but it does not appear annually. There is a *Northern Rhodesia Official Handbook* issued at Lusaka, with an extensive bibliography. A full survey on *The Soils, Vegetation and Agricultural Systems of Northwestern Rhodesia,* by C. G. Trapnell and J. N. Clothier, was published at Lusaka in 1937. On Nyasaland an *Annual Report* is issued in London (His Majesty's Stationery Office). F. Debenham's *Nyasaland* (London: H.M.S.O.) 1956, written by a geographer, is particularly informative. See also I. S. Van Dongen, *Focus,* October 1956 (Angola), March 1956 (The Federation of Rhodesia and Nyasaland). For Portuguese territories see James Duffy, *Portuguese Africa* (Cambridge: Harvard University Press), 1959.

[4] *Geog. Rev.,* **XXXVII**, 1947, 351–368.

CHAPTER TWENTY

South Africa[1]

Historical introduction

Mastery of the Cape of Good Hope meant the control of the commerce between Europe and India. That was the reason for the early Portuguese interest in the Cape; that was the reason that the Dutch East India Company sent Jan van Riebeeck in 1652 to establish a settlement on the shores of Table Bay under the shadow of Table Mountain; that was the reason that the British dispossessed the Dutch temporarily in 1795 and permanently in 1806. It is van Riebeeck's ship which has long been pictured on the penny stamps of the Union of South Africa, and the Afrikaans-speaking South Africans regard this as their "Mayflower." Little remained of former Portuguese interests, and it was not the intention of the Dutch to establish a colony—simply a rewatering and revictualing halt on the way to India. But, as we have already indicated in Chapter 2, when the settlement became firmly established, expansion was inevitable. The hinterland was occupied by Hottentots, who, their tribal organization broken down and decimated by plague, became the white man's servants while nominally remaining free. From the first the settlement and later the colony depended upon these Hottentot servants and on imported Malay and African slaves. Unlike the Hottentots, the Bushmen farther in the hinterland showed an incapability of benefiting from contact with the white man and sought only to preserve their isolation by bows and poisoned arrows. They became practically extinct.

By 1795 the Dutch colony had expanded to some 15,000—free "burghers" who had retired from the company and remained, together with a few pioneer settlers on the one hand and the servants of the Dutch East India Company on the other. The whole colony resented the harsh restrictions im-

---

[1] I am greatly indebted to Dr. Monica Cole for valuable comments on this chapter. Her work on *South Africa* (1961) should be consulted on all aspects of the geography of the southern part of the continent.

posed by the company, and they were ripe for revolt when in August 1795 the Dutch capitulated to the British, whose occupation of the Cape was a strategic move against the French. Actually the British held the Cape from 1795 to 1803 in the name of the Prince of Orange, then a refugee from the French, living in England. Although the British removed all restrictions on trading, things did not go smoothly for long. The flow of European goods was cut off; the Dutch, although willing to work hard for themselves, had the tradition that to work for others was for blacks and slaves. The British objected to the harsh Boer attitude toward the Africans, though it differed but little from the attitude of white people in European North America at the time. It has already been indicated how eventually the Great Trek started in 1836. The establishment of the Orange Free State and the Transvaal Republic followed. By way of contrast, Natal was proclaimed British in 1843 and made a province of the Cape Colony the next year. With the recognition of the independence of the Transvaal in 1852 and of the Orange Free State in 1854, the four provinces of the future Union of South Africa—two British (Cape of Good Hope and Natal) and two Boer—were broadly defined.

In 1877 the impoverished Transvaal was being harassed by several warlike African tribes. The British stepped in, annexed the country, and restored order. But the old problem remained. The Boers needed military assistance but hated interference by the British government; the British felt the need to protect whites against blacks but regarded the Boer treatment of Africans as the root of the trouble. The result was the First Boer War (1880–1881), with a British defeat and the Transvaal again independent.

Then came the discovery of the richest goldfield in the world, the Rand Goldfields. The Boers had no capital to work the deposits; British capital and Western industrialization poured into the country. The patriarchal Boers, headed by President Paul Kruger, hated these "outlanders" (uitlanders); they tried to tap their wealth by taxation while denying them rights of citizenship. The coup d'état, known as the Jameson Raid, failed, and the British found themselves involved in the costly Boer War of 1899–1902 against a wily foe, thoroughly used to the terrain. The British were several times besieged, notably at Ladysmith and Mafeking. The relief of the latter on May 17, 1900, resulted in such wild rejoicing by crowds in London that the word "mafficking" was long used to denote extravagant crowd behavior.

By the Treaty of Vereeniging (1902) the Boers surrendered. Fortunately great men on the British side like Lord Milner were matched by great men among the Boers—General Botha and General Smuts. The Boers were granted British citizenship and given 15 million dollars with which to restock their farms, and other measures were immediately put in hand to restore the devastated areas. Within three years the Transvaal and Orange Free State were granted responsible government; a little later, after two years of discussion, the four colonies joined to form the Union of South Africa with dominion status (1910). In the World Wars of 1914–1918 and 1939–1945 South Africans, Boer and British alike, fought side by side with Britain.

Before considering subsequent events it will be well to examine the population problem.

The population of South Africa

In order to maintain the domestic life of the settlement the Dutch East India Company, especially between 1685 and 1688, sent out numbers of orphan girls as well as about 150 French Huguenot refugees. There was little to tie either the Dutch orphans or the French refugees to their mother countries, and the growth of illiteracy is not surprising. With little contact or fresh immigration from Holland after 1688, they even abandoned their own language of Holland for a limited patois, the *Taal*—the origin of Afrikaans, which includes many African, especially Kaffir, words. For twenty years after the British occupation in 1795 the colony remained essentially Dutch, but the British supplied troops as protection against Kaffir and Bantu inroads. It was largely to secure a new frontier that 4000 selected (out of 90,000 who applied) British immigrants were settled on the west side of the Fish River in 1820 (the Albany settlement). By that time the European population, mainly of Dutch descent, numbered 42,000. The Albany settlers founded Port Elizabeth and Grahamstown and drifted to Cape Town. The more influential worked for freedom of speech and forced not only a more liberal government policy but a substitution of English institutions for Dutch. With the abolition of slavery and the Great Trek, the stage was set for the Cape to become predominantly English speaking.

The other English-speaking stronghold was Natal. The original settlers of 1824 whose presence deterred the Boer trekkers formed a small group, so that Natal was annexed to Cape Colony in 1844, placed under a separate government in 1845, but in 1856 was established as a separate colony. Zululand was added to Natal in 1897 and some districts of Transvaal transferred in 1903.

In the white colonization of South Africa there are certain interesting points of comparison with North America. South Africa is outside the tropics and climatically a "white man's country," just as North America is. Colonization was with the object of cultivating the land, and permanent settlement in both cases took place from the seventeenth century onward. In South Africa there were two language streams—Dutch-speaking and English-speaking—which may be compared with the French-speaking and English-speaking in North America. Afrikaans has moved farther from the original Dutch than has French-Canadian from French mainly because of the incorporation of African words. At the time when the South African settlers spread out over what became the Cape Province the Bantu had not yet reached the area, so that apart from the Hottentots and Bushmen the whites did not have to dispossess the Africans of their lands as the Indians were gradually dispossessed in North America. The clash occurred in the southeast Cape Province in the area still designated as the Border.

The need for labor led to importation of slaves from other parts of Africa and Malaya and later of indentured labor from India and elsewhere. The immigrant labor has remained to constitute a race problem—in which East Indians in South Africa may be compared with Negroes in the United States. We are familiar with the old frontiersman's adage, "The only good Indian is a dead one." This bears comparison with the older white South African's view of the blacks; not that they were better dead, but must be regarded only as inferior beings to be used as servants and could not be treated as equals. To some the old slavery was the right answer.

Just as the United States revolted from rigid and stupid control so the Dutch in South Africa were ripe for revolt in 1795. What in the ordinary course of human affairs might have become a separate Afrikaans-speaking United States of South Africa and an English-speaking Dominion of South Africa became, by supreme statesmanship on both sides after the Boer War, the Union of South Africa in 1910.

To the United States and Canada the Indian problem has become essentially a moral one—responsibility for the remnants of erstwhile fine people. To the United States the Negro problem is one of a difficult minority. Here South Africa is in a very different and vastly more difficult position. The whites are in a minority of about 1 to 4; there is a bottomless reservoir of Negro Africans in the whole continent to the north. A democracy of equal citizenship for white and black and equal voting rights would immediately give the Negro African control of South Africa; hence the present dilemma.

The Representation of Natives Act of 1936 provided for the direct representation of native Africans in the Senate—four additional to the twenty-eight elected Senators and eight nominated (four with special knowledge of native affairs), but all Senators had to be of European descent. The House of Assembly had 153 elected members, of whom three were native members. Thus the African point of view was directly represented, but obviously in no sense in proportion to numbers. A very comprehensive study of the whole racial position at the time is contained in Professor J. M. Tinley's book, *The Native Labor Problem of South Africa.*[2]

The conclusions that Professor Tinley drew were depressing. He pointed out that to all intents and purposes the Union of South Africa was already an independent republic, and its policies such as those towards the Africans

[2] University of North Carolina Press, 1942. See also G. W. Broomfield, *Colour Conflict,* London (Edinburgh House Press), 1943.

could and did contrast sharply with those of the British government in London administering the British African colonies and protectorates.[3] Although successive South African governments varied in their liberality toward the Africans, the Nationalists under Dr. D. F. Malan (elected to power June 4, 1948) became much less tolerant than the previous United Africa party under General Smuts, and all were bent on maintaining the supremacy of the whites and regarding South Africa as a white man's country. The Malan government declared its policy to be one of "apartheid"—the segregation of the Africans into specific areas.

The white man made South Africa, and it would be wrong to assume that the determination for the country to remain under white control came exclusively from the Afrikaans-speaking population. But the whole policy of racial discrimination was and is opposed to world trends and to the policy of other members of the British Commonwealth. In that regard, coupled with South Africa's refusal to admit United Nations authority over Southwest Africa, the Union of South Africa had become an embarrassment to Britain and the Commonwealth. On October 5, 1960, a referendum was held among the 1,800,426 white voters for or against the Union's becoming a republic on May 31, 1961. The voting was 52 per cent in favor, the voting in the Cape being almost equal, that in Natal overwhelmingly against. A republic was declared, and almost immediately South Africa left the Commonwealth.

Table 20.1   South Africa: Area and Populations of the Four Provinces

Year	Area in square miles	Europeans	Non-Europeans	Total	Density
1904	472,550	1,116,806	4,059,018	5,175,824	11
1911		1,276,242	4,697,152	5,973,394	13
1921		1,519,488	5,409,092	6,928,580	15
1936		2,003,857	7,586,041	9,589,898	20
1946	472,494	2,335,460	8,923,398	11,258,858	24
1951	472,359	2,641,689	10,029,763	12,671,452	27
1960		3,067,638	12,773,490	15,841,128	33

Increase of Europeans (white) over 42 years, 1904–1946, was 2.6 per cent per annum, but in 9 years, 1951–1960, was 1.6 per cent per annum.

Increase of non-Europeans over 42 years, 1904–1946, was 2.9 per cent per annum, but in 9 years, 1951–1960, was under 1.0 per cent.

This table illustrates the very rapid population growth after the establishment of the Union of South Africa (see also Figure 20.1). Both European and non-European populations have been growing at a rate roughly twice that of the world average.

[3] See *Labour Supervision in the Colonial Empire, 1937–1943*, London, His Majesty's Stationery Office, 1945.

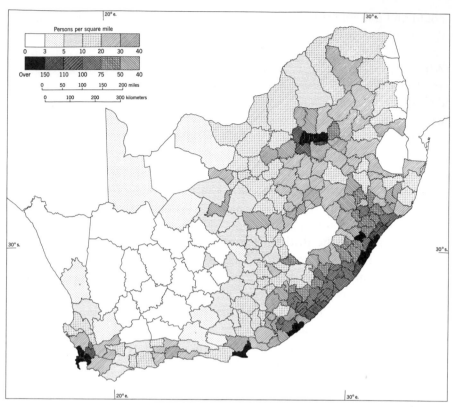

Figure 20.1 The density of population in South Africa by magisterial districts, based on the Census of 1946.

Officially Republic of South Africa, or Republiek van Suid-Afrika, is bilingual; government servants are required to know both Afrikaans and English. Though agreed previously by the Decimal Coinage Act of 1959, the declaration of the republic came only a few weeks after the Rand, equivalent to 10 shillings (2 Rand = £1), divided into 100 cents came into use.

The white adherents of the Dutch Churches in 1957 numbered 1,402,709; this is a clue to the number of Afrikaans-speaking whites. These Boer descendants definitely outnumber the English-speaking. This is predominantly the case in the Orange Free State and in rural Transvaal, but not in the other two provinces or in the urbanized Witwatersrand. Of the non-Europeans the majority are Bantu, but 3 per cent (over 285,000 in 1946—see Figures 20.2 and 20.3) are Asian and over 10 per cent (nearly a million) are "other races"—including the numerous "Cape Coloured" discussed later.

South Africa never has been a black man's country. Its development is due almost entirely to white settlement and enterprise, but essential labor has been provided either by those of nonwhite races brought in for the purpose or who have been attracted there by economic advantages to such an extent that numerically they are in the majority. To a large number of white South Africans *apartheid* and the maintenance of white rule is the only solution, and after 1948 the Nationalists not only maintained but gained power. But the whole concept of racial segregation, antimiscegenation laws, and minority rule is against the trend of world opinion, and particularly opposed to the views of all other members of the British Commonwealth of Nations. While many regretted to see undone the great work of Smuts, when the Union of South Africa became the Republic of South Africa and withdrew from the Commonwealth in 1961, a source of great embarrassment to Britain and the rest of the Commonwealth was removed.

The question now is: can a vast territory controlled by only 2½ million whites, so opposed to world trends, for long survive? The first two years of the Republic saw a further development of *apartheid* and also a strengthening of the national economy.

Figure 20.2   The racial composition of the population of South Africa by provinces and with High Commission territories.

Figure 20.3   The urban population of South Africa showing racial composition, 1946.

The Africans

In the Republic of South Africa the Africans are described officially as "natives," and their affairs are in the hands of the Department of Native Affairs. Practically all the Africans in the Republic are Bantus; the majority belong to the two major groups, the Nguni and the Sotho. Originally they were all tribally organized and lived in kraals or small villages. Whether or not the dwellers in an individual kraal were actually related, the kraal was regarded as a family unit, and there was no marriage permitted between dwellers in the same kraal. The kraals were controlled according to tribal law by a headman, who was usually a member of the traditional Bantu aristocracy, and nominally all allocation of tribal land was carried out autocratically by the chief. In actual fact, though grazing was common, cultivated fields tended to remain in the hands of the same families for many decades. Under the old organization the men provided food by hunting and took care of the stock, whereas the gathering of fruits and roots and the cultivation of fields were women's work.

Broadly speaking, the Africans in South Africa can now be divided into three classes. There are the tribal natives, living in the reserves, where to a varied extent the old tribal organization is still maintained. There are the "squatters" on the farms belonging to the white Africans, who in many cases continue to recognize more or less directly their tribal obligations. And, third, there are the town dwellers, who do not recognize any such obligation. In addition to these three groups are the African workers recruited for work in the mines, especially the gold mines of Witwatersrand. They come mainly from Mozambique, Basutoland, Bechuanaland, Swaziland, and from various parts of tropical Africa. The recruitment of these workers in the mines is carried out systematically by the Native Recruiting Corporation Limited for the three High Commission territories, and under various agreements and regulations where other countries are concerned. For example, in Mozambique there is a convention between the South African government and Portugal dating from 1928 and revised at intervals since then whereby a maximum number is permitted (it was fixed at 100,000 in 1940) and whereby conditions of work such as a period of acclimatization of 28 days of service are laid down. On leaving the mines the workers are not allowed to remain in the Republic.

The steady breakdown of tribal organization among the Bantus may be attributed to several causes. There is a poll tax, early fixed at 20 shillings ($2.80) for every adult male, and there is also a local hut tax, then 10 shillings ($1.40) per hut, imposed upon the occupier of every dwelling in a native location. These taxes must be paid in cash, and thus there is an immediate incentive for the earning of money. It is still the rule for young men to pay in kind or cash to the parents of their brides, and the increasing tendency is to pay in cash rather than in cattle. Thus the desire on the part of the young men to obtain the necessary cash is probably the strongest inducement for them to leave their kraals and to obtain work in the mines, on farms, or as laborers in the towns. There is a constant demand for domestic servants in all the larger towns, and the number of Bantu female servants has been increasing rapidly. It is urged by some that missionary enterprise is also largely responsible for the process of detribalization. Approximately half the total native population in the Republic is recorded as belonging to various Christian denominations. With missionary enterprise has come the spread of education, and as we have pointed out elsewhere modern ideas of democracy are in conflict with autocratic tribal organization.

The squatters on the farms provide the greater part of such farm labor as is available. Arrangements differ in different parts of the country. A common arrangement in the Free State is for the head of a family to contract to serve the farmer throughout the year in return for which he receives a small cash remuneration plus the right to graze an agreed number of stock and to cultivate an agreed area of ground free of charge. In the Transvaal the agreement is to work for the farmer without wages for 90 days, with complete liberty for the remainder of the year, either to hire himself out to the best bidder or to work land provided by the farmer.

It is illegal for the farmer to sell land to the African squatters. It is generally agreed that the system is unsatisfactory and the labor indifferent.

The general trend in South Africa—a trend much accentuated by the accession to power of the Malan government in 1948—is toward residential segregation of the three "racial" groups, white, colored, and native, with Asiatics included in the colored group. Under the Group Areas Act passed in July 1950 persons of one group are not permitted to own or occupy property in the controlled area of another group, except under permit. This involves registration, together with details of race, of all persons resident in the Union; and under the Immorality Amendment Act, also passed in July 1950, sex relations were entirely prohibited between Europeans and non-Europeans, that is, both colored and native groups. Previously the prohibition had applied only to marriages between Europeans and natives.

Segregation of course works both ways. A few years ago I was the guest of an Afrikaans minister in Pretoria. But not even he could visit, or get me permission to visit, the far-famed Voorhekker Monument—it was visiting day for the Africans. Similarly at one of the new slum-clearance villages near Johannesburg, only the responsible government officer is allowed to enter the gates through the high wire fence without special permission, and for me to see the neat little homes with their attractive gardens and the central shopping center and to sample the Kaffir beer brewed at the very modern brewery required a permit difficult to obtain and not valid after dark.

It will be seen that the trend in legislation is diametrically opposed to the general trend in other parts of the African continent. It is based essentially on the concept that South Africa is and should remain a white man's country. The initial step was really taken as long ago as 1913 with the passing of the Natives' Land Act, in which native reservations were demarcated. This of course was as much for the protection of the natives as anyone, and they have since obtained some increases in their land.

The "Cape Coloured"

The community known as the "Cape Coloured" is a critical element in the complex population structure of the Republic. It owes its origin to three centuries of miscegenation between the immigrant Europeans—especially of Portuguese, Dutch, and British stock—with the original Bantu, Hottentot, and other African peoples and also with slaves of West African, Malayan, East Indian, and other origins. It is reported on contemporary evidence that in the early years of European settlement in the Cape three-quarters of the children born to slave mothers had European fathers. Officially the term covers the relatively pure-blooded original non-Negro peoples, such as the Bushmen, Hottentots, and Griquas, about 25 per cent of a total of about a million. The remaining three-quarters are the mixed peoples properly speaking, whose cultural affinities are with the mass of Europeans. Nearly 90 per cent live in the Cape Province, where they are concentrated in the western parts, constituting there over half the total population (Figure 20.4). Except for the small English-speaking groups in Natal, the majority of Cape Coloured speak Afrikaans. Large numbers are employed on Afrikaans farms, especially in the more intensively farmed districts. In the towns they provide unskilled labor, domestic servants, and industrial workers. Only a small "upper class," tending to remain aloof from the majority, includes teachers, skilled workers, and professional men. The worst elements drift to the underworlds of the larger towns, especially Cape Town. Nearly all the Cape Coloured are nominally Christians but adhere to English denomina-

Figure 20.4   Distribution of Cape Coloured. (From K. M. Buchanan and N. Hurwitz, *Geog. Rev.*, 1950. Courtesy of the *Geographical Review*, American Geographical Society.)

tions even more than to the Dutch Reformed church. Among the Coloured the birth rate is 50 per cent above that of the Europeans, but poverty, bad housing and malnutrition have resulted in high mortality. On the whole the position of these people has steadily deteriorated. Employers prefer Europeans wherever possible, and the tendency under the racial discrimination policy of the Nationalist government which came into power in 1948 was to squeeze them out of the slightly advantageous position which they had held over the African.[4]

The Asiatics

Ninety-seven per cent of the Asiatic immigrants[5] living in the Republic of South Africa speak Indian languages, so that the designation in the census return "Asiatic" may be read "Indian." It was in 1859–1860 that the sugar planters and other colonists in Natal secured legal permission to bring "indentured" coolie labor from India. After completing five years the Indians were free to choose their own job; after ten years they were entitled to a free return passage. Many came, few returned. They became traders and market gardeners, and with their low standard of living were able to undercut the European settlers in many fields. The reaction was inevitable. Natal, where seven-eighths of the total are found, prohibited free entry in 1896; the Union government in 1913 prohibited further immigration entirely. By that time the numbers had come to exceed numbers of Europeans in Natal, but with cessation of Indian immigration numbers of Europeans drew slightly ahead after about 1925. In 1946 there were 285,000 Asiatics in the Union; by the census of 1960 this had increased to 477,400.

The Indians came from many parts of India—Muslim Gujaratis from Bombay and Tamil-speaking Indians professing Hinduism from the Madras coasts are most numerous, but there are many Hindi speakers from North India and Telegus from the south. Muslims constitute nearly a fifth of the total.

Among the Indians men heavily outnumber women (a legacy from the old days), but the birth ratio is high and the total is rapidly increasing. In the British Commonwealth as a whole Indians enjoy a citizenship status of equality with Europeans. In South Africa their official status was different and closer to that of the Africans, hence the continuing source of friction between India and Pakistan and South Africa. In 1927 inducements in the form

---

[4] An excellent study of these people by K. M. Buchanan and N. Hurwitz appears in the *Geog. Rev.,* **XL,** July 1950, 397–414. ("The 'Coloured' Community in the Union of South Africa.")

[5] K. M. Buchanan and N. Hurwitz, "The Asiatic Immigrant Community in the Union of South Africa," *Geog. Rev.,* **XXXIX,** July 1949, 440–449. In South Africa the word Asiatic is officially retained; the modern trend elsewhere is to substitute Asian.

of a free passage and a bonus were offered to Indians to return to India, and in the following twenty years about 100,000 took advantage of the scheme. But the majority have little wish to leave. They are economically better off than they would be in India. They make good livings as traders, as market gardeners, and in some of the professions. Some have become very wealthy.

The physical background

What are the essential characteristics of the land into which Briton and Boer penetrated, and which is today the Republic of South Africa?

In common with other parts of the African continent there is in the south a great central plateau separated from the shores of the Indian and Atlantic oceans by a varied width of lower country.

In southern Africa the plateau reaches remarkably high elevations, especially over the eastern half. Nearly all this eastern half has an elevation of more than 4000 feet, and considerable stretches exceed 6000 feet above sea level. The eastern and southeastern edge of the plateau forms a remarkable feature known as the Drakensberg or the Quathlamba Mountains, and the gigantic rocky wall viewed from the east is one of the world's spectacular features. Although the edge of the plateau is somewhat less marked along the south, where it receives various names, it is nevertheless a distinctive feature. In the dry country of the west the edge is less distinct and the elevation reached, though almost everywhere over 3000 feet, is less, and only a few points reach the level of 6000 feet. The plateau itself is over large stretches almost flat. At other times it is rolling, and sometimes low, flat-topped hills rise from its surface. The latter feature is associated particularly with the presence of the almost horizontal sheets of sandstone associated with igneous rocks, belonging to the Karoo[6] beds (see above, Chapter Three). A marked change of scenery is associated with a change from the Karoo beds to the underlying ancient rocks.

In southern Africa the surface of the plateau sinks greatly towards the center, and over the heart of the dry land of Bechuanaland the average elevation drops below 3000 feet. In the Republic of South Africa the greater part of the plateau lies in the basin of the Orange River, together with its main tributary the Vaal. Only the northern half of the Transvaal comes within the drainage of the Limpopo.

Climatically the elevation of the plateau lowers the general temperature 10° to 20°F. throughout the year, and the frost danger is of considerable importance (Figure 20.5). Since the plateau is a region of summer rain and falls in the winter are infrequent, snow is rare except on the mountains of the edge.

---

[6] Linguists now agree that the spelling "Karoo" is to be preferred to the older "Karroo." Previously, "Karoo" was the Afrikaans spelling; "Karroo" was commonly used in English works.

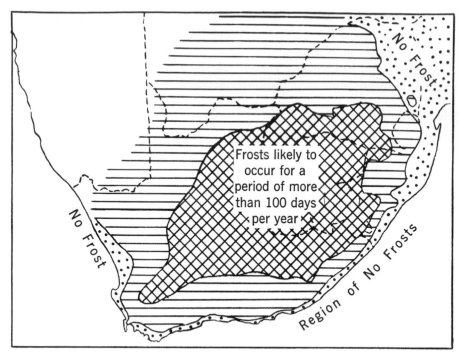

Figure 20.5   Frost map of South Africa.

By a curious coincidence, on my first visit to the Witwatersrand, in the month of July, I awoke in the early morning when my train was approaching Johannesburg to find the whole veld as far as the eye could see thickly mantled in 4 or 5 inches of snow. It proved to be the first time that snow had fallen for some five years, and most of the small children were seeing it for the first time.

The plateau lies in the so-called trade wind belt. The rain-bearing air masses of summer are from the Indian Ocean, and the heaviest fall is consequently in the east; but only on the higher eastern parts of the plateau does the average exceed 30 inches a year. It is possible to consider the high plateau as divided into eastern and western halves by the isohyet of 15 inches a year (Figure 20.6). With less than this amount cultivation except by irrigation becomes impossible. Even where the fall is between 15 and 20 inches a year crop production is precarious, and perhaps it is better to say that normal arable farming is limited to those eastern regions of the plateau which have more than 20 inches a year. Furthermore, the rain tends to fall in sudden storms, and the quantity from year to year is subject to serious variation. The sudden falls are conducive to serious soil erosion and the rapid formation of deep *dongas,* or gulleys. In addition to direct soil erosion the rain falling suddenly on the hard parched surface of the land does not readily soak in but runs off instead of enriching the soil. It follows that most of the South African rivers, the tributaries of the Orange, are liable to sudden floods, whereas for a large proportion of the year the watercourses are mainly dry.

The country between the high plateau and the sea is not in southern Africa a coastal plain. In the east throughout Natal under the great scarp of the Drakensberg Mountains there is a belt of very varied hilly land, and visitors to Pietermaritzburg who pass through the Valley of a Thousand Hills will recognize in that name the essentially broken-up nature of this tract. Here the underlying rocks are the same Karoo Beds that underlie neighboring parts of the plateau. But they are here gently folded, and the process of subaerial weathering has cut through the horizontal or gently inclined layers to carve out a varied relief which because it is still actively in course of being sculptured geologists would describe as a "young relief." Only along the coasts of Natal is there a strip which can be described as a coastal plain, fringed along the ocean itself by lines of sand dunes against which pound the everlasting breakers from the Indian Ocean.

In the south, that is, in Cape Province, the land between the plateau edge and the sea is much more varied. Here, in contrast with the whole of the heart of Africa but in common with the northwest of the continent, the rocks

Figure 20.6   The rainfall of South Africa. The heavy line marks the limit of predominantly winter rainfall of the southwest.

have been considerably folded, and one gets the familiar features of folded mountain ranges. Though these ranges differ in detail in direction, elevation, and degree of dissection, on the whole they tend to be parallel to the edge of the plateau. Between them are broad or narrow valleys, sometimes wide enough to form extensive plains. And it may be said, therefore, that the descent from the plateau to the sea is by a series of gigantic steps, each separated from the next by a range of mountains. In the most typical development the lowest step is a narrow coastal plain, or coastal plateau, then a range of mountains—the Langeberg and Outeniquas—followed by the second step, a dry plateau known as the Little Karoo. The Great Black Mountains (Groote Zwarte Bergen) are followed by the third step, the plateau of the Great Karoo. The Great Karoo itself is overshadowed by the scarp here known as the Nieuwveld, which forms the edge of the plateau.

This southern tract is the one where the summer rains of the type associated with the trade wind belt alternate with the winter rains from the westerlies and so receives a rainfall well distributed throughout the year. The rainfall is largely relief rainfall, with the consequent sharp differences between an exposed hill ridge and a sheltered valley. But there are numerous small rivers, rising among these favored mountains of the Cape Province. They naturally tend to flow as far as possible along the valleys, but at intervals they cut through the intervening mountain ridges by great gaps known in South Africa as *poorts*. Several of the rivers are naturally of considerable importance in providing water for irrigation of the flat valley plains.

Best known of South African mountains are those which lie in the southwest. Table Mountain, under which nestles the town and port of Cape Town, is in fact a prototype of flat-topped mountains found throughout Africa wherever beds of resistant rock are approximately horizontal. Nearby, overlooking Gordon's Bay, are those more varied mountain forms associated with irregularly folded rocks. This southwest region, of course, is the region of winter rain, South Africa's belt of Mediterranean climate, with the consequent reproduction of so many physical features reminiscent of southern California or southern Portugal.

Farther north and in Southwest Africa the land between the plateau edge and the sea is the desert stretch known as the Namib, of varied but not very distinctive relief. Throughout the vast stretch from 30° South to the border of Angola in 17° South only one permanent stream, the Orange River, reaches the coast.

Gold

For many decades South Africa has led the countries of the world as a producer of gold. The African continent is responsible for about three-fifths of the world's output, and of this total some 80 per cent comes from South

Africa. Through recent discoveries an important part is now played by gold-fields in the Orange Free State. From 1887 to 1949, inclusive, nearly all the gold came from the single goldfield of the Witwatersrand, with a total yield approaching 500 million ounces. This field alone in 1948 was furnishing 97 per cent of South Africa's output, nearly 48 per cent of the estimated world output, and its value represented two-fifths of all the commercial exports of the whole continent of Africa, excluding Egypt. Geological experts are satisfied that South Africa's output can be maintained at comparable levels for at least another quarter century even if no further reserves are discovered. Although serious production only began in 1951, by 1959 the new Orange Free State fields were producing more then a quarter of South Africa's gold —5.58 million fine ounces out of a total of 20.07 million. Up to the end of 1960 South Africa had produced over 700 million ounces of fine gold. The year 1961 saw a record of over 22.5 million ounces, only to be beaten by 1962.

The Witwatersrand Goldfield has been described from the geographical point of view by Peter Scott.[7] He points out that the field, commonly known as the Rand, extends for 50 miles from Randfontein eastward to Springs and for 20 miles southward from Springs to Heidelberg. Structurally it comprises the areas where gold-bearing conglomerates called "reefs" or pre-Cambrian age either outcrop at the surface or dip steeply southward under a cover of younger rocks. Twelve-thousand feet is regarded as the possible limit to economic mining. At a depth of 9000 feet in the Crown mines the rock temperature is 109°F., and in order to protect the miners from phthisis and silicosis the air has to be kept saturated with moisture; deeper mining is possible only if dry methods with dry air can be adopted.

Structurally the gold field may be divided into four main regions: the Central Rand, the Far East Rand, the West Rand, and the Far West Rand. As shown in Figures 20.7 and 20.9, these areas are separated by structural features.

The gold was discovered in 1884, the field was proclaimed in 1886, and production became important in the following year; by 1888 the whole length of the outcrop of the Central Rand was being mined by numerous companies. Gradually, as surface working gave place to mines and the mines had to go ever deeper, the work passed into the hands of large units. The Central Rand dominated production until 1897, and it was during this period that the cyanide process made possible the recovery of gold from pyritic ores which had previously been regarded as valueless. The process was introduced in 1890 and generally adopted from 1892 onward.

There followed the great development of the West Rand from 1898

[7] *Geog. Rev.,* **XLI,** October 1951, 561–589.

Figure 20.7

Figure 20.8

Figures 20.7–20.10   Four maps of the Witwatersrand Goldfield. In the 1948 map (Figure 20.10) the largest circles represent companies producing between 500,000 and 1,000,000

to 1911 and then the Far East Rand (1912 to 1923), which became dominant in the years 1924 to 1938 when the Far West Rand, previously insignificant, began to be important. The years since 1951 have been marked not only by further expansion east and west but by the rise of the new fields in the Orange Free State to the South. In the Rand itself a production peak of over 14 million ounces was reached in 1941. A drop to 11.5 million in 1948 was followed by a rise consequent upon the devaluation of sterling in 1949. In 1950, however, the export value of gold from South Africa dropped below the total for other commodities. By 1959 the total again exceeded 14 million ounces but largely from poorer ores. In 1898 for every ton of reef which was milled, 9.78 pennyweights (0.489 ounce) of gold was obtained. By 1948 this had fallen to 4.01 pennyweights (0.2005 ounce), but vast additional areas had been proved.

It should be noted that the development of the goldfield was made possible by the near-by existence of coal, first in the neighborhood of the Far

Figure 20.9

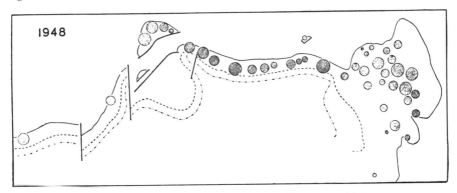

Figure 20.10

fine ounces a year, the smaller circles 100,000 to 500,000 and under 100,000. (From Peter Scott, *Geog. Rev.*, 1951. Courtesy of the *Geographical Review*, American Geographical Society.)

East Rand itself, latterly from the Witbank field where the seams are almost undisturbed, the coal of excellent quality, and the reserves very great. An electric power supply, vital to deep mining operations, was built up after 1907 on the basis of unlimited coal resources.

The great problem of the Rand has always been labor. There was an early attempt to use demobilized European soldiers as unskilled labor. There was also an attempt to recruit Africans in Central and East Africa. In 1904 Chinese laborers, on a three-year indenture system, were introduced, and at one time as many as 53,000 Chinese were employed in the mines; but repatriation was decided upon and was completed in 1910. Since then Africans have been recruited under the regular systems mentioned elsewhere, and increased technical efficiency has steadily lowered the average number of employees per 1000 tons of ore milled—now under 6. The mines in 1961 were employing 51,000 Europeans and 415,000 non-Europeans.

The development of the Rand has given rise, naturally, to many other problems. One of the most serious is adequacy of water supply, which may prove to be a limiting factor in the future. The spread of the gigantic conurbation based on Johannesburg has been rendered difficult by the huge areas occupied by mining dumps of white crushed quartzose conglomerate. Naturally, apart from the important iron and steel industries, the development has given rise to a wide range of industries designed to supply local needs.

Diamonds

Gold is far from being the only mineral of importance in South Africa. Until the discovery in 1908 of diamonds in Southwest Africa and later discoveries in Tanganyika and elsewhere, South Africa was almost the only source of diamonds in the world. A pebble from the banks of the Orange River was identified as a diamond in 1867; but the most famous diamond field is at Kimberley in Cape Province, where diamonds were first found in 1871. They were found in a decomposed rock known as *yellow ground* outcropping at the surface in oval or circular patches corresponding to depressions, or pans. It was found that underneath the decomposed yellow rock was a hard igneous rock, known as *blue ground,* and the momentous discovery of the diamond industry was the realization that this blue ground was the parent rock of the diamonds. The geologist knows blue ground as kimberlite, an igneous rock occupying pipes going down into the earth's crust which probably represent old volcanic necks. There are large numbers of these pipes though only a few are diamond-bearing. At first they were excavated in great pits from the surface to depths of 400 feet or more. Then it became necessary to follow the blue ground by underground mines, which took the diamond-mining industry out of the hands of individuals or small companies and made it a monopoly of large combines, such as De Beers, able to command the necessary capital, human skill, and technical equipment. In due course the great diamond combines were able to control and restrict the output in order to maintain prices. Their principal mines were near Kimberley, at Jagersfontein, Koffie-fontein and finally, the largest single mine of all, the Premier diamond mine near Pretoria, from which the world's largest diamond, the Cullinan, was obtained in 1905. In the years 1925–1927 when discoveries of rich diamond-bearing alluvial deposits were made elsewhere, especially in Southwest Africa, diamond mining was temporarily shut down to counteract the output of alluvial stones. But recent years have seen South Africa again in control with three quarters of the world output passing through the Central Selling Organization and worth in 1962 nearly 300 million dollars.

Other minerals

Since 1952 uranium oxide has been extracted by some twenty mines in the Rand—all existing gold mines. In 1961 11 million pounds were worth 110 million dollars, and output is still increasing, the Rand is believed to be the richest source of uranium in the world.

The fortunate possessor of the only extensive fields of bituminous coal in Africa, South Africa has in the Orange Free State, in the southern Transvaal, and in Natal vast reserves of valuable fuel. The coal occurs in the lower part of the great Karoo system. Principal workings are at Witbank and Middelburg in the Transvaal, which supply Johannesburg, and around Newcastle in Natal. Output has climbed steadily from 30 million tons in 1952 to over 45 million tons in 1962.

Among other minerals of South Africa there are copper ores in Namaqualand and at the mines of Messina in the northern Transvaal, as well as in Southwest Africa. Tin ore occurs in the Transvaal Bush Veld, and South Africa has such other minerals as silver ore, asbestos, chromite, platinum ore, mica, manganese, and chrome ores, as well as limestone for local use. A natural alloy of osmium and iridium is a by-product in the Rand.

Thus the Republic of South Africa is far from being dependent upon a single mineral commodity, however important.

The iron and steel industry

The development of the South African iron and steel industry affords a very interesting example of progress towards economic self-sufficiency which marks the growth of so many of the "newer" countries of the world. The start dates only from 1910 to 1916, when three plants using scrap were established in the Witwatersrand, mainly to supply some of the needs of the gold-mining industry, and another also using scrap was located on the Vaal River at Vereeniging and received government support. The curtailment of overseas supplies during World War I (1914–1918) helped the industry, but it was hurt by the postwar depression. Nevertheless, the Union Steel Corporation (USCO) of Vereeniging established a blast furnace at Newcastle in Natal in 1926 and an additional steel works on the Klip River at Vereeniging in the same year. The South African Iron and Steel Corporation (ISCOR) was established at Pretoria in 1934 to use the local medium-grade quartzitic bedded ore deposits, and by 1949 it was producing three-quarters of South Africa's output of about 650,000 tons of steel. The discovery of rich hematite deposits at Thabazimbi, 156 miles from Pretoria by a railway which was pushed there in 1934, soon made that the chief source of ore. Though only some of the seams are suitable for making metallurgical coke, the Witbank coal workings are only 70 miles from the ISCOR works. But Vereeniging has proved to have an even better location; it is actually on a coal field, other suitable coal from northern Natal is near, water supply is good, and the location is central for South Africa's railway system. In 1944 a site at Vanderbijl Park, 10 miles west of the old works and on the bare veld, was chosen. Five years later this South African Gary had blast furnaces and steel and engineering works and was a fast-growing town of 20,000 people. Despite expanding demand South Africa in 1950 was on the verge of being completely independent of imports of iron and steel. The old works on the goldfield had expanded into a considerable industry but were completely overshadowed by Pretoria and Vereeniging. The geographical aspects of the industry have been considered by Peter Scott,[8] who has kindly permitted me to reproduce the accompanying map (Figure 20.11). By 1952 output of steel from Pretoria and Vanderbijl Park exceeded a million tons; by 1961–1962 this had been doubled.

The regional divisions of South Africa

Some years ago when I was working in South Africa in collaboration with the late Mr. J. N. Jamieson, we agreed that, from the geographical point of view, southern Africa falls naturally into a number of regions, each with a distinctive character, whether regarded from the point of view of natural endowments or from the point of view of human reactions as illustrated by land use and types of farming. We used this scheme of regional divisions in a number of geographical textbooks which have been widely used in South African schools.[9] At a later date Professor J. H. Wellington of the University of Witwatersrand, in a paper entitled "Land Utilization in South Africa,"[10] independently drew up a series of regions based on land use, which agree so closely that it is possible to combine the two concepts. The account which follows is based essentially on modifications of my original scheme suggested by Professor Wellington's work.

As he very rightly says, "Two facts stand out in any consideration of land development in South Africa. The physical environment is inexorable, and the geographical advantages can be realized to the full only when the country realizes its true economic relationships with the rest of the world. Of the inexorable physical circumstances rainfall is of foremost importance."

On the basis of rainfall Wellington recognizes three main divisions. The eastern is where the rainfall is adequate and land may be utilized in the production of crops requiring a summer fall. The southwestern is where crop production is also possible because of sufficient rainfall, either coming this time in the winter or distributed throughout the year, or where there are

---

[8] "The Iron and Steel Industry of South Africa," *Geography,* **XXXVI**, 1951, 137–149.
[9] *The World: A General Geography for South African Schools,* 1st Edition, London, 1927.
[10] *Geog. Rev.,* **XXII**, 1932, 205–224.

Figure 20.11   The iron and steel industry. (After Peter Scott.)

Key (legend):
- ⊙ Blast furnaces and steelworks
- ○ Steelworks only
- ▲ Iron
- ✕ Chromium
- ● Coking coal
- ■ Limestone
- ⊠ Dolomite
- ☐ Fluorspar
- △ Fireclay

perennial streams which permit continuous irrigation. The third, which he calls the middle area, perhaps more appropriately the western, is where rainfall of less than 15 or 20 inches a year is insufficient for crop production.

The three main divisions and subdivisions proposed and named by Professor Wellington are indicated on Figure 20.12. We may consider each in turn.

The Cape region. This is essentially the area of winter rainfall where the rainfall is sufficient for crop production. It is an area of mountain ridges and

Figure 20.12　The regions of South Africa.

intervening valleys or plains. There is the socalled *swart* land in the west, and the *ruens* or ridge lands of the Caledon and Bredasdorp districts to the south-east. This is the birthplace of European agriculture iñ South Africa, and it is the region which bears the closest comparison to other parts of the world enjoying a Mediterranean climate, but notably to southern California.

The farmlands are used mainly for wheat production, with about half the land under crops and the other half lying fallow. But there is a natural infertility of the soils, and the yields are lower than in other countries relying chiefly on wheat production. Farms are large. Wellington quotes an average size of 1600 acres, but this includes land within farm boundaries which cannot actually be farmed. In certain areas there is a specialized development of viticulture, and the holdings are naturally smaller. On the scanty natural pasture of shrubby Mediterranean type, sheep farming is a profitable secondary industry, and the animals graze also on the stubble and fallow lands. There is little cattle farming; the summer is too dry. But this suggests that more land should be devoted to fodder crops, to enable the pastoral industry to be expanded.

The production of wheat has tended to rely to a considerable extent on the protection afforded by duty on imported wheat. This is not a region, however, which need necessarily rely primarily on agricultural production. Its climate has the attractive features of sunny southern California. Quite apart from the early start enjoyed by Cape Town and the facilities which it has for easy communication by rail (Figure 20.13) and lately by road with the whole of the subcontinent, this Cape region is one which naturally attracts those who have worked elsewhere and saved sufficient to retire into a part of the country climatically most attractive. The Atlantic coast near Cape Town itself now has a succession of resorts with hotels and holiday apartments; the sheltered nature of False Bay (Figure 20.14) attract bathers and pleasure boatmen. Cape Town itself, previously very congested between the slopes of Table Mountain and the shores of the bay, now has plenty of room, still only partly used, for expansion, with offices on the reclaimed harbor area (Figure 20.15), and light industry on the flats mark the land.

Incidentally, the botanists include a large tract of Southwest Africa in the region of the "Cape flora," the richest in the whole of Africa and one characterized by a great wealth of flowering plants, especially those of shrubby habit.

Figure 20.13   The main Cape Town–Johannesburg rail at Tulbagh Kloof. The South African railroads are 3 feet, 6 inches gauge, and the train shown is the express "Blue Train" about 70 miles from Cape Town. (Courtesy South African Railways.)

Figure 20.14   General view of Cape Town and docks, sheltered by Table Mountain. The original site afforded some shelter, but the modern port is entirely artificial. In the foreground is the older dock; beyond it is the larger and newer dock, with reclaimed foreshore. (Courtesy South African Railways.)

The drier southwestern region. This region differs from the preceding one in that the rainfall is almost everywhere too small for agriculture. It includes many of the folded mountain ranges, but interest centers on certain of the valleys which lie between them. These include the valley of the Olifants River in the north, the Breede River and its tributaries in the south, as well as the famous Ceres valley and the Hex River valley. Both the Olifants and the Breede are perennial streams, and therefore water can be used for irrigation during the dry summer season. Fortunately the land which can be irrigated has good fertile soils, and soils which are suitable for fruit growing command very high prices per acre, fifteen or twenty times that which cannot be irrigated, and the use of which is restricted to grazing. This is the main area of production of grapes, but it also includes some of the best deciduous fruit orchards of the country, notably plums and apples. Some tobacco, especially of Turkish types, is grown, and there are winter crops of oats and barley. This fruit-producing region has the advantage that the seasons are the reverse of those of the northern hemisphere and consequently there is a large export of South African fruits to British and other European markets at a time when local supplies are nonexistent.

In the valleys of this region such small towns as Paarl and Worcester are primarily concerned with fruit drying, fruit packing, and the manufacture of wines and brandies. Much progress has been made in the technique of wine production. In particular South Africa has succeeded in producing excellent wines of the sherry type, able to compete on their own merits with the long-favored products of Spain. Light table wines, though they cannot be matched directly with German hocks or with French wines, have been proving their popularity, especially in Canada and Britain.

The expansion of quick freezing has opened up new possibilities in the marketing of fresh fruits.

This too is a country of magnificent scenery: long sinuous passes between the lofty mountain barriers (Figure 20.16), through which go river courses filled with roaring, surging cataracts and flood waters in the wet season. The wealth of spring flowers as in the Cape flora is remarkable, but the sheltered valleys with their neat fruit orchards and tidy vineyards and attractive, compact, color-washed farmhouses also offer a picture of great beauty.

Though originally introduced by the early Dutch settlers, both viticulture and fruit farming owe much of their development and success to the influence of the French Huguenots who, after the revocation of the Edict of Nantes in 1685, settled in this part of South Africa.

In contrast to other Mediterranean climatic regions, neither climate nor soil seems suitable to olives.

The southern coastal region. This is the region where there is a gradual

Figure 20.15   New office buildings on the reclaimed land at Cape Town, looking towards the docks. (Courtesy South African Railways.)

Figure 20.16   The road through Meirings Poort, Groot Zwartbergen. One of the finest of the "poorts" or gaps through the ranges which bound the Great Karoo (Courtesy South African Railways.)

merging of the winter type of rainfall into the area of summer rain. Heavy mists are frequent on the southern slopes of the boundary ranges known collectively as the Langebergen, and the more even distribution of rainfall results not only in perennial streams but in soils with a character different from those of other parts of southern Africa.

Where the soils are derived from the Table Mountain sandstone they tend to be poor and leached, but where they are formed from shales and the rainfall is moderate or low, soil acidity tends to disappear and the land is particularly productive. Unfortunately the area concerned is strictly limited in extent. Among field crops oats and potatoes are important, wheat relatively less so. The well-distributed rainfall results in a comparatively luxuriant grass growth in wetter regions. An improvement in pasture grasses would mean a definite increase in beef and dairy breeds of cattle, whereas sheep flourish on the drier hill slopes. There is obviously great variation from place to place according to local conditions, with the result that land values, types of farming, and intensity of production also show marked variation. Some of the best land is on the alluvial soils by Gamtoos River between Port Elizabeth and Humansdorp. Irrigated land commands a high price.

George is a fruit-growing center with special interest in apples; Knysna, with a heavier rainfall, lies in a forested area where afforestation has assumed importance on the neighboring hillslopes. Mossel Bay is a port lying in a sheltered bay commanding two passes into the interior, so that it is an outlet for the Karoo country behind. But in this respect it does not rival Port Elizabeth on Algoa Bay, which is the natural outlet of a large and productive hinterland, including not only the eastern part of Cape Province but also much of the Orange Free State which lies behind, and has also been provided with a good harbor.

The Karoo. Both the Great Karoo and the Little Karoo are treeless plains hemmed in by mountains and lying below the main scarp of the great African plateau. They both suffer from a small rainfall—everywhere less than 15 inches and in the west less than 10 inches—and a rainfall which is very irregular in its incidence during the year as well as from year to year (Figure 20.17). On the whole the flora is that of the Mediterranean Cape region, with an admixture of those plants characteristic of the dry Upper Karoo on the

Figure 20.17 Districts classified as drought stricken and entitled to state relief measures. The heavy line shows the limits of the Orange Basin. (After J. H. Moolman, *Geog. Rev.*, 1946. Courtesy of the *Geographical Review*, American Geographical Society.)

Figure 20.18   Hartebeestpoort Dam, near Johannesburg. This is typical of the many modern dams designed primarily to provide irrigation water and, in this case, for urban water supply. (Courtesy South African Railways.)

surface of the plateau itself. Usually drab and monotonous, with the gray-leafed shrubs separated by tracts of bare soil, after a shower of rain the shrubs and the succulent plants burst into flower. This is country of which it can truly be said, "The desert shall blossom as a rose." The streams are nearly all intermittent in flow, with the exception of a few which derive from the Swarte Bergen range. Here it is possible at the foot of the great escarpment and near the higher mountain ranges of the region to use the water for the cultivation of crops of wheat or lucerne, together with tobacco and grapes. Where major conservation dams (Figure 20.18) have been constructed on the Dwyka, Olifants, and Sundays Rivers, lucerne and citrus fruits (Figure 20.19) are intensively cultivated. The Sundays River valley is a leading area.

Oudtshoorn was long famous as a center of the ostrich-farming industry which flourished in those days when women of fashion in many parts of the world took pride in their ostrich feather fans and boas, or wore the plumes as a decoration to their headgear. With changes in fashion, ostrich farming became a dying, almost dead industry, but there is a modest industrial demand for the making of feather dusters. Oudtshoorn has now become the center of extensive irrigated lands with an intensive form of agriculture.

Outside such specialized irrigation settlements, the Karoo is essentially a pastoral area, supporting considerable numbers of Merino sheep and Angora goats from which mohair is obtained. The bushes typical of the Karoo vegetation appear to have a high nutritive value as well as medicinal properties which keep the animals in good condition, though the carrying capacity of the land is low. Farms are 4000 to 10,000 acres in area; their value where they cannot be irrigated is less than a dollar an acre.

Apart from Oudtshoorn in the Little Karoo, Beaufort West in the heart of the Great Karoo is the chief settlement. Since the main railway from Cape Town to Johannesburg or Rhodesia passes through the heart of the Great Karoo, the country is not isolated.

The dry regions of the plateau. To the north of the Great Karoo and beyond the great escarpment are the dry regions of the plateau. In general, aridity increases toward the west and north, and a dry pastoral region where cattle can find a fair pasturage fades into the Kalahari Bush Veld and Kalahari Desert.

The southern part of the region immediately north of the great escarpment is often known in South Africa as the Upper Karoo or the Karoid

Figure 20.19 Picking oranges on a citrus farm, Cape Province. (Information Service of South Africa.)

Plateau. This vast flat or very gently undulating treeless plain is broken by flat-topped hills, sure indication of the existence of horizontal beds of Karoo sandstone and Karoo dolerite. Everywhere the soil is shallow and rocky, and the vegetation consists of small scattered bushes capable only of supporting a few sheep and goats. The small population depends upon underground water which may be reached by wind-driven pumps.

Not only is the rainfall low, but it is extremely irregular, and it is not unusual for two or three years to pass without appreciable rainfall. Such small towns as Carnarvon and Victoria West are centers of the pastoral industry, but the farmers require anything from 4000 to 20,000 acres in order to maintain a flock of reasonable size. The Persian fat-tailed sheep seems to be the best adapted to the area where the Karoo shrubs occur. The industry which has brought at least a tolerable prosperity to this region is the Karakul fur industry. Karakul is the name given to the fur obtained from newly born lambs of this fat-tailed sheep. The killing of the lambs is not as cruel as it sounds: the mothers are able to survive on the herbage, which they could not do if they had to suckle their lambs. Northward in Namaqualand the bushman grass and other coarse grasses provide winter pasturage for a few thousand cattle. In the bush veld to the north of the Orange River cattle may find a fair pasturage in the summer, which here becomes the nominal rainy season.

Although little water reaches the Atlantic Ocean, the Orange River itself is a perennial stream, and along its banks are terraces large enough to be worth irrigating. As shown in Figure 20.6, winter frosts occur over most of the area, but summers are long enough and hot enough for cotton to be possible on the alluvial soils of these terraces. In a few favored areas an interesting type of cultivation may become possible, as, for example, in the Zak River basin. When this river comes down in flood its waters are diverted into shallow basins separated by low earthen banks. After the soil has been thoroughly soaked the water is allowed to flow through sluice gates into other prepared basins (saaidam or zaaidam irrigation). Wheat is then sown on the damp mud and matures with this single flooding. Clearly such a cash crop is precarious and possible only in certain years.

The Namib. Although the greater part of the Namib Desert lies in South west Africa, it stretches into the Cape Province and is in fact the coastal strip where are to be found the most extreme of the desert conditions known in South Africa. The irregular rainfall even on an average does not exceed 5 inches a year.

The High Veld. The regions so far considered lie within the Cape Province of the Republic of South Africa. Although the surface of the high plateau as a whole may be called and often is called the High Veld, this term can be properly restricted to the eastern part of the plateau surface, covering the larger part of the Orange Free State together with the neighboring parts of the Cape Province and stretching northward into the southern Transvaal. Geologically, the surface is of almost horizontal beds of the Karoo system, sandstone predominating in the south and east with some dolerites and lavas in the northwest. The whole is a great expanse of rolling grassland, treeless except where shade trees have been planted around some of the farms and near villages or towns. It is in this area that the rainfall, more than 15 inches, tends to average between 20 and 30 inches a year, and is of greater reliability than in the drier parts. The even surface has moderately fertile, loamy soils, but the elevation, usually between 4000 and 6000 feet, results in a great range of temperature, as well as a frost period extending certainly for more than 100 days in the year. Although there is much land in pasture, this is essentially a region of South Africa characterized by extensive arable cultivation. Although some wheat is grown in places as a winter and early summer crop, corn (maize) is the mainstay of the region. This is the so-called "maize triangle" (Figure 20.20), where this is outstandingly the most important crop. With the development of mixed farming, however, the term has become something of a misnomer.

Some years may be affected severely by droughts, and occasionally the summer rains arrive too late for the late-sown corn to ripen before the advent of winter frosts. The corn has then to be used for silage.

Although the dry climate results in a dry and compact grain, yields are low when compared with the Rhodesian maize area. Commonly the yield is little over four bags, or 800 pounds, an acre, which can be doubled or even trebled by the use of fertilizers, but is only about one-third of yields which have now become common in the corn belt of the United States.

Corn is the staple food grain of the Africans, and a considerable proportion is used as human food. It might be thought that a better use of the corn

Figure 20.20   The distribution of corn (maize) and wheat. Each dot represents 10,000 bags of 200 lb. (1000 short tons) in a good average year. The so-called "maize triangle" lies in the wetter eastern part of the High Veld. Wheat is important in the Mediterranean area.

would be for the development of cattle, pig, and sheep farming. It is true that silage has been made regularly for Hereford and Friesian cattle on the better farms in the Standerton area, but this is far from general. The High Veld is indeed a great sheep area, but with Merino rather than mutton sheep. It would seem that the natural grasses of the High Veld are far from being as nutritious as they should be. It is believed that this is due to a lack of phosphorus, and that the comparatively poor quality of South African beef and mutton is in large measure due to this deficiency. It has been shown that a ration of bone meal or calcium phosphate can double the milk yield and more than double the market value of cattle or sheep intended for slaughter. In the meantime this has long been a corn-exporting region, yet the low yields combined with the relatively expensive and inefficient labor previously mentioned render the growing of corn for sale economically unproductive. Among the other difficulties faced by the farmer in the past was the liability to locust plagues. The menace still exists, but there are effective control measures. Nevertheless, the High Veld is dotted all over with its attractive little farms, each often sheltered by a plantation of pines or gum trees, or the Australian wattle, the bark of which has a value in tanning leather. Many farms too have their apple orchards, and a windmill pumping water is an almost inevitable adjunct to the whole.

Edward Ackerman has expressed the view that even the relatively favored "maize triangle" is a problem area. More than three-quarters of the cultivated land of South Africa is inside the triangle, which has long been a one-crop region, though changing to mixed farming. Crop failures recur because of uncertain rainfall, with heavy summer thundershowers (when much-needed moisture is lost in runoff), high evaporation, and destructive hailstorms. The possibilities of crop failure do not encourage permanent investment in farm buildings, implements, or fertilizers. Plentiful early rains encourage shallow root systems, a liability for the plant if dry months follow.

Since 1951 the economic position has materially changed with the development of the new goldfields.

The administrative center of the Free State, Bloemfontein, is the natural clearing and distributing center for the agricultural products of the High Veld. It lies rather to the drier side of the state in a wheat and sheep area slightly outside or on the margins of the main maize-cattle triangle. In the maize triangle itself Kroonstad and Bethlehem are clearing centers, and most of the corn is now handled in bulk through storage elevators and not by the old system of bags.

North of the Free State the High Veld stretches into the Transvaal. Here are to be found the same scattered farms, until the great Witwatersrand industrial region is reached. This extends for 70 to 100 miles east and west through the great city of Johannesburg and follows roughly the belt of the gold-producing banket reefs.

The Rand. Although this is not an agricultural land-use region in the same sense as those already described, the Rand, or correctly the Witwatersrand, is so distinctive that it merits separate consideration. It lies where the ancient rocks of the great complex crop out from beneath the Karoo beds which hide them farther south. It lies in fact between the High Veld properly speaking and the region of the northern Transvaal known generally as the Transvaal Bush Veld. As already described, it is the greatest gold-producing region of the world. The ore, extracted from depths of up to 9000 feet, must be crushed by powerful machinery before the gold can be extracted by chemical means.

This implies large-scale organization with adequate capital. An essential factor in the development of the region has been the supplies of cheap coal from the great field which extends from the eastern end of the Rand over the edge of the plateau into Natal. The focal point of the Rand is the great modern city of Johannesburg (Figure 20.21), second only to Cairo in population among African cities, and with a population exceeding a million. East and

Figure 20.21 The skyscraper city of Johannesburg. Notice the mine dumps of white quartz in the background. (Courtesy British Overseas Airways Corporation.)

west of Johannesburg are such industrial towns as Springs, Germiston, Benoni, Krugersdorp, Brakpan, and Boksburg, which together form the nearest approach in Africa to a conurbation.

Johannesburg was founded in 1886, and its progress was rapid. At first the surrounding veld was scarred by the huge dumps of waste white sand left after the gold-bearing blanket was crushed and the gold extracted. But Johannesburg itself has been beautified by plantations of trees, notably Australian gum trees, which not only add character to the region but also are economically important as supplying pitprops and mining timber.

Rather naturally subsidiary industries have developed in the Rand, including chemicals, engineering works, and the preparation of agricultural products for food.

The Transvaal Bush Veld. This complex and interesting region occupies the northern two-thirds of the Transvaal between the Witwatersrand and the Limpopo River (Figure 20.22). There is thus a full range from the temperate climatic conditions characteristic of the high plateau at 6000 feet to the tropical climate of the Limpopo valley at under 2000 feet.

The gently rolling surface of the High Veld of the south gives place to a more broken and diversified relief where the older rocks outcrop. It is possible to distinguish a whole succession of low hill ranges, separated by relatively flat areas, in fact a number of distinct physiographic regions in each of which a distinctive agricultural economy is developed.

The name Bush Veld suggests that here the treeless, grassy, High Veld

Figure 20.22 The Transvaal, showing main ranges (numbered) and subregions. (From J. H. Wellington, *Geog. Rev.*, 1932. Courtesy of the *Geographical Review*, American Geographical Society.)

gives place to a vegetation so characteristic of tropical Africa as a whole, here one with scattered bushes rather than trees. As the altitude drops towards the north, average temperatures become higher and the frost decreases until along the Limpopo itself frost is completely absent, or at least rare. In comparison with other parts of the Republic of South Africa this is a region of recent development. A simple subdivision of the whole is not easy, but South Africans frequently distinguish the following parts.

(1) *The Bankenveld,* otherwise the banken or slopes. Around Pretoria the country consists of lines of hills running from east to west with gentle northern slopes, grass covered and steeper southern rocky slopes with thorny bushes. Pretoria, the capital of the Republic, lies in this country. Somewhat similar ridges, but trending north to south, lie northeast of Pretoria.

A short distance eastward from Pretoria is the famous Premier diamond mine, for many years the largest diamond mine in the world, and certainly one of the largest man-made holes in the African continent.

(2) *The Central Bush Veld* lies to the north of Pretoria, and here are remarkable irrigable valley floors such as the fertile Springbok Flats. An important tract is irrigated by the Hartebeestpoort Dam on the Crocodile River around the settlement of Brits. This is a land of new and flourishing farming developments with large citrus orchards. Still larger is the area irrigated from the Loskop Dam and the Olifants River.

(3) *The Waterberg, Sandveld, and Pietersburg Plateau* lie to the north of the Transvaal Bush Veld, and here the excessively sandy soils in the valleys limit productive capacity, so that the land becomes pastoral rather than agricultural.

(4) *The Limpopo Bush Veld* occupies the broad valley of the Limpopo. Again soils are sandy, and dense bush covers much of the area, which resembles similar country to the north of the river lying in Southern Rhodesia. It may perhaps be regarded as cattle-ranching country, but owing to natural conditions some 80 acres are regarded as necessary for each beast.

Apart from the first modern iron smelting works in all Africa being at Pretoria, where smelting began early in 1934, there have been many other recent developments in the northern Transvaal. The completion of the railway through to the Limpopo River, which it crosses by the famous Beit Bridge, made it possible to work copper deposits at Messina. It was the intention that this railway should link up directly with the Southern Rhodesian system, but the connecting link in Southern Rhodesia has been long delayed though the Beit Bridge is used by through road traffic.

Where communications make settlement attractive in the northern Transvaal have come the development of spacious orchards, the cultivation of cotton, tobacco, and peanuts, and the possibility of extensive development of other tropical or semi-tropical crops.

The Basuto highlands. Returning to the southeastern margin of the High Plateau, the High Veld in the Orange Free State gives place southeastward before the crest is reached to country where the horizontal Karoo sandstones, capped by resistant basaltic beds, reach elevations of 6000 feet and over, but where the land has been deeply dissected to form a series of precipitous crags and deep narrow valleys. Most of the country of this type lies outside both the Free State and the Cape Province and for the most part within the limits of Basutoland. Because Basutoland is a territory under direct British colonial administration and not part of the Republic of South Africa, it is separately considered.

The eastern uplands. Professor Wellington uses this name—perhaps not a very satisfactory one—for the broad stretch of foothill country below the great escarpment and lying mainly in Natal and including the middle veld.

The great scarp of the Drakensberg needs to be seen to be appreciated. Its highest point—incidentally the highest point in South Africa—is Giant's Castle, reaching over 11,000 feet. There are forests in some parts, but many slopes are covered with grass, so that this area has been called the Mountain Grass Veld or Sourveld.

Basaltic rocks of the plateau cap the great scarp, and below are the almost horizontal Karoo beds with their seams of coal. It is, therefore, in this belt that the Natal coalfield has been developed, the focal point being the town of Newcastle. There is an obvious advantage that the export of coal to the Port of Durban is essentially downhill, and gravity does much of the work of haulage.

Towards the coast the mountain grass veld stretches into what is sometimes called the grass veld and thorn bush belt, where much more cultivation is possible and where there is a very extensive population of Africans.

The Sourveld (where the word "sour" indicates the occurrence of grasses lacking in food value) gives place to a grass veld where the rooi grass is much more nutritious and where others have been introduced to provide even better grazing. To some extent this has become a dairying and even a beef-producing region. It includes the old land of the Zulus, Zululand. The staple food grain over much of the tract is Kaffir corn, but Indian corn, or maize, is very extensively cultivated.

South Africa has almost a world monopoly in production of wattle bark for tanning, and 70 per cent of the acreage of plantations is in the intermediate belt of Natal between 2000 and 4500 feet above sea level. There are large and small plantations on farms concerned primarily with other crops or stock and also larger plantations controlled by companies producing the extract. It was an English trader between Australia and Natal, John Vanderplank, who brought seeds of the Black wattle (*Acacia mollissimma*) from Australia to attempt to grow a thicket to shelter his home in Natal. Boer farmers soon observed the rapid growth of the wattle in wind-swept localities and quickly adopted it; not until 1884 was its value as a source of tanning material appreciated. Commercial planting began, and by 1950 nearly 100,000 tons of extract were being exported in addition to large quantities of bark.[11]

The eastern Low Veld and coastal region. This is the coastal strip itself, and broadly can be taken to include the land below the 2000-foot contour. Here frost becomes rare and near the coast completely absent. Although rainfall averages well over 40 inches, there is both seasonal and local variation; but everywhere rainfall is adequate for agriculture. Temperature variations on either side of a 70°F annual average are low when compared with the plateau. At Durban, for example, the range is from 64° to 76°F. Both temperature and rainfall conditions are naturally most reliable near the coast itself. Though there are good alluvial soils in the valleys, elsewhere the ancient rocks with their granite intrusions which here outcrop give rise to some sandy and poor tracts. The whole region carries a heavy population, whether in the European areas of Natal or in Zululand and other areas occupied mainly by Africans. The development of commercial crops has laid emphasis on tropical products. Sugar cane comes first, and with its development South Africa became self-supporting in sugar. Now, with a production of over a million tons of sugar, there is a surplus for export. Cotton is of some importance, but in the years between the World Wars cotton growers were greatly discouraged in Zululand by the unexpectedly violent rainfall fluctuations as well as low prices. Tropical fruits, citrus fruits, bananas, pineapples, and pawpaws are widely cultivated and sent to the interior parts of the country. Market gardening, the production of vegetables for consumption in the towns, has also extended greatly, and it is here that one sees the conflict between European and Indian. With a higher standard of living to maintain, the European market gardener can easily be undercut in the markets of Durban and the other towns by the Indian squatter, content to live in a hut made of old gasoline cans.

Climatic conditions, British settlers, the introduction of fodder grasses and the local urban demand have combined to encourage a flourishing dairying industry so that a section of Natal has become the premier dairying belt of South Africa.

Northward from Natal, the coastal belt passes into Portuguese East Africa, and Swaziland, which is separately described, lies inland. The Low Veld along the eastern margin of the Transvaal remained until World War I but little developed, and it is here that the enormous nature reserve, the Kruger National Park, is to be found. Then came a rapid and important development.

---

[11] M. D. Birkby, "The Wattle Industry in Natal," *Geography*, XXXVI, 1951, 150–164.

Figure 20.23 A model of Port Natal (the site of Durban) as it was in 1852. (Copyright Aerofilms Library.)

The administrative center of Natal is Pietermaritzburg, founded as early as 1839. In size it is eclipsed by Durban (the port of Natal). The harbor of Durban is a natural bay of very considerable size with a narrow entrance which was formerly obstructed by a sand bar (Figure 20.23). This has in large part been removed by constant dredging, and the largest vessels using the Indian Ocean are able to dock alongside the quays adequately protected from the stormy seas of the South Indian Ocean (Figure 20.24). Durban has naturally become the principal coal- and mineral ore-exporting center of the Republic. It is the third town in order of size, and the population is roughly one-third African, one-third Indian and one-third European. It still has a whaling industry.

The sandy coasts in the neighborhood form attractive holiday resorts, and surf bathing under adequate safeguards is as popular in South Africa as anywhere in the world. Resorts like Warner Beach, with their crowds of sun- and surf-bathing Europeans, add a final touch, if such were needed, to South African contrasts. Although geographically Natal and the coastal regions have here been treated as a whole, it might have been more logical to describe separately the European areas and the native reserves.

Mining versus agriculture in South Africa

It is often urged that the economy of the Republic of South Africa is insecurely based because of its marked dependence upon the production of one commodity, which is gold. If for some reason or other world demand for

Figure 20.24   An air view of Port Natal with Durban in 1952, showing a hundred years of change. (Copyright Aerofilms Library.)

gold should cease, it is argued that the whole country would find itself in a very precarious position.

During and after World War II figures for the production and value of gold for export were not published, but the state of affairs in the years between the World Wars is a sufficient indication of the general trend. On an average for 1921–1925 gold represented more than half by value of the total exports of the Union of South Africa. Another 10 per cent was represented by diamonds (Figure 20.25), so that gold and diamonds together made up over 60 per cent of all exports. The only others of significance then were wool and mohair and corn (maize), with limited quantities of coal. As years went by the position in 1933–1935 was that gold had come to represent nearly two-thirds of the total value of exports. Although nominally diamonds had decreased in relative importance, this position was essentially the result of deliberate restriction. Before the outbreak of World War II fruits and sugar had come to exceed corn in value among exports.

It has been said with considerable truth that a tremendous part of South Africa's effort is directed towards digging gold out of the deep mines in the Witwatersrand for it to be buried, not quite so deeply, in vaults at Fort Knox in the heart of the United States. How long is this process likely to continue? The position in 1963 is that output is still on the increase.

In the meantime agricultural development proceeds steadily and against considerable difficulties. To a large extent South African agriculture is primarily the concern of the Afrikaans-speaking population (with the exception

Figure 20.25   The most famous hole in the world, the old Kimberley diamond mine. (Copyright Aircraft Operating Company.)

of the tropical products in Natal) whereas mining has become rather more the concern of the English-speaking section. This is admittedly only a very broad half-truth. Those who look to the future development of South Africa as bound up with agricultural production, though pointing to such factors as good sunshine records, are forced to recognize the numerous natural disadvantages—the inadequacy and irregularity of rainfall, the poverty of soils and liability to soil erosion, all of which combine to result in low and irregular yields. There is also the unsatisfactory labor position which many regard as being made worse rather than better by the restrictive racial legislation. If, however, South Africa is forced to rely more than in the past on agricultural production, this account should have made it clear that there are considerable possibilities, especially in parts of the country still largely underdeveloped. Thus the lines of future development in the Republic of South Africa would seem to rest especially with (1) the development of irrigation, (2) the control of soil erosion, (3) the introduction of fodder crops and nutritious grasses which have proved so successful in New Zealand, and the consequent development of more intensive mixed farming with high yields of crops, meat, milk, and other products. Long discussed, a vast project to regulate the Orange River has been started.

Nothing has been said in the foregoing account of the important fisheries around the coasts of South Africa, which will be found described in detail in a paper by Peter Scott.[12] The author concluded: "Unlike other areas of the world's fisheries, South African coastal waters could be far more intensively fished than at present without depleting resources." He commended a long-term program of survey and research, since fishing had previously been restricted to certain areas only. The home consumption of fish in the country was only 7 pounds per head per annum. Existing taboos against the eating of fish held by many Bantu tribes are doubtless destined to disappear. There is little doubt that the health of these people, who suffer seriously from protein deficiency, would be improved by the addition of fish to their diet. Since Scott wrote, the industry has expanded enormously, and South Africa is the largest producer of fish in the Southern Hemisphere. Together with South-west Africa 7500 fishermen and a further 20,000 employed on shore handle over 500,000 tons of fish annually—notably, pilchard, maasbanker, and mackerel. Much is converted to fishmeal and oil or is canned. Trawlers, especially from Cape Town, land the bulk of fish consumed locally. The three other ports concerned are Port Elizabeth, East London, and Mossel Bay. The bulk of the fish caught is known as "stock fish," otherwise Cape hake, which is a cold-water species, closely allied to the European hake. It is obtained by trawling in the cold waters off the southwest coast. The other principal fish is the Agulhas sole, representing 5 per cent by weight, but 16 per cent by value. During and after World War II South Africa sent snoek (or barracouta) to Britain, but it was not popular and certainly not an advertisement for South African fisheries. Rock lobster or crayfish, of which the tails are exported frozen or canned, are, however, much appreciated.

Communications in South Africa

South Africa is well served by an excellent railway system, despite the fact that the gauge is only 3 feet, 6 inches. The first railway from Cape Town to Wellington was begun in 1859, and by 1960 over 13,590 miles of railway had been constructed in the Union. The railways and harbors are owned and controlled by the government, being administered by a special department. South Africa may be quoted as a good example of the excellent results which may be achieved with a narrow gauge and unified control.

At first the construction of lines from Cape Town was based partly on strategic considerations; then it was dictated by the discovery of the gold of the Rand and the diamonds at Kimberley, and later by the need to develop

[12] "The Otter Trawl Fisheries of South Africa," *Geog. Rev.,* **XXXIX,** 1949, 529–551.

productive or potentially productive agricultural regions and to provide a comprehensive network to all habitable parts of the country. The later functions are clear from the special arrangements made by the railways for the handling of coal direct from the collieries to the wharves in the main harbors. The construction of a series of maize elevators in the corn-growing districts and at the ports was undertaken to secure ease and economy in handling one of the principal agricultural exports of the country. In comparison with the rest of Africa the Republic is fortunate in its adequate and accessible reserves of coal. This has not prevented the extensive use of electrification, and Natal was able to boast one of the earliest and longest stretches of electrified main line in the world.

The railway map now shows how the lines serve the four main ports of South Africa—Cape Town, Port Elizabeth, East London, and Durban—and also the eastern Transvaal with its natural outlet at the Portuguese port of Lourenço Marques. These lines leading to the main ports have now been joined up in such a way as to give a reasonable network, but it is still a torturous journey, for example, from Cape Town to Port Elizabeth by rail. The concentration of development on the four main ports has meant that in many years the trade passing through the minor ports, such as Mossel Bay, Port Nolloth, Simonstown, and Knysna, is less than 1 per cent of the whole.

In the years between the World Wars and subsequently there has been a great expansion in the development of motor roads and the use of motor transport. South Africans claim that they make a greater use of automobiles than any country in the world outside the United States and Canada. Whether this claim is true or not, the old ox wagon, with its span of 16 oxen, has become a rare sight. Although South Africans still use the expression "to outspan" when they intend to call a halt, the majority have forgotten what it really means and certainly would be as puzzled as to how to do it if they were asked as any European or American town dweller.

As in other dry countries, vast stretches of the land can be covered by automobile without special preparation of roads. The difficulty is in the wetter regions, with the sudden rise of streams and the unfortunate habit which the floods have of cutting deep gulleys across roads. This is obviated, for example in Natal, by the construction of concrete stretches so that the flood waters can find their way across the road with the minimum of damage. Traveling salesmen who have to tour extensively in South Africa were (at least until World War II) granted a special allowance to enable them to hire cattle to pull their cars out of unsuspected bogs or *spruits* unexpectedly deep.

Side by side with the development of motor transport has come the very extensive use in South Africa of the airplane.

Southwest Africa (Suidwes Afrika or Zuid-Wes Afrika)

This vast territory, totaling nearly one-third of a million square miles, occupies the drier side of the continent from the arid scrublands of the Bechuanaland border to the absolute desert or Namib which parallels the Atlantic Ocean from the mouth of the Orange River northward to the lower course of the Cunene River, which forms the frontier with Angola. Throughout the whole of this stretch no permanent watercourse reaches the ocean. The southern tropic runs through the heart of the country in such a way that a larger area lies to the north within the tropics than south outside the tropics. Only locally, as near Windhoek, does the African plateau rise to sufficient heights to cause marked amelioration of the hot dry climate. The white population in 1960 was only 73,000 out of a total of 525,000. The average of all human inhabitants over the whole territory is under two per square mile.

It is believed that this territory was inhabited at an early date by wandering Bushmen, who some six or seven centuries ago were replaced along the coastal regions by Hottentots. They were followed in due course by the Ovambos, and early in the eighteenth century by the Hereros. The last were checked in their southern movement by the Hottentots under a leader known generally as Jonker Afrikaner, who has since become a legendary figure. Living near the banks of the Orange River, he organized the Hottentots, equipped them with firearms, and became their leader and champion until his death in 1860, when the Hereros succeeded in forcing the Hottentots southward.

As early as 1486 Bartolomeu Dias landed at Angra Pequena, now known as Lüderitz, and erected a cross to record his landing. Later travelers recorded that the Hereros in the area had great herds of cattle, and it was in 1792 that the Dutch took possession of the chief natural harbor of the coast, Walvis Bay.

In 1805 missionaries of German nationality, though in the service of the London Missionary Society, established missions in Namaqualand. It was an American shipmaster, Captain B. Morrell, who in 1828–1830 explored the coast, made journeys into the interior, and drew attention to the deposits of guano on the islands off the coast. This led to the exploitation of these guano islands in 1843–1845, and to their annexation by Britain between 1861 and 1867. It was in the following year, 1868, that the great German leader, Bismarck, became interested in the area and asked whether the British government was prepared to safeguard the lives and properties of German missionaries. The British reply was noncommittal, though a few years later the Cape government sent a special commissioner who fixed limits for the territories of the two chief tribes, the Namaquas and Damaras.

A couple of years later, in 1878, Walvis Bay was annexed by Britain. In the eighteen-eighties, when Germans were active in so many parts of Africa, a German merchant, Lüderitz by name, acquired land south of Walvis Bay and soon after purchased the harbor of Angra Pequena, where with the approval of Bismarck the German flag was hoisted. This led naturally to the annexation by Germany of the whole territory north of the Orange River, excepting only Walvis Bay and the guano islands. The German government took over responsibility for the administration of the territory from the German company, the Deutsche Kolonial Gesellschaft. Jonker Afrikaner's old headquarters were made the seat of administration and renamed Windhoek.

The Germans were subsequently concerned with long and costly wars with the Hereros and Hottentots, but it was the discovery of diamonds on the Lüderitz Bay coast in 1908 which showed the whole potential importance of this arid area.

When World War I broke out, the Germans advanced into Union territory but were quickly countered by Union forces under General Botha; on July 9, 1915, the German army surrendered. In 1919, at the end of World War I, the League of Nations granted a mandate to the Union of South Africa to administer the area, which became known as the Territory of Southwest Africa. Germans, including all officials, were repatriated. This was a Class 3 mandate, under which the territory was to be administered as an integral part of the territory of the Mandatory Power. But a curious situation lasted for many years. The people of Southwest Africa in due course expressed their wish to be incorporated in the Union of South Africa, but this was prevented by the United Nations Assembly in 1946. The South African Government has persistently refused to recognize that the United Nations have any right to interfere and the Republic regards Southwest Africa as an integral part of its territory.

The country as a whole is essentially a stock-raising country, scarcity of water and poor rainfall rendering agriculture virtually impossible. Between 3 and 4 million sheep and goats and more than 1½ million cattle exist in the area, and considerable attention has been paid to the improvement of the quality of cattle and to the production of butter for home consumption and export. An important product is Karakul pelts, a valued fur in temperate lands. The area producing diamonds has been steadily expanded, and their recovery from alluvial sands and gravels takes place over a 300-mile stretch of the coastline from the Orange River northward. In the north of the country ores of vanadium (important), tin, lithium, lead, copper, and zinc are worked, the last three especially from the Tsumeb mine. Walvis Bay, the chief port, is linked by railway with the main South African system at De Aar Junction. Within the territory of Southwest Africa are over 1000 miles of railway of the South African 3 feet, 6 inches gauge. The railway administration also operates well-developed road-motor services, covering several thousand miles of road.

Despite aridity it is clear that Southwest Africa is far from being an unimportant area. There are some parts where subterranean water can be reached by wells, and this makes possible the extension of cattle rearing. Salt is obtained from some of the salt pans in the Kalahari, which occupies the northern and eastern parts of the country.

The High Commission territories of South Africa

Within the area which may broadly be called South Africa are three territories which for various reasons remain distinct from the four countries which united in 1910 to form the Union of South Africa. They are under the direct protection of the British government in London, represented by a High Commissioner who is also the United Kingdom Ambassador resident in South Africa.

Basutoland. The story of this little mountain state reads more like a romantic historical novel than a story from real life. Its foundation dates from the troubled times of 1820 when the Bantu, including the Zulus, Matabele, and Korannas, were sweeping southward from central Africa, exterminating all those who stood in their path. A warrior named Moshesh welcomed refugees fleeing from the invaders and constituted himself their leader. The territory he chose was well suited for guerilla warfare; it stretches westward from the edge of the Drakensberg and is for the most part more than 6000 feet above sea level. Only the western border and the westward-draining valleys are at a lower elevation. Moshesh succeeded in building up what was almost unique in Africa, a nation as opposed to a tribe. In due course the Voortrekkers reached the country (1835–1837), and Moshesh took a hand in the troubled political relationships between the Boers and the Cape government. The latter was anxious to avoid trouble, and when action had to be taken in 1852 Moshesh was too good for the punitive force. The British abandoned the territory. The local Boers constituted it an independent Boer republic, but their attitude towards the Basutos was such that the chief appealed to Britain for help. So Britain intervened, and in 1869 Basutoland became a British Territory under the direct protection of the British government in London. When the Union of South Africa was formed by the South Africa Act of 1909, provision was made for the transfer of Basutoland to the Union, but forty years later the inhabitants showed no wish to come under the Union. So Basutoland is a native territory, all the land being owned by the people, who form a Christian nation ruled since 1960 by a paramount chief with an advisory council of chiefs advised by a handful of British officials. Previously the country had been ruled by a woman— Ma'Ntsebo—styled the Paramount Chieftainess Regent (widow of the great-great-grandson of Moshesh). At the head of the British officials is a resident Commissioner under the direction of the High Commissioner.

Is it possible for such an island of tribal Africa to survive in the modern world? A careful and detailed study by Hugh Ashton makes depressing reading. Not only does it seem to show that progress is impossible in a system of hereditary chieftainship but also that economic conditions resulting from isolation have led to the survival or resuscitation of some of the most undesirable features of African life even culminating in ritual murders.[13] In recent years there has been an ever-increasing fear of South Africa's racial policy and a strong desire to remain under the direct protection of Great Britain—which is true also of Swaziland and Bechuanaland. The economic position is assisted by the strong demand for Basuto labor in the Rand mines. In 1960 the population was estimated at 675,000 with an additional 125,000 temporarily absent for work in South Africa. This movement of labor is carefully regulated from the capital, Maseru, which is linked with the South African railway system though only one mile of line is actually in Basutoland.

Swaziland. Swaziland[14] was settled in the early part of the nineteenth century by the Swazis, who had retreated northward in the face of Boer settlement, only to find themselves menaced by the warlike Zulu raiders. It was at a time when British prestige was high; Mswazi, the Swazi chief, sent a deputation to Theophilus Shepstone seeking protection. Shepstone used his influence with Mpande, the Zulu chief, to such good effect that the Swazis and the Zulus have remained ever since on friendly terms. Mswazi died in 1868. Both he and his successor Mbandeni made numerous "concessions" to individual prospectors with the result that the country was overrun by undesirable characters, often in conflict. Again came an appeal to the British in 1887, but this time it was in vain. So the chief simply appointed the son of old Theophilus Shepstone as his resident adviser! There followed a short period of self-government by European residents with Swazi consent, then administration by the South African Republic, then by the Transvaal until 1907. Since that year Swaziland has been administered by its own paramount chief with a resident British commissioner. In 1924 the Swazis objected strongly to the suggestion that their territory should be incorporated in the Union of South Africa, and that has remained their attitude.

The country has an area of 6704 square miles and in 1960 had an estimated population of 264,300, including 8700 Europeans, 1600 colored, and the remainder nearly all Swazis. The few Zulus in the south acknowledge allegiance to the paramount Swazi chief.

The main occupation of the people is subsistence farming, but the country is rich in minerals. Asbestos is the leading export, but in 1954 a rich

---

[13] Hugh Ashton, *The Basuto*, New York, 1952.

[14] D. M. Doveton, *The Human Geography of Swaziland*, Institute of British Geographers, Publication 8.

deposit of high-quality hematite iron ore was located and awaits exploitation. A railroad was planned for completion in 1964 to take the ore to Lourenço Marques. China clay also exists. Europeans have developed fruit and vegetable farming, helped by irrigation, and there is considerable afforestation.

Bechuanaland Protectorate. This is as large as the whole of France and thus much more extensive than the other two territories.

Unlike Basutoland, which is entirely surrounded by Republic territory, and Swaziland, which is essentially an enclave of the eastern Transvaal, the third of the British High Commission territories in southern Africa, the Bechuanaland Protectorate, stretches away northward from the Cape Province and the Transvaal to occupy a huge area in the heart of the continent only separated from the Zambezi itself by a narrow tongue, the so-called Caprivi Strip, which was ceded to Southwest Africa. The southern boundary of the present Bechuanaland Protectorate is the Molopo River, a nonpermanent stream which drains or should drain to the Orange. The southern half of the country is essentially the Kalahari Desert, without any surface streams; the northern half is in the basin of Lake Ngami and the Okovango swamp, from which the water overflows in favorable seasons to the Zambezi. We may, therefore, regard northern Bechuanaland as lying in the Zambezi basin.

Few political divisions in Africa coincide either with natural features or frontiers between tribes, and the present Bechuanaland Protectorate is no exception. The southern part of the land of the Bechuanas lies in the Cape Province of the South African Republic. The country south of the Molopo was first declared a British crown colony under the title of British Bechuanaland, and a protectorate was established over the northern area by agreement with the leading chiefs. In 1895 the British area was incorporated in Cape Colony and today forms part of Cape Province. The protectorate was administered for a short time by the South Africa Company, but the chiefs protested and in 1896 the protectorate came permanently under the direct administration of London. In 1896–1897 the Bechuanaland Railway Company constructed the line linking South Africa with Rhodesia. It runs through the entire length of eastern Bechuanaland and makes the country an essential link in African communications.

Eight different Bantu tribes, each with an elaborate tribal organization, inhabit Bechuanaland together with a few nomadic Bushmen and some Damaras who fled from the Germans in Southwest Africa before the 1914–1918 war.

Bechuanaland may well be called "Livingstone's Africa" since it was here that he spent his early days in Africa and from which he went on to explore Zambezi land.

Over that greater part of the protectorate which coincides with the Kalahari, perhaps misnamed a desert, the fine yellow Kalahari sand is an almost universal covering of the surface. The African population is collected in large reserves, mainly in the eastern half of the country, leaving 60,000 square miles in two large areas of crown lands. These have practically no population because there is no surface water but might be made suitable for large-scale ranching. The first need would be deep wells to provide watering points for cattle. There is need of fencing for control of grazing because overstocking for even a short time could begin a dust bowl and serious erosion. The natural grasses are said to be excellent in some places and at least edible in others, but droughts occur about one year in every three so that other fodder, best provided by hay in good years, must be available. All this clearly means large-scale operation; there is real danger of land damage in small-scale ranching or private ownership. Just as most of the Protectorate suffers from lack of water, so the northwest corner, the tsetse-fly-infested Okovango swamps, suffers from too much. There development is possible only with improved communications as well as control of water and the provision of incentives to the Africans—here the Batawana tribe.[15] The Okovango River rises in the Angola plateau where there is a good summer rainfall and after a course of some 800 miles enters the Ngami depression by the Popa Falls. There its waters spread out into a great swamp towards Lake Ngami, which lies at the southern end of this inland delta. Lake Ngami is being steadily invaded by thorn bush and is a mere fragment of the lake Livingstone discovered. At times waters from the swamps and lake escape southeastward to the Makarikari depression (which has water only after floods), the lowest part of the northern Kalahari. At other times it seems that the waters of the Okovango escape into the Linyanti swamps and so into the Zambezi. Apparently the Zambezi is capturing the waters of the Okovango. Whatever may be the exact hydrological relationships, these swamplands are potential rich farmlands if the same methods can be applied as used by the French in the inland Niger delta.

The Bamangwato Reserve in eastern Bechuanaland, with its capital at Serowe, came into the world limelight in 1950 because of the marriage of the chief-designate Seretse Khama to a white girl in England and of the conflict of loyalties which resulted. This has already been discussed in Chapter 7.

BIBLIOGRAPHY

Apart from the references quoted in the text, the following should be noted:

Official Year Book of the Union of South Africa (published annually). Often with articles of general interest and results of research; now *Republic of South Africa*.

[15] The views expressed here are those of Frank Debenham; see *Geography*, **XXXVI**, 1951, 107–109.

A. Gordon-Brown, *Year Book and Guide to Southern Africa,* published by the Union Castle Mail Steamship Company, London.

Cambridge History of the British Empire, Vol. VIII, London, 1936.

A. L. du Toit, *The Geology of South Africa,* 2nd Ed., London, 1939.

L. C. A. and C. M. Knowles, *South Africa,* London, 1936.

W. J. Talbot, *Land Utilization in the Cape,* Cape Town, 1950.

The South African Geographical Journal. Includes many articles of importance.

J. H. Wellington, *Southern Africa,* Vol. I, London, 1955; Vol. II, London, 1955.

Monica M. Cole, *South Africa,* London, 1961.

W. J. Talbot, "*South Africa,*" in *A History of Land Use in Arid Regions,* Paris: UNESCO, 1961.

Lester C. King, *The Scenery of South Africa,* 2nd. Ed., London, 1963.

See also *Focus,* November 1960 (Southwest Africa) and December 1963 (High Commission Territories).

Though published in Capetown, Edwin S. Munger's *African Field Reports* (1961) range widely over Africa south of the Sahara and are a valuable source of information.

N. C. Pollock and Swanzie Agnew, *An Historical Geography of South Africa,* London, 1963.

CHAPTER TWENTY-ONE

African Seas and Islands

Continental and oceanic islands

Emphasis has already been laid upon the uninterrupted character of so much of the coast of Africa. The absence of deep bays and gulfs is a marked feature, and associated with this smoothness of so much of the African coastline is the absence of islands, which are to be found in such numbers bordering the coasts of other continents. Geographers commonly distinguish between continental islands and oceanic islands. Those belonging to the first group rise from the continental shelf at no great distance from the mainland. They are associated structurally with the neighboring parts of the mainland, and consequently the environmental conditions which they offer to human inhabitants differ but little from those of the neighboring shores. Oceanic islands, on the other hand, frequently rising from great ocean depths and cut off from the continental masses by stretches of water which are commonly both deep and wide, may bear no close relationship with the continental masses, and are not infrequently the summits of submarine volcanoes or the higher peaks of otherwise submerged mountain ranges.

Africa has but few continental islands or groups of islands and but few oceanic islands in the neighboring seas. But members of both groups have in Africa assumed a rather special significance.

Continental islands

The coastlands of Africa have been described earlier in this book as inhospitable. Their inhospitality in the physical sense is particularly marked where large stretches of desert shore are fringed by sandy coastlands, against which pound the oceanic rollers in everlasting lines of surf. Through these breakers boats propelled by hand—for the larger modern vessels cannot approach within miles—make their way in constant danger of damage or destruction.

Other stretches of the coastline are backed by mangrove swamps, in turn giving place to thick forests affording constant cover to enemies. It is not surprising that those who sought to explore or establish trading relationships with the peoples of Africa, approaching the continent by sea, placed particular value on any natural inlet which might serve as a haven. Later, when they sought to establish bases from which to carry on their trading, whether the nefarious slave trade or more legitimate efforts at commerce, it is obvious that they would choose easily defensible sites. Some such sites are afforded by rocky promontories, sheltering some bay to serve as a harbor, with land approaches which could be defended with relative ease. Considerations of this sort entered into the choice of sites for such settlements as Saint Louis, or Dakar in Senegal, or even Freetown in Sierra Leone. It is not surprising that maritime peoples approaching by sea, used to life on the sea and able to use their ships for escape purposes in case of need, favored especially the use of continental islands close to the coasts for their trading settlements. Examples are numerous around the coasts of Africa.

With the development in modern times of peaceful trading relationships these island sites have often proved inconvenient for establishing lines of communication with the interior, as with Gorée. In some cases the best has been made of a bad job. In other cases, new settlements have been chosen and developed. Some interesting examples of island sites are afforded by Bathurst, the capital of the British colony of the Gambia, built on an island at the entrance to the Gambia River and consequently developed with difficulties which have not yet been fully overcome in an attempt to improve communications with the interior. In Portuguese Africa and Nigeria are examples of settlements on islands, where the irregular swampy coast still remains undeveloped. Lagos is on an island in a sheltered lagoon, but what might have originally been a good choice has necessitated the construction of deep-water wharves and the commercial terminus of the railways into the heart of Nigeria on the opposite mainland at Apapa.

Elsewhere around the coasts of Africa are examples of larger islands which have served and continue to serve as more extensive bases for European powers. Spain remains in possession of Fernando Po; Portugal remains in possession of the islands of São Tomé and Príncipe. The British occupancy of the Guano Islands off the southwest African coast (now Southwest Africa) had a different objective, the recovery of a substance of economic importance.

But the general story is repeated along the east coast of Africa, where islands are few but of considerable importance. The large and relatively fertile island of Zanzibar and its neighbor Pemba form the base from which the Sultans of Zanzibar exercised control over very large stretches of the mainland. Though the fortunes of the mainland changed, the islands remained in the possession of the Sultan; today they form an independent republic.

In more recent times, in World War I, during the campaigns against German East Africa, British troops from India landed on and used the island of Mafia. The great Arab stronghold and port of the east coast, Mombasa, was built on an island, which again has presented certain difficulties in the development of the railway system through Kenya to Uganda.

Farther north a very interesting example of the changing importance of islands is offered by the tiny island of Perim in the midst of the narrow entrance to the Red Sea. Like so many islands of strategic importance, its significance was appreciated by Britain in the days of imperial expansion. Perim became a naval base, a signals stations, a point for recoaling and refueling. But with their increasing size, warships and merchant ships were no longer able to use its limited facilities. Its functions have been transferred to the port of Aden on the mainland coast of Arabia, another defensible position, but one with a harbor of magnificent size and depth.

There are other groups of islands farther removed from the coasts of Africa which may still be considered continental islands. In the northern Atlantic Ocean, lying off the northwest African coasts, are the Canaries. These partly volcanic islands with their rich soil, favorable climate, and moderate, well-distributed winter rainfall and abundant sunshine proved attractive to the Spaniards. The islands are administered as an integral part of Spain. The existence of natural harbors, or harbors improved without difficulty to meet the needs of modern vessels, has led to the use of Santa Cruz de Tenerife and Las Palmas as ports of call for ocean liners from Europe bound for South America or South Africa.

The important island of Madeira, farther off the continental shores of the northwest, long in the hands of Portugal, provides an alternative, again with a good harbor, at Funchal. Like the Canaries, Madeira is an island intensely productive and extremely attractive climatically and scenically. In the early days of exploration and of trading with merchant vessels equipped only with sail, the group of the Azores, much farther out into the Atlantic, afforded like and equally important facilities, immortalized in the lines, "At Flores in the Azores Sir Richard Grenville lay" and the story of the *Revenge*. But they are in the latitude of Portugal, not of Africa.

Nearer the coasts of desert Africa are the Cape Verde Islands, climatically much more arid and less favored for settlement, whose significance therefore has tended to wane with the passing of time. These are almost the only groups of islands in the Atlantic.

In the Indian Ocean special attention must of course be given to the great island of Madagascar. Excluding the island continent of Australia and the great island of Greenland, Madagascar can claim to be one of the largest islands in the world. Although it is structurally connected with continental

Africa, it is a subcontinent which has had a long story of development of its own. Associated with Madagascar to the north are several groups of islands, but of no very great importance.

Oceanic islands

In the midst of the Atlantic Ocean there are several truly oceanic islands, far removed from land, notably Ascension, St. Helena, and the Tristan da Cunha group. It might be thought that mention of these has no place in a book on Africa, but, in the days when exploration of the African coastlands was still actively taking place, these oceanic islands had an immense significance as ports of call, as havens of refuge in time of storm or other need, and as stepping stones on far-flung ocean routes. They took on a new significance with the development of submarine electric telegraph cables, when some of them became cable stations. For a brief period it seemed that the development of transoceanic air transport would bring them once more into permanent prominence. But this has been prevented by the ever-increasing speed and range of modern aircraft.

In the wide expanses of the Southern Ocean there are other islands which again have strategic importance and a significance in the whaling industry.

In the Indian Ocean islands are far more numerous, but certain ones, notably Réunion, Mauritius, and the Seychelles, have played a part comparable with that of the oceanic islands of the Atlantic. Mauritius and Réunion are sufficiently large to have a permanent existence and life of their own.

No excuse need be offered therefore for a consideration of at least some of the features of these islands which lie in the oceans around the African continent.

The Azores

The three groups of islands making up the Azores have a total area of a little over 900 square miles and a population approximating a quarter of a million. They lie well out in the Atlantic between latitudes 37° and 39°, which is in the extratropical high-pressure belt, but far enough north to receive an adequate rainfall from the winter cyclones of the westerly wind belt. They are volcanic, and the peaks of the old volcanoes reach considerable elevations, for example, 8500 feet in Picot, so that the islands attract a sufficient relief rainfall to prevent serious drought. The chief town and port of Ponta Delgada is on the largest island, São Miguel.

The islands produce foodstuffs in adequate quantities for the people in cereals, fruits, wine, cattle products, and fish, and there is a small trade with Portugal, which lies almost due east. The scenery and climate are attractive to tourists, but the islands are rather off main ocean routeways.

Madeira (or the Madeiras)

This group consists of the one large island, Madeira itself, about 300 square miles in area, and four smaller ones.

Farther south than the Azores, the dry summer season is longer, the period of winter rainfall shorter. But again the volcanic rocks of Madeira rise to 6500 feet, and a considerable relief rainfall results even at Funchal, on the southern coast, where the average is 30 inches. The climate, with abundant sunshine even in the winter, and the scenery are both delightful, so that very large numbers of residents have been attracted to Madeira to live their years of retirement.

The once forested hillslopes, which might easily suffer from very serious soil erosion, have been carefully terraced (Figure 21.1). Attractive little houses, each with a terraced garden resplendent throughout the year with flowers, climb up the hillsides in the vicinity both of Funchal and of other settlements.

Careful cultivation yields abundant harvests of wheat and barley, but it is for its fruits—its pineapples and bananas, and particularly its grapes—that Madeira is famous. The Madeira wine, a specialty for so long of the island, is only one of the types which are made.

Though the local handcrafts, such as lace making and the making of cane

Figure 21.1   Terracing on the steep slopes of Madeira. (Copyright Geographical Publications Limited.)

chairs, are maintained to a large extent for the benefit of the numerous passing tourists, they form a lucrative sideline for the peasant population. Clearly also Madeira has a strategic significance in its position. The old treaties of friendship which have existed between Portugal and Britain for the past two centuries form the basis on which rather special commercial relationships have been established between Madeira and Britain, and it was in full accord with this tradition of friendship that Britain obtained temporary air bases in the Azores during World War II, when Portugal remained neutral.

The Canaries

The Canaries form a larger group of seven main islands, again of volcanic origin, with a total area of 2800 square miles and a population of over half a million. In the island of Tenerife the dormant snow-capped volcano, Pico de Teide, rises in a magnificent cone to a height of over 12,000 feet. As a result of these elevations rainfall may be considerable on higher ground, though near the coast on the eastern sides of the islands it may fall to 10 inches or less. In addition, the drying harmattan blows from the African mainland, which is nearer than in the case of Madeira.

Shrubby Mediterranean vegetation with numerous succulent plants is found on the hillslopes, though Mediterranean trees such as the holm oak (*Quercus ilex*) are found in the damper areas. Again careful cultivation, especially with irrigation, has made possible the cultivation of cereals and vegetables, notably onions for home use, together with olives, citrus fruits, and tobacco. A small and very sweet variety of banana, which is much liked in European markets, has been very specially developed.

Again there is an extensive tourist trade. Santa Cruz in the island of Tenerife is rivaled as a tourist center and a port of call for steamers by Las Palmas, on the northeastern coast of the island of Gran Canaria and with an excellent modern harbor developed on the eastern side of a tombolo.

The delightful smaller island of Palma is essentially the top of a single extinct volcano with a huge blown-out crater. Less frequently visited, it is an island of great beauty inhabited by a cheerful agricultural peasantry.

The Canaries form an integral part of Spain, just as the Madeiras are administered as an integral part of Portugal.

The Cape Verde Islands

Ten islands and a few islets form the Cape Verde Islands, a Portuguese colony, covering rather over 1500 square miles, and with a population of about 200,000. Being situated in latitude 15° to 17° due west of St. Louis in Senegal, they lie in the belt of the Trade Winds throughout the year and are extremely dry. The total rainfall, between 5 and 10 inches, falls mainly in

August, September, and October, in contrast to the Mediterranean rainfall of the Canaries or Madeira.

Sisal, a vegetable oil, purgeira, resembling castor oil, and oranges are among the agricultural products produced in excess of local requirements.

The capital of the islands is Praia, but the chief port, a former coaling station mainly used by vessels on the South American run, is São Vincente.

Ascension

Ascension is an isolated volcanic island in the South Atlantic less than 8 degrees south of the equator, but no less than 700 miles from its neighbor to the southeast, St. Helena, and a still greater distance from the African coast.

It was occupied by the British in 1815, and its importance was as a haven or refuge in case of need by vessels of the British fleet. Consequently it was for long controlled by the British admiralty and organized as if it were a battleship, governed by a British naval officer. In 1922 it became a part of the colony of St. Helena.

Ascension takes its name from the fact that it was discovered by the Portuguese on Ascension Day in 1501. The several volcanic cones of which it is formed have rocks colored red and brown, but the central and highest one, rising to 2817 feet, owes its name, Green Mountain, and its covering of vegetation to the mists which frequently clothe the summit and a relief rainfall exceeding 30 inches. This is in striking contrast to the arid and often bare lava surfaces occupying the lower levels of the island.

It became and still is a cable station, and the handful of people living there are all employees of the British Cable and Wireless Limited, now under government control.

In World War II it suddenly became again of immense strategic importance. An airstrip of the size suitable for the largest transport planes, together with the necessary buildings, was built by the American forces and became known as Wideawake Field. When the American forces left the island in 1947, transatlantic air transport had already become virtually independent of such stepping stones. Radio has made cable communication out of date so that this question almost automatically arises: Is there a future for this little island of 34 square miles, other than as a breeding ground for the sooty tern, which comes to Ascension three times in every two years to lay its eggs, or the sea turtles, which use the warm sands for the same purpose between January and May? It has a possible temporary function in the United States rocket testing through the South Atlantic.

St. Helena

St. Helena, though only slightly larger—47 square miles—than Ascension and similarly an isolated volcano, with its peak rising to 2700 feet, is by comparison an important island. It too was discovered by the Portuguese, in 1502. It too is just a rocky top of a gigantic volcanic pile resting on the floor of the Atlantic Ocean, but St. Helena has been British for over 300 years, since 1571, and has a greater importance for several reasons. Its position in 16° South is right in the path of the southeast trade winds, so that the island was of utmost importance as a haven of refuge in the days of sailing ships. It was first occupied by the East India Company for the benefit of their ships rounding the Cape of Good Hope to India. Naturally the port and chief settlement, called Jamestown, is on the sheltered northwestern side of the island.

When vessels began to use coal it became a coaling station, especially for the ships of the British navy. It is 1200 miles from the nearest point, the Port of Mossamedes, on the African mainland, and its very isolation led to its being used as a base for whalers. It is now, however, too far from the chief whaling grounds to serve this function.

The first time that the British captured Napoleon Bonaparte of France he was imprisoned on Elba, off the coast of Italy, and escaped. The second time, after his defeat at Waterloo in 1815, the British took no chances, and he lived a prisoner on St. Helena until his death in 1821. St. Helena is famous, therefore, as the place of exile of perhaps the most dangerous prisoner-of-war of all time. At a later stage St. Helena became a cable station, with the cable running from Cape Town on the one hand to Ascension and Europe on the other. The island still has importance in collecting messages from the feeble radios of small ships and passing them on. The pleasant climate is another factor which has led to a population approaching 5000 living happily on this island. They have as much meat as they need; they grow such excellent potatoes that some in the past have been exported. New Zealand flax has been introduced, and the industry started by the government mill in 1908 includes the preparation of rope, string, and lace for export.

Again, however, the question clearly arises: What is the future of such an island? Efforts to establish an airstrip during World War II revealed the absence of any suitable land.

St. Helena is a British crown colony, with a resident governor.

Tristan da Cunha

Even more remote and inaccessible than St. Helena is the group of islands which make up Tristan da Cunha, and which since 1938 has formed a dependency of St. Helena. Tristan da Cunha itself is another old volcano of which the highest point reaches 8000 feet. The islands lie in 37° South, which is south of the southernmost point of Africa, and in the belt of the westerly winds, almost in the latitude of the "roaring forties." The handful of people, between 100 and 200, who lived there on the main island were descended mainly from shipwrecked sailors. Despite the cold, stormy climate and the extreme isolation, because Tristan da Cunha, unlike Ascension and St. Helena, is not near well-used oceanic routeways, they had a deep affection for their island and no desire to leave. They lived on a low plateau on the northwestern side of the island, growing potatoes and fruit, apples and peaches, and rearing cattle and geese. They had abundant fish in the surrounding seas.

During World War II the isolation of Tristan da Cunha was broken and the island became officially a British warship, under the name of *H.M.S. Atlantic Isle,* its function being primarily as a meteorological and radio station.

In 1961 the volcano, long believed extinct, showed ominous signs of activity and later erupted. The inhabitants were compelled to leave and were evacuated via South Africa to Britain. After a scientific investigation of the position the majority returned early in 1963.

Réunion or Bourbon

Turning now to the oceanic islands of the Indian Ocean, there are three volcanic islands, Réunion (French), Mauritius (British), and Rodriguez (British), forming a chain sometimes called the Mascarenhas, from the name of their Portuguese discoverer. Like the isolated islands of the Atlantic, they are volcanic. They lie in the trade wind belt, approximately in latitude 21° to 22°South, with a moderate to heavy rainfall derived from the Southeast Trades and augmented in the summer months by frequent tropical cyclones which are sometimes of a very violent nature. Only on the low-lying sheltered parts is there any real dry season, but the oceanic position moderates the temperature which at sea level ranges only between monthly means of 68° and 69°F. Prior to their discovery by Europeans, the islands, densely covered with forest, were uninhabited. In the course of time forests have been almost entirely destroyed. Their place has been taken by plantations of sugar cane, the chief economic crop of the islands. The population has been derived mainly from settlers from France and Britain, settlers or imported laborers from India, together with a few Negroes, the descendants of slaves, or natives from Madagascar. A certain number of Chinese have also settled on the islands.

Réunion was occupied by France in the middle of the seventeenth century, and, except for a short period during the Napoleonic wars when it came into British hands, it has remained French. The quarter of a million people are largely of French descent. With an area a little under 1000 square miles, it rises to 10,000 feet. The range of altitude makes possible the cultivation of a great variety of crops. The earlier ones of coffee, cloves, vanilla, and sugar have given place to a greater variety, including tea, cinchona, cocoa, manioc, cassava, and rice. Wheat and temperate fruits and vegetables can be grown at higher levels. The principal economic crop is sugar cane, so that large quantities of sugar and rum are exported.

It is to be noted that this production is achieved in a tropical island with white labor, or labor of predominantly white descent.

The capital is St. Denis. The only harbor accessible to large vessels is Pointe-des-Galets, which is a partly artificial port.

Mauritius

Mauritius is situated some 500 miles east of Madagascar and almost on the direct line between South Africa and Ceylon and India. It was certainly known to early Arab or Moorish sailors, and, though it was discovered by the Portuguese, the Dutch first settled on the island in 1598. They left, however, in 1710, and it was more than fifty years before the French arrived in 1767 and named the island Île de France. The British occupied the island in 1810; it was formally acknowledged as British by the Treaty of Paris in 1814.

Like Réunion, it is a large island for an oceanic island, having an area of about 720 square miles. It is less elevated than Réunion, the highest point rising to 2711 feet. In consequence there is a much larger proportion of cultivable low ground with rich volcanic soils, and very large numbers of emigrants have crowded into Mauritius from densely peopled India, so that the population approaches 650,000. Vegetables and farm crops are grown for home use. Salt is obtained by evaporating sea water in salt pans around the coast. Sandy areas of the coastlands are covered with coconuts and yield copra, but the mainstay of the island is its production of sugar. Mauritius is essentially a sugar island; its prosperity depends on the production and the price of sugar. The porous volcanic soils, the marked seasonal rhythm, the low to moderate rainfall, are just those conditions so well known in the West Indies as eminently suitable for the growth of sugar cane. By value Réunion and Mauritius have each a higher per capita export trade than any mainland country of Africa except the Rhodesias.

The principal town of Mauritius is Port Louis, situated on the northwestern side of the island and now linked to all parts by the motor roads which have replaced the former island railways. Port Louis is a little too hot and humid for Europeans, who favor the small hill station of Curepipe, 1800 feet above sea level, but only a dozen miles away. In contrast to Réunion, however, there are few pure Europeans in Mauritius. Apart from the Indians, the Mauritians are largely of mixed blood, together with Negroes and Chinese.

Rodriguez, lying 300 miles northeast of Mauritius, is much smaller. Only 42 square miles in area, it has only a few thousand inhabitants, who engage in fishing and the cultivation of food crops for their own sustenance.

Madagascar (République Malgache)

The huge island of Madagascar covers an area of 227,736 square miles. It is not far short of 1000 miles from the extreme northern to the extreme southern point, and in places its breadth reaches 360 miles. It supports a population of 5,184,000 (1960), yet it is true to say that this island remains almost an unknown land to English-speaking peoples. As a former French colony nearly 90 per cent of the shipping visiting Madagascar is French; the air services which of recent years have linked it with Paris by three different routes are also French. It comes as a surprise to English readers to realize that there is a very extensive, voluminous, and well-informed literature on the geography and resources of Madagascar, but very little published in English. In the *Geographical Review,* **XXVII,** 1937, Dr. Elizabeth T. Pratt gave a resumé of recent literature under the title "Madagascar: Great Isle, Red Isle, a Bibliographical Survey." There are no less than 59 works referred to in footnotes. Special attention is called to the fact that Madagascar is well equipped with both maps and bibliographies covering the description of the country. In the great work of G. Grandidier, brought up to date by a later volume covering the period to 1933, more than 8000 items are included. There is a reconnaissance map of the country on the scale of 1:500,000, and various sections of the island have been covered on larger scales, including the important series on 1:100,000. A very useful summary of the geography of Madagascar was given by W. A. Hance in *Focus,* May 1958.

Although it is only separated from the African continent by the Mozambique channel, some 250 miles wide, and although the basic crystalline complex which occupies the eastern two-thirds of the island does not differ greatly from the crystalline complex of the African continent, Madagascar has had a history entirely its own. Populated from the far side of the Indian Ocean rather than from the continent of Africa, isolated for a very long period previously so that both its fauna and flora have many distinctive characters, Madagascar can claim to be an island continent. In the island there are no large quadrupeds, but a number of distinctive species of lemurs. There are no poisonous snakes, and its flora is equally distinctive.

Outline of history. Although some have urged that the peoples of Madagascar may have come at least in part from the African mainland, the general view is that the island was settled by those who traveled across the Indian Ocean, and that this peopling began somewhere about the twentieth century B.C. It is to be noted that the winds blow towards Madagascar from across the Indian Ocean, whereas there are no regular winds *from* the African continent towards Madagascar. The first inhabitants were probably Indonesians of Negro characteristics, whose descendants still constitute one of the important elements of the population. These were reinforced by large incursions of the Hovas, allied to the Malays racially and linguistically. In later times the island became well known to the Arabs, who came from the Persian Gulf as well as from the east coast of Africa and who settled on the northwest and part of the eastern coastlands. Indians also came by sea and populated part of the southeast coast.

There are strong Negro elements, especially on the western side of the island. Some of these may have come as free settlers at a later stage, or may have been mainly brought as slaves. The final Malayan migration to the island seems to have finished actually after the first appearance of European explorers. This was in fact the main invasion by the Hova, who may be said to constitute perhaps one-quarter of the population, and who have profoundly influenced the character of the other island peoples. They offer many points of contrast physically and mentally to the Negroes of Africa.

The mixture of Arab blood, or influence of Arab culture, in the north has tended to result in peoples who are industrious and frugal and who make both excellent cultivators and good merchants.

The island was definitely sighted by the Portuguese Diego Dias in 1500. At the time when the French were active in the Indian Ocean they had military posts on the east coast for part of the seventeenth century and most of the eighteenth century, but early in the nineteenth century they relinquished them all except the island of Ste. Marie. In 1811 Tamatave was occupied by British troops, and under the Treaty of Paris, 1814, the French settlements in Madagascar were recognized as coming under British control. The British, however, made no attempt to settle on the island and were content to leave it to the control of the Hovas, whose king—Radama I—established friendly relations with the British government; a British agent was sent to reside at his court. The London Missionary Society established the first Christian missions in 1820, but when Radama was succeeded in 1828 by one of his wives, she persecuted the native Christians to such an extent that most of them lost their lives. In 1836 all missionaries were compelled to leave the island, and for some years all Europeans were excluded from the country. Radama II, though he ruled for only two years before being murdered (1861–1863), reopened the island to European trade. His wife, who succeeded him, effected treaties with British, French, and American governments.

Queen Ranavalona II, who ruled from 1868 to 1883, became a Christian, and during her reign much progress was made both in the spread of Christianity and in education. But relations became strained with France because the Hova queen refused to recognize the French claim that certain tracts on the northwest coast had been transferred to them by local chiefs, and in 1883 Tamatave was bombarded and occupied by French marines. In the subsequent peace terms it was agreed that Madagascar's foreign relations should be directed by France, that a French governor should remain in the capital, and that Diégo-Suarez should be ceded to France. In 1890 Britain recognized this French protectorate over Madagascar. After further disputes, a French expeditionary force in 1895 effected the conquest of the island; consequently, in 1896 the ruling Hova queen was exiled, and Madagascar became a French colony.

With the recall to power of General de Gaulle in 1958 and the institution of the Fifth Republic of France, Madagascar in common with the other French colonies in Africa was offered the chance to decide its own future. The vote was to remain a member of the French Community (1958) followed by the declaration of an independent republic on June 26, 1960 and admission to the United Nations later that year.

Structure and relief. The essential structural element in the island of Madagascar is a high plateau, part of the ancient continent of Gondwanaland, built up basically of crystalline rocks, with a whole range of granites and other igneous rocks which outcrop over vast stretches of the country. Here and there gold-bearing veins have decomposed to give rise to small placer deposits, and there are deposits of graphite which constitute one of the main mineral resources of the island. There are areas where precious stones occur, deposits of radioactive ores of nickel, copper, and lead. But over a very large part of the country the ancient rocks are hidden beneath a mantle of laterite or of lateritic decomposition products. The red lands which result are liable to extensive erosion and cause many of the streams draining to the coast to be deep red in color; hence the name sometimes given to the island is "Red Isle."

The crest of the plateau lies nearer the east than the west, and outcrops of volcanic rock give rise to high ground reaching to more than 6000 feet. Around the crystalline plateau, sedimentary rocks have been deposited which are especially important on the western third of the island, and become younger in age as traced towards the Mozambique Channel.

The eastern coast tends to be straight, free from indentations, and fringed with coral reefs. There are an onshore wind and a constant swell, and anchorages are very few and far between. From the crest of the plateau the land descends very sharply to the east coast, but to the west the drop is less, though there are some steep scarp faces overlooking the lower territory formed by the sedimentary rocks. Along the east coast is an almost continuous string of lagoons between the coral beaches and the steep rise inland. Linked by cuts this forms a valuable waterway.

Climate. Climatically the island lies within the Trade Wind Belt, so that southeasterly winds predominate. They bring a heavy rainfall to the eastern side of the island, comparatively little to the west. Thus four climatic divisions are distinguished:

1. The eastern slopes and the coast, much of which has a rainfall of over 100 inches even at sea level in the rainy period from December to July, but where a considerable fall comes in every month (Figure 21.2).
2. The plateau, where altitude reduces the temperature from the 70° to 80°F. usual on the coast to a range of 55° to 67°F., typical of Antananarivo, 4600 feet above sea level. Such climatic conditions suggest suitability of the terrain for white settlement.
3. The south and southwest, where the prevailing winds are descending from the plateau and become warm in the process. They deposit little or no rain, so that southward the southwest coasts are really to be described as arid and receive only some 15 inches of rain. For two-thirds of the year the rivers are dry.
4. The northwest. This resembles the southwest but has some northwesterly winds during the midsummer period, with a heavy rainfall and a dry season lasting from about May to November.

Vegetation. The vegetation corresponds closely with these climatic divisions (Figure 21.3). It may be hazarded that the original vegetation cover consisted of a continuous evergreen rainforest over the wetter areas of the east and north, giving place to a savanna or perhaps to steppe on the plateau and to semiarid types in the driest regions. French workers in Madagascar believe, however, that the natural vegetation has been almost completely destroyed throughout the whole island by the process of burning by the inhabitants, so that over at least four-fifths of the whole surface a vegetation resulting from human interference has replaced that which is natural. Many species have been thereby extinguished, and the density of woodland or savanna is much less than it would otherwise be. The map of vegetation reproduced from the work of Professor Maurette shows the distinction which is drawn between the evergreen forests of the east and the deciduous vegetation of the west. The bamboo forests which are common at high altitudes are probably entirely secondary, and the laterite soils found when forests have been cleared are not very fertile, so that clearings are soon abandoned and allowed to degenerate into bush, locally called "savoka." This is easily burnt, but often as a result there is bare soil with a hard barren crust, rendering the land virtually useless. The French have established a Forestry Service to do what is possible to repair the damage. A small amount of timber, notably ebony, is produced, and products collected from the forests include gum copal.

Agriculture. It will be clear that this island which seems to be favored climatically is far from being as agriculturally rich as might be expected. Little plantation agriculture has been developed. Rice is the principal food

Figure 21.2　Rainfall and winds of Madagascar.

Figure 21.3   The vegetation of Madagascar.

Legend:
- Evergreen rainforest
- "Savoka"
- Deciduous forest
- Savanna-steppe regularly burnt over
- Semi-arid
- Mangroves
- Limit between evergreen and deciduous trees
- Limit of semi-arid vegetation

crop; many varieties are grown but most of them are rather poor and the yield low. Some upland rice is grown in forest clearings. Manioc is second to rice as a food crop, especially in the wetter regions. Corn (maize) can be grown even in the dry parts during the rainy season, and is therefore of first-class importance in the southwest. Sorghum, yams, and beans are other food crops, and sugar cane may be grown where irrigation is possible. Crops which point the way to possible future development include coffee, of *arabica* type grown by villagers and of *liberia* or *robusta* types grown on European plantations in the east. Vanilla, cloves, and locally cocoa have been introduced. Cotton, coconuts, sisal, and flax have all been tried. The agricultural people of the east have few animals, but on the plateau cattle rearing is a mainstay of the native agricultural economy. Cattle, however, are mainly of the zebu type, and cows give but a minute yield of milk, so that hides form the principal product. Fat-tailed sheep and goats are to be found in drier regions, and every Madagascan farm has a few pigs.

Human geography. The bulk of the African population lives in small villages, usually surrounded by a protective stockade. Most of the cities over part if not the whole owe their development to European influence. Antananarivo, now more usually called Tananarive, is a curious example of a mountain capital situated far from the sea or a river port and with no apparent geographical advantages unless inaccessibility can be claimed as one. A jumble of villages linked by tortuous streets and ancient stairways can scarcely be reached from the more modern sections, and the rugged terrain presents sudden obstacles to building as well as to water supply and drainage. Before the French occupation of Madagascar it was the seat of government of the Merina people, an old trading and once a slave-trading center. The French established their rule there in 1895, and the population rapidly increased to make it the commercial and cultural as well as the political capital. It is situated on the edge of the Imerina plains, and in the capital and the surrounding highland plains live possibly one-third of all the people of the island.[1] It is connected by railway with Tamatave, the principal port, and a branch from this railway runs northward to Lake Alaotra. Whether the planned extensions of Madagascan railways will ever take place becomes increasingly doubtful, because of the rapid modern development of roads.

Roads suitable for motoring in dry weather cover at least 20,000 miles and are served by an extensive and even elaborate network of motor services covering some 1500 miles. In 1957 80 per cent, or 16,000 miles, were described as all-weather roads.

In any study of Africa seriously scientific and objective, Madagascar deserves special consideration. It repeats on a smaller scale many of the re-

[1] W. A. Hance (*Focus,* May 1958) has a striking map showing the concentration of population in a few parts of the island.

lief, climate, soil, and vegetation features of the tropical parts of the continent itself. It is claimed by many observers that the Madagascan or Malagosy peoples have greater vitality and initiative than characterize the Negro peoples of the continent and that therefore it should prove an easier task to forward development. Yet quite clearly this vast area is far from being an important contributor to world sources of foodstuffs. The bulk of the trade is with France.

The completion of half a century of effective French occupation in Madagascar (1896–1946) was the signal for a stock taking of the island's agricultural economy.[2] The total area of cultivated land is given at 3,310,000 acres, of which rice occupies 40 per cent, other subsistence crops rather more, and commercial crops about 18 per cent. The last are now characterized by the great variety of products for export. Coffee holds first rank and accounts for one-third the total value of exports. But more than half the production is in one district, the Fianarantsoa district. Although rice is the basic subsistence crop, the amount exported accounts for less than 4 per cent of the total. About 11 per cent of the ricelands of Madagascar are irrigated. The other commercial crops grown for export include cocoa, vanilla, cloves, pepper, cinnamon and other spices, copra, raffia, tobacco, sugar cane (sugar and rum), manioc (for flour), and tapioca. Reference is made to the marked development of the livestock industry, which at the time of the survey boasted 6 million cattle, 420,000 pigs, and 300,000 sheep and goats, with an export in 1945 of 12,500 tons of meat and meat products (including canned meat) and about 400,000 hides. Cut off as it was during the years of World War II, agricultural production dropped, and when the foregoing figures are viewed against the background of the enormous area of the island, Madagascar must still be regarded as an underdeveloped land. As pointed out in the conclusions, however, it is necessary first of all to raise the standard of living of the indigenous peoples, four-fifths of whom are cultivators.

Among the major developments of recent years may be noted hydro-electric power. This in turn has stimulated industrial development, including silk and cotton weaving (with a large cotton-weaving plant at Antsirabe) and cement. Compared with figures given above, in 1960 coffee still led in exports, but vanilla, sugar, rice, tobacco, and cloves were all important and showed the expansion in cash-crop agriculture.

The Comoro Islands

This group of islands lies midway between the northwest coast of Madagascar and the mainland of Africa and is administered by France as the *Territoire des Comores*. There are four main islands, with a total population

[2] Cinquantenaire de Madagascar, *Rev. int. de botanique appliquée*, **XXVI**, 1946, 333–504. Summarized in *Geog. Rev.*, **XXVII**, 1947, 495–496.

at the 1958 census of 183,133. The two chief are Grand Comoro (720 square miles) and Mayotte (140).

The climate is wet tropical. The natural forests have been largely cleared for agriculture, but some timber (exported as railroad ties) is obtained from those that remain. Sugar cane and vanilla are leading crops, but the farmer has suffered from more effective production of sugar elsewhere. As a result there has been considerable emigration to Madagascar and the mainland. Cocoa, coconuts, and sisal are also grown.

Statistical Summary

An independent republic; linked with Syria as the United Arab Republic (U.A.R.). An independent kingdom from 1922 to 1952 when Farouk I, who succeeded in 1936, abdicated in favor of his infant son after a military *coup d'état*. In 1953 the new king, Fuad II, was deposed by a military council under General Neguib, who proclaimed a republic with himself as President, but had to give way in 1954 to Lieut. Col. (later General) Gamel Abdul Nasser. In 1958 the republics of Egypt and Syria combined as the United Arab Republic with Colonel Nasser as joint President. This was dissolved in September 1961 but reformed in 1963.

Area. Including deserts, 386,198 square miles (settled area 13,500 square miles).

Population. 19,087,304 (1947 census); 26,065,000 (1960 census).

Density. Over settled area, at 1960 census, 1900 per square mile.

Towns. 1960 census (with 1947 in parentheses): Cairo (capital) 3,346,000 (2,100,506); Alexandria 1,513,000 (925,081); Port Said 244,000 (178,432); Gîza 250,000, Tanta 184,000 (139,965); Mahalla el Kubra 178,000 (115,509); Suez 203,000 (108,250); Mansûra 152,000 (102,709); Damanhûr 126,000 (102,709); Zagazig 124,000; Asyût 122,000; Ismailia 111,000; Faiyûm 102,000; Minya 94,000.

Religion. In 1947, Moslems 91.5%; Christians 8.2%; Jews 0.3%.

Land use, 1957

Arable and land under tree crops:	6,449,460 acres
Forested:	2,471 acres
Unused but potentially productive:	1,275,066 acres

Cultivation

	1949–1950	1959–1960
Cotton	2,049,592 acres	1,826,111 acres
Corn (maize)	1,506,563 acres	1,929,896 acres
Wheat	1,424,133 acres	1,532,056 acres
Rice	726,868 acres	756,143 acres

Livestock, 1957–1958. Horses, 45,000; donkeys, 950,000; mules, 11,000; cattle, 1,390,000; buffaloes, 1,395,000; sheep, 1,259,000; goats, 723,000; camels, 157,000; pigs, 17,000.

Mineral production, 1959 (long tons). Phosphate rock, 629,000; crude petroleum, 3,399,000. Also alabaster (gypsum), salt, iron ore, manganese ore.

499

Trade, 1959

Exports: £E 153 million ($439 million).

Imports: £E 213 million ($611 million).

Exports, 1959: raw cotton, 72%; cotton yarn and fabrics, 7%; minerals, 5%.

Currency

£E 1 (one Egyptian pound) = 100 piastres or 1000 mils
                          = in sterling 16 shillings (1964)
                          = U.S.A. 225 cents. (1964)

Exchange £1 (sterling) = 120–125 piastres; $1. = 42–45 piastres (1964)

MOROCCO (AL-MAMLAKA AL-MAGHREBIA)

An independent kingdom. Former Sultanate under Mohammed V, who changed the royal title to king in 1957 and on his death in 1961 was succeeded by his son as King Hassan II. In 1956 France and Spain relinquished the protectorates which they exercised over the greater part of Morocco, and the powers (including the United States) which exercised control over the Tangier International Zone also restored that territory to the Sultan. New forms of government include a cabinet system, a council of ministers, and a consultative assembly.

Area. Estimated at 158,500 square miles (former Spanish zone about 18,000 and Tangier 225).

Population. 11,626,470 (1960 census).

Towns. Casablanca, 961,000; Marrakesh, 242,000; Fez, 216,000; Tangier, 142,000; Rabat, 225,000; Meknes, 177,000; Oujda, 129,000; Tetuan, 101,000; Agadir (before its devastation by an earthquake on March 1, 1960), about 50,000.

Land use, 1960

Arable and land under tree crops:	25,750 square miles
Permanent pastures (mostly rough grazing):	35,500 square miles
Forested:	20,500 square miles
Built on, waste, etc:	76,750 square miles

Cultivation, 1959–60. Wheat, 4.225 million acres; barley, 4.440 million acres; corn (maize), 1.267 million acres.

Livestock, 1958–1959. Horses, 257,000; asses, 1,128,000; mules, 269,000, cattle, 2,560,000; sheep, 10,262,000; goats, 5,349,000; pigs, 57,000; camels, 208,000.

Minerals, 1961 (long tons). Phosphate rock, 7,949,702; anthracite, 457,324 (1959); iron ore, 1,245,043 (1959); manganese ore, 463,000 (1959); crude oil, 80,000.

Trade, 1961

Exports: DH 1,731,312,000 ($346 million).

Imports: DH 2,257,381,000 ($451 million).

Chief exports: phosphates, citrus fruits, preserved fish, wine in casks.

Currency. Linked with French franc. National currency introduced in 1959; unit, the dirhan (DH = 0.9756 new French franc); exchange rate (1964), about 5 DH to the dollar.

REPUBLIC OF ALGERIA

Under the constitution of the Fifth Republic, with amendments adopted in June 1960, the "French Republic" consists of four groups of Departments: A, Metropolitan; B, Algerian; C, Saharan; and D, Overseas. Following a referendum early in 1962 a cease-fire between the French forces and the Algerians was declared and Algeria became an independent republic on July 4, 1962.

Area. Northern Algeria is divided into 13 departments, with an area of 114,000 square miles. Southward it merges into the Algerian Sahara, which has an estimated area of 838,000 square miles, making a total of 952,000 square miles.

Population, 1960 (census). Northern Algeria, 10,197,000; Algerian Sahara, 589,000; total 10,786,000.

Towns, 1960. Algiers, 884,000; Oran, 393,000; Constantine, 223,000; Bône, 164,000; Sidi-Bel-Abbès, 105,000; Mostaganem, 69,000; Sétif, 94,000; Tlemcen, 83,000; Philippeville, 88,000; Blida, 93,000; Bougie, 63,000.

Land use, 1959–1960

Arable and land under tree crops:	27,000 square miles
Permanent pastures (rough grazing):	150,000 square miles
Forested:	12,000 square miles

Balance: desert, otherwise waste or built on.

Cultivation, 1959–1960. Wheat, 4,200,800 acres; barley, 2,693,453 acres; grapes, 906,878 acres (production, 2,386,000 metric tons).

Livestock, 1958–1959. Horses, 217,000; donkeys, 388,000; mules, 298,000; cattle, 645,000; sheep, 5,478,000; goats, 2,014,000; pigs, 57,000; camels, 120,000.

Mineral production, 1960. Iron ore, 2,444 metric tons; phosphate rock, 419,000 tons; crude petroleum, 8,841,000 tons.

Trade, 1960

Exports: 194,654 million francs ($389 million)
Imports: 624,531 million francs ($1249 million)

Exports: wine, 49.5%; minerals, 12%; fruits, 9%.

Currency. Linked with the French franc. Exchange: about 5 New Francs to the dollar.

TUNISIA

A sovereign independent republic with an elected president. France surrendered her protectorate in 1956 but has maintained a naval base at Bizerta in opposition to Tunisia's demands for its evacuation. Gradual withdrawal is agreed.

Area. 48,332 square miles.

Population. Mid-year estimate 1960: 4,168,000 (Moslems 3,750,000; Tunisian Jews, 60,000; French and Italians, 250,000; others, 108,000).

Towns, 1960. Tunis, 680,000; Sfax, 65,685; Sousse, 48,172; Bizerta, 46,681; Kairouan, 39,968.

Land use, 1957

Arable:	18,965 square miles
Permanent meadows:	405 square miles
Forested:	3,784 square miles
Unused but potentially productive	11,595 square miles
Built on, desert, or otherwise waste:	13,583 square miles

Cultivation, 1957. Wheat, 3,281,570 acres; barley, 1,949,664 acres; grapes, 240,000 tons; citrus fruits, 74,000 tons; olive oil, 58,000 tons.

Livestock, 1958–1959. Horses, 85,000; donkeys, 200,000; mules, 54,000; cattle, 604,000; sheep, 3,793,000; goats, 1,276,000; camels (1957–1958), 216,000; pigs, 8,000.

Mineral production, 1959. Phosphate rock, 2,151,000 metric tons; superphosphates (concentrates), 122,000 tons; iron ore, 966,148 tons; lead ore, 90,300 tons.

Trade, 1959

Exports: 59,585,000 dinars ($142 million).

Imports: 64,202,000 dinars ($153 million).

Exports, olive oil, 25%; phosphates, 13%; wine, 12%; wheat, 6%; iron ore, 5%; barley, 4%.

Currency. Unit (introduced November 1958): dinar, of 1,000 millièmes. Exchange value: 1 dinar = $2.38 = 17s.

LIBYA

An independent sovereign kingdom constituted after World War II by the Allies from the former Italian territory of Libya. It was divided into three provinces— Cyrenaica, Tripolitania, and Fezzan—which were federated in December 1951 as the United Kingdom of Libya, with the Amir of Cyrenaica as the first hereditary King, Idris I.

Area. 679,000 square miles, of which Cyrenaica occupies 49 per cent and Fezzan 37 per cent, leaving 14 per cent for Tripolitania.

Population. Mid-year estimate, 1960: 1,195,000. Reversing the order of the provinces in size, Tripolitania, the smallest, is the most densely populated, with about 70 per cent of the total; Fezzan, though the second of the provinces in size, has the smallest population; inland and largely desert, it supports only about 5 per cent of the total population; while Cyrenaica, the largest province, contains under 30 per cent.

Towns. Tripoli, the joint capital, claims a population of 184,000; and Benghazi (Cyrenaica), the alternate capital and royal seat, has 140,000. Other towns are comparatively small, mainly in the nature of agricultural centers. Barce, on the chief agricultural plateau behind the coast, is a municipality of 10,000 in a district of some 36,000; it was severely damaged by earthquake, February 1963.

Land use. Under 2 per cent of the total area is arable land or under tree crops, and under 5 per cent is classed as meadow land; only about a quarter of 1 per cent is forested. All the rest, except where built on, is waste or desert, though the location of oil promises a measure of commercial utilization.

Livestock, 1958–1959. Horses, 29,000; donkeys, 97,000; cattle, 100,000; sheep, 1,220,000 (700,000 in Fezzan); goats, 1,129,000; camels, 175,000.

Trade 1960
Exports: Libyan £3,107,000 ($8.7 million).
Imports: Libyan £59,053,000 ($165 million).

Exports: oil seeds, nuts, and kernels, 27%; cattle and sheep, 16%; hides and skins, 7%. The heavy imports are mainly of equipment for developing the oilfields. Export of oil by the first pipeline to the coast began in October 1961.

Currency. The Libyan £ is equivalent to the £ sterling. It is divided into 100 piastres and 1000 millièmes. Libya is in the sterling area.

SPANISH TERRITORIES IN AFRICA

Places of Spanish sovereignty	*Area,* *square miles*	*Population,* *1960*
Alhucemas, Ceuta, Charafinas		
Melilla, Penon de Valez	82	146,000[2]
Ifni Territory	741	54,000[2]
Spanish Sahara		
Territories of Rio de Oro and		
Sekia el Hamra	105,448	25,000[1, 2]
Spanish Guinea		
with the islands of Fernando Po,		
Corisco, Elobey and Annobon	10,852	245,989
Total	117,123	470,989

[1] Exclusive of nomads who enter the territories after the rainy season.
[2] These are United Nations estimates of "questionable reliability."

FORMER FRENCH WEST AFRICA (AFRIQUE OCCIDENTALE FRANÇAISE)

Until the recall of de Gaulle in 1958 French West Africa was part of Overseas France (France d'Outremer) under a governor-general at Dakar; divided from 1946 into eight territories.

Area, square miles		*Population, 1949*	
Senegal	81,050	Senegal	1,992,000
French Guinea	108,400	French Guinea	2,180,000
Ivory Coast	129,800	Ivory Coast	2,065,000
Upper Volta	122,900	Upper Volta	3,069,000
Dahomey	44,650	Dahomey	1,505,000
French Sudan	461,300	French Sudan	3,177,000
Mauritania	364,000	Mauritania	518,000
Niger	494,700	Niger	2,029,000
Total	1,806,000	Total	16,535,000

Europeans numbered   52,000 (40,000 French)

The eight separate republics which have existed since 1960 (Guinea since 1958) are detailed on pages 504 to 506.

SENEGAL (RÉPUBLIQUE DU SÉNÉGAL)

An independent and sovereign republic in tropical West Africa, bordering the Atlantic Ocean, formerly a territory of French West Africa.

Area. 76,125 square miles.

Population, 1960. 2,973,285.

Towns. Dakar (1960), 367,000; Rufisque, 50,000; Kaolack, 47,000; Saint Louis, 48,000; Thiès, 39,000.

Principal crop. Peanuts; cultivated area (1959–1960), 2,268,431 acres; production, 860,000 tons.

Livestock, 1958–1959. Horses, 78,000; donkeys, 90,000; cattle, 1,500,000; sheep, 450,000; goats, 550,000; pigs, 35,000.

Mineral production. Titanium, phosphates, and cement are exported, the last supplying a large part of the requirements of neighboring countries.

Trade, 1959. Senegal's special exports, coupled with those of Mauritania and Mali, were valued at 28,600 million francs CFA (Colonies Françaises d'Afrique = 2 old French francs, or about 0.4 cent) or $114 million. Shelled peanuts and peanut oil constitute 80 per cent of the total.

Special imports, 44,037 million francs CFA ($176 million).

GUINEA (RÉPUBLIQUE DE GUINÉE)

Former territory of French West Africa which refused to join the French Community in 1958 and elected to become an independent republic. It fronts the Atlantic Ocean between Portuguese Guinea and Sierra Leone.

Area. 95,000 square miles.

Population, 1960. Mid-year estimate; 3,000,000.

Towns. Conakry (capital), 112,000; Kankan, 29,000.

Chief agricultural products. Cassava, rice, peanuts, palm kernels.

Minerals (exports 1959). Diamonds, 657,000 carats, valued at £1,858,000 ($5.2 million); bauxite, 297,000 tons; iron ore, 347,000 tons.

Currency. Unit the Guinea franc, on a par with the franc CFA (see under Senegal).

IVORY COAST (RÉPUBLIQUE DE CÔTE D'IVOIRE)

An independent and sovereign republic, formerly a territory of French West Africa, situated in West Africa on the Gulf of Guinea, between Liberia and Ghana.

Area. 124,500 square miles.

Population. Mid-1960 estimate: 3,230,000.

Towns. Abidjan (capital), 170,000 Africans, 7,500 Europeans; Bouaké, 70,000; Grand Bassam, 11,500.

Crops. The Ivory Coast grows more coffee than any other country in Africa— 160,000 long tons in 1959–1960, when also the cocoa crop reached 60,000 tons. The republic also exports large quantities of palm kernels (14,000 tons in 1959–1960), as well as several thousand tons each of palm oil and peanuts.

Minerals. Diamonds and manganese ore produced and exported.

Trade, 1959.

Special exports: 33,821 million francs CFA ($135 million) of which raw coffee provided nearly a half, cocoa beans nearly a third, timber 12%, and diamonds (230,900 carats), 1%.

Special imports: 28,259 million francs CFA ($113 million) principally motor vehicles, 10%; machinery, 9%; cotton fabrics, 9%; petroleum products, 7%; base metals, 7%.

UPPER VOLTA (RÉPUBLIQUE DE HAUTE-VOLTA)

An independent republic in the interior of West Africa, north of the Ivory Coast and Ghana, formerly part of French West Africa.

Area. 105,840 square miles.

Population. Mid-1960 estimate: 4,400,000.

Towns. Ouagadougou or Wagadugu (capital), 51,000; Bobo-Dioulasso, 57,500.

Chief crops. Millet and sorghum, 590,000 tons in 1957–1958.

Cattle. 1,550,000 in 1955–1956.

Trade, 1957

Exports: 896 million francs, CFA ($3.6 million); chiefly livestock, fish and peanuts.
Imports: 1612 million francs CFA ($6.4 million).

DAHOMEY (RÉPUBLIQUE DU DAHOMEY)

An independent republic in West Africa, between Ghana and Nigeria, formerly a territory of French West Africa.

Area. 44,695 square miles.

Population. November 1960 census: 1,934,447.

Towns. Porto Novo (capital), 31,500; Cotonou (chief port), 56,200; Abomey, 19,000; Ouidah, 14,000.

Chief crops. Maize (1957–1958), 180,000 tons; palm kernels (1959–1960), 50,000 tons exported; also a few thousand tons of palm oil; millet and sorghum (1958–1959), 40,000 tons.

Trade

Special exports: 2833 million francs CFA ($11.3 million); palm kernels 60%, palm oil 14%, raw coffee 6.6%, shelled peanuts 5%.

Special imports: 3956 million francs CFA ($15.8 million).

MALI (RÉPUBLIQUE DU MALI)

An independent republic (formerly the French Sudan) in the interior of West Africa, lying between Algeria and the Volta Republic; formerly part of French West Africa.

Area. 465,000 square miles.

Population. Mid-1960 U.N. estimate: 4,100,000.

Towns. 1957: Bamako (capital), 120,000; Kayes, 29,500; Ségou, 21,000; Timbuktu, 7000.

Chief crops, 1957–1958. Millet and sorghum, 785,000 tons; rice (paddy), 176,000 tons; peanuts, 125,000 tons; maize, 62,000 tons.

Livestock, 1955–1956. Horses, 80,000; donkeys, 230,000; cattle, 2,900,000; camels, 95,000.

Trade formerly included with Senegal.

MAURITANIA (RÉPUBLIQUE ISLAMIQUE DE MAURITANIE)

An independent republic in Northwest Africa, fronting the Atlantic Ocean and stretching inland between Spanish Sahara and Senegal; formerly a territory of French West Africa. Claimed by Morocco.

Area. 419,000 square miles.

Population. 1960 U.N. Estimate: 727,000.

Towns. Nouakchott (capital), small coastal town; Kaédi, 8500; Atar, 4200; Port Etienne, 1200.

Minerals. Overlapping the Sahara, the chief wealth of the country lies in large deposits of iron ore, with an estimated minimum content of 215 million tons, to be linked with the coast at Port Etienne by a railway 400 miles long, carrying an initial output of 4 million tons a year. Large deposits of copper are also earmarked for exploitation.

NIGER REPUBLIC (RÉPUBLIQUE DU NIGER)

An inland, independent republic in West Africa, lying mainly north of Nigeria; formerly a territory of French West Africa.

Area. 459,000 square miles.

Population. U.N. estimate: 2,870,000. Capital, Niamey, 30,000.

Crops, 1957–1958. Millet and sorghum, 921,000 tons; peanuts, 193,000 tons.

Trade, 1959

Special exports: 2851 million francs CFA ($11.4 million), of which shelled peanuts provided 70%; peanut oil, 14%; live animals, 6%; hides and skins, 4%.

Special imports: 1787 million francs CFA ($7.2 million). Cotton fabrics, 16%; sugar, 12%; motor vehicles, 7%; machinery, 6%.

TOGO

An independent republic in West Africa since April 27, 1960; formerly French Togoland, a trusteeship territory under the United Nations (formerly part of German Togoland).

Area. 21,893 square miles.

Population. 1955 census: 1,439,772. 1,089,877 Africans and 1277 Europeans; 1960: Lomé, 65,000 including 1000 Europeans in 1958.

Trade

1949

Exports: 844.7 million francs CFA ($3.3 million)
Imports: 1454.4 million francs CFA ($5.8 million)

1959

Exports: 4348 million francs CFA ($17 million)
Imports: 3755 million francs CFA ($15 million)

Exports, 1949: Cocoa, 23%; coffee, 15%; palm oil and kernels, 15%.
Currency. West African Francs (CFA): see Senegal.

LIBERIA

An independent republic in West Africa.
Area. 43,000 square miles (estimated).
Population. Estimated between 750,000 and 2,500,000, including 12,000 to 20,000 Americo-Liberians and 6,000 Europeans and Americans.
Towns. Monrovia (capital), estimated 80,000.

Trade

	1949	1960
Exports:	$14,327,865	$78,873,427
	1947	
Imports:	$8,762,728	$69,190,435

Exports: rubber, palm kernels, gold.
Currency. Liberian dollar was raised to parity with the U.S. dollar in 1944.

GAMBIA

A British colony and protectorate in British West Africa.
Area. 4101 square miles.
Population. 250,000 in 1944 [Bathurst (capital), 21,152]; Protectorate (in 1948 census), 229,284. 1960 estimate: 284,000 including Bathurst, 31,490.

Trade

	1949	1959
Exports:	£1,753,915 ($4.9 million)	£2,956,822 ($8.3 million)
Imports:	£2,356,300 ($6.6 million)	£3,148,308 ($8.8 million)

Currency. As in Britain, pound sterling.

SIERRA LEONE

An independent country in West Africa since April 27, 1961, and a member of the British Commonwealth, previously a British colony and protectorate.
Area. 27,925 square miles.
Population. 1,858,000 (1948 estimate); 2,450,000 (1960 estimate); Capital, Freetown, 125,000 (1960).

Trade

	1949	1960
Exports:	£4,243,099 ($11.9 million)	£25,926,801 ($73 million)
Imports:	£6,171,910 ($17.3 million)	£26,342,213 ($74 million)

Exports: palm kernels and palm oil, coffee, cocoa, iron ore, diamonds, kola nuts, ginger, piassava.
Currency. As in Britain, pound sterling.

GHANA

An independent African Republic since 1957 but remaining a member of the British Commonwealth. Formerly the Gold Coast, a British colony and protectorate in West Africa.

Area. 91,843 square miles (including 13,041 square miles of Togoland).

Population. 4,111,680, including 6,770 non-Africans (census of 1948), including 382,717 in Togoland; 6,690,730 (census of 1960).

Towns. 1948: Accra, 135,926; Kumasi, 190,362; Sekondi-Takoradi, 44,557. 1960: Accra, 325,977; Kumasi, 190,362; Sekondi-Takoradi, 101,532.

Trade

	1949	1961
Exports:	£48,246,334 ($135 million)	£115,203,000 ($323 million)
Imports:	£52,942,041 ($159 million)	£142,735,000 ($400 million)

Exports: cocoa, 60%; gold, 10%; manganese, 6%; timber, 12%; diamonds, 8%; (1960).

Currency. Ghana pound (£G) equivalent to and freely interchangeable with pound sterling.

FEDERATION OF NIGERIA

An independent state in West Africa consisting of Northern, Western, and Eastern Regions and a federal capital (Lagos). A member of the British Commonwealth; prior to October 1, 1960 a British colony and protectorate.

Area. 356,669 square miles (approximate).

Population. 25,000,000 (1949 estimate); 35,297,000 (1960 estimate). For 1963 census see p. 313.

Towns. 1948 estimates, 1960 figures in parentheses. Ibadan, 335,500 (600,000); Lagos, 230,000 (450,000); Kano, 102,000 (130,000); Iwo, 86,000 (100,000); Ogbomosho, 84,500 (140,000); Oshogbo (123,000); Ife (111,000); Abeokuta (84,000).

Trade

	1948	1961
Exports:	£37,527,112 ($85 million)	£160,914,000 ($451 million)
Imports:	£44,897,309 ($126 million)	£215,319,000 ($603 million)

Exports, 1960: palm oil and kernels, 34%; cocoa, 23%; peanuts, 21%; tin, cotton, timber.

Currency. As in Britain, pound sterling.

FORMER BRITISH TOGOLAND

Formerly a United Nations trusteeship under Britain, administered by Gold Coast, now part of Ghana (since 1957).

Area. 13,041 square miles.

Population. 382,717 (census of 1948).

FORMER BRITISH CAMEROONS

Former United Nations Trusteeship under Britain, administered by Nigeria; when the former French Cameroons and Nigeria both became independent, small northern parts were added to Nigeria; the larger southern part with Mount Cameroon and the town of Victoria elected to join Cameroun.

SUDAN

Until 1951 a condominium ruled jointly by Britain and Egypt under the title Anglo-Egyptian Sudan. When Egypt abrogated the treaty, the King of Egypt was declared King of the Sudan, but effective administration remained in British hands. Became an independent republic on January 1, 1956.

Area. 967,500 square miles.

Population. 10,262,536 (census 1955–1956), including 537,000 non-Sudanese; 1960 U.N. estimate: 11,770,000.

  Towns. Omdurman, 113,551; Khartoum (capital), 132,185; Port Sudan, 47,562; Atbara, 42,000.

Trade

	1949	1960
Exports:	£E 26,435,396 ($74 million)	£S 60,679,266 ($170 million)
Imports:	£E 23,869,569 ($67 million)	£S 63,743,828 ($178 million)

Exports: cotton, 55%; cottonseed, 5%; gum, 11%; sesame 8%; peanuts 7%.

Currency. Formerly the Egyptian pound (£E) of 100 piastres or 1,000 mils; since 1956 the Sudanese pound (£S), slightly more than the pound sterling.

FRENCH SOMALILAND (CÔTE FRANÇAISE DES SOMALIS)

An overseas territory of the French Community.

Area. 9,071 square miles.

Population. 48,210 (estimated 1949), Europeans 2,034; 1961 estimate: 81,000, including 24,000 Somalis, 7000 Europeans. Capital: Djibouti (41,200 in 1961).

SOMALIA

Since July 1, 1960, an independent republic consisting of former Italian Somaliland (a trusteeship territory of the United Nations administered by Italy from 1950 to 1960) and British Somaliland, a former British protectorate.

Total population. Estimated (1960) at 1,990,000. Capital Mogadishu (Mogadiscio).

Former British Somaliland

  Area. 68,000 square miles (estimated).

  Population. 600,000 (estimated).

Former Italian Somaliland:

  Area. 189,000 square miles (estimated).

  Population. 1,270,000 (estimated 1950), including 4,500 Italians. Mogadiscio, 86,643, (Census, December 31, 1958).

ETHIOPIA (ABYSSINIA)

A sovereign independent state or empire. Emperor Haile Selassie I, re-entered after Italian occupation, 1942.

Area. 350,000 square miles (estimated), making with Eritrea a total of 395,000.

Population. Official estimate (1960) 18 to 20 million (including Eritrea), but probably an exaggeration. Leading race Amhara (2,000,000) and official language Amharic.

Towns. Addis Ababa (capital), 900,000; Dire Dawa, 40,000; Harar, 40,000.

Trade

	1949	1960
Exports:	$28 million	$77 million
Imports:	$30 million	$88 million

Exports: coffee, 34%; hides and skins, cereals and pulses.

Currency. Ethiopian dollar of 100 cents ($Eth.) = 2 shillings East African = £0.1 or 28 cents U.S. (1951–1952); now 40 cents U.S.

ERITREA

Autonomous province under Ethiopian Empire, former Italian colony.

Area. 45,000 square miles.

Population. 2,000,000 (estimated), including 21,000 Italians (1949; many still remain). Asmara 120,000 (1960).

FORMER FRENCH EQUATORIAL AFRICA (AFRIQUE EQUATORIALE FRANÇAISE)

Until the referendum of 1958 a French colony under a governor-general, divided into four territories, each under a governor.

Area

Gabun (Gabon), capital Libreville	104,000 square miles
Middle Congo (Moyen Congo), capital Pointe Noire	172,000
Ubangi-Shari (Oubangi-Chari), capital Bangui	236,000
Chad (Tchad), capital Fort Lamy	400,000
Total	912,000

Population	*Estimated January 1, 1950*		*January 1, 1960*
	European	Others	
Gabun	3,378	405,400	430,000 (estimate)
Middle Congo	9,050	675,400	794,577
Ubangi-Shari	4,391	1,067,400	1,193,000
Chad	3,301	2,238,200	2,581,080
Total	20,120	4,386,400	

Brazzaville had 6,505 Europeans on January 1, 1951.

Livestock, 1944. Horses, 125,000; asses, 175,000; cattle, 4,000,000; sheep and goats, 5,000,000; camels, 200,000.

Trade, 1949

Exports: 7,253,800,000 francs CFA
Imports: 13,393,600,000 francs CFA

Exports: cotton, 36%; wood, 24%; gold, 12%; palm oil, rubber.

Currency. Francs CFA = 2 old French francs (see Senegal).

Since 1960 Gabun and Chad have been independent republics. Ubangi-Shari has become the Central African Republic (République Centrafricaine) and the Middle Congo has become the Congo Republic (République du Congo), not to be confused with the former Belgian Congo.

CAMEROUN (RÉPUBLIQUE DU CAMEROUN)

A republic since January 1, 1960, when the trusteeship territory administered by France on behalf of the United Nations became fully independent and later (1961) was increased in area when the southern part of British Cameroons voted to join the Republic in preference to joining Nigeria. Prior to World War I, German Kamerun.

Area. 166,489 square miles plus about 30,000 square miles of former British Cameroons.

Population. French portion, 8998 Europeans; 2,997,164 Africans (1950), 3,223,000 (1957); mid-1960 U.N. estimate, 4,097,000.

Towns. Yaounde (capital), 53,833 (1957); Douala, 118,857 (1957).

Trade

	1949	1959
Exports:	6661 million francs CFA ($26 m)	20,767 million francs CFA ($83 million)
Imports:	8776 million francs CFA ($35 m)	20,153 million francs CFA ($81 million)

Exports: cocoa, 35%; coffee, 18.5%; bananas, 3.4%; cotton, 4%.

CONGO REPUBLIC (RÉPUBLIQUE DU CONGO)

Formerly Belgian Congo, a Belgian colony under a governor-general. Became independent June 30, 1960.

Area. 904,750 square miles (estimated).

Population. 11,073,311 Africans; 53,176 Europeans; 1063 Asians (census of December 31, 1949). 13,540,182 Africans and 112,759 others (census of January 1, 1959). Mid-1960 U.N. estimate: 14,150,000.

Towns, 1949. Léopoldville (capital), 160,304; Elisabethville, 48,734.

Minerals. In 1949: copper, 176,000 metric tons (1950); gold, 10,504 kilos; diamonds, 9,700,000 carats (1950); cobalt, tin, zinc, cadmium. In 1959: copper, 282,094 metric tons; gold, 10,520 kilograms; diamonds, 14,855,000 carats.

Trade

	1949	1959
Exports:	10,968 million francs ($219 million)	25,004 million francs ($500 million)
Imports:	10,346 million francs ($207 million)	14,994 million francs ($300 million)

Exports (1949): copper, 25%; palm oil and kernels, 17%; cotton, 13%; other metals, rubber.

Currency. Congolese franc (officially 50 fr. = $1.).

RUANDA-URUNDI (RWANDA AND BURUNDI)

United Nations trusteeship territory, formerly administered as part of Belgian Congo, formerly part of German East Africa; administered directly by Belgium 1960–1962, now two independent countries.

Area. 20,900 square miles.

Population. 3,882,392 Africans; 3407 Europeans; 2894 Asians (census of 1949); 4,847,931 Africans; 8127 Europeans; 2869 Asians (census of 1959).

Trade. Included under Belgian Congo until 1960, figures given above.

SÃO TOMÉ AND PRÍNCIPE

Two Portuguese islands in the Gulf of Guinea.

Area. 372 square miles.

Population. 60,490 (1940); 60,159 (1950); 66,000 (U.N. estimate, mid-1960).

Trade. Exports: cocoa, coffee, coconuts, copra, cinchona.

UGANDA

An independent country of East Africa since 1962 and a member of the British Commonwealth, previously a British protectorate over Buganda and other kingdoms.

Area. 93,981 square miles, but including 13,690 square miles of water.

Population. 4,993,965 (census of 1948). 4,953,000 Africans; 3448 Europeans; 37,517 Asians. Census of 1959: 6,523,628 Africans; 69,103 Indians; 2830 Goans; 4259 Arabs; 10,866 Europeans. Mid-1960 U.N. estimate: 6,677,000.

Trade

	1949	1960
Exports:	£23,433,182 ($66 million)	£41,588,000 ($116 million)
Imports:	£12,817,633 ($36 million)	£26,030,000 ($77 million)

Exports (1960): cotton, 36%; coffee, 40%; cottonseed, 4%; copper 9%; tea 3%.

Currency. East African shilling divided into 100 cents. 20 shillings = one pound sterling.

KENYA

An independent country of East Africa since 1963 and a member of the British Commonwealth; previously a British colony and protectorate.

Area. 224,960 square miles (219,790 land area).

Population. 5,379,966 (census of 1948). 5,225,120 Africans; 29,660 Europeans; 97,687 Indians and Goans; 24,174 Arabs. Estimated population mid-1960: 6,550,000 (6,300,000 Africans).

Capital: Nairobi, 250,800 (1960).

Trade

	1949	1960
Exports:	£29,173,704 ($82 million)	£40,195,000 ($113 million)
	(including re-exports	(including re-exports
	£18,209,570 or $51 million)	£5,007,000 or $14 million.)
Imports:	£54,123,277 ($152 million)	

Exports (1960): sisal, 13%; coffee, 29%; tea, 12%; pyrethrum, 9%; meat, 5%; hides and skins, 5%.

There is a customs union between Uganda, Kenya, and Tanganyika, so that it is difficult to separate the trade of the three countries. Many of the exports of Kenya are destined for Uganda; most of the exports of Uganda pass through Kenya.

Currency. As in Uganda.

TANGANYIKA

An independent country of East Africa since 1961 and a member of the British Commonwealth; formerly a United Nations trusteeship held by Britain; previously German East Africa (part).

Area. 362,000 square miles approximately, including 20,000 water.

Population. 7,487,305 (census of 1948). 7,410,269 Africans; 16,299 Europeans (including 5397 Polish refugees); 60,737 Asians. Mid-1960 estimate: Europeans, 22,300; Indians, 87,300; Arabs, 25,400; Africans, 9,183,600.

Dar-es-Salaam (capital), 128,732, including 4478 Europeans (census 1957).

Trade

	1949	1960
Exports:	£20,124,985 ($56 million)	£56,601,000 ($158 million)
Imports:	£27,576,110 ($77 million)	£37,817,000 ($100 million)

Exports: sisal, 28%; cotton, 16%; coffee, 13%; diamonds, 9%; gold, hides, and skins.

Currency. As in Uganda.

ZANZIBAR

An independent country, consisting of two islands off the east coast of Africa, formerly a British protectorate. Became independent in 1963; the sultanate was replaced by a republic in 1964 and in April was united with Tanganyika.

Area. Zanzibar island, 640 square miles; Pemba, 380.

Population. 264,162 (census of 1948); 299,111 (census of 1958). Mid-1960 U.N. estimate: 307,000. Zanzibar, 149,575; 165,353 in 1958. Pemba 114,587; 133,858 in 1958. 279,935 Africans and Arabs (about 50,000); 18,334 Indians; 507 Europeans; 335 others. Zanzibar town 45,284; 57,923 in 1958.

Trade

	1949	1959
Exports:	£2,823,336 ($7.9 million)	£4,775,596 ($12.4 million)
Imports:	£2,979,874 ($8.3 million)	£5,509,128 ($15.4 million)

Exports: cloves and clove-oil, 55%; coconut oil, copra, and ivory.

Currency. As in Uganda.

MOÇAMBIQUE (PORTUGUESE EAST AFRICA)

A Portuguese colony under a governor-general.

Area. 297,731 square miles.

Population. 5,085,630 (census of 1940). 5,031,955 Africans; 27,438 Europeans; 15,641 mixed; 1449 Chinese; 9147 Indians. Total in 1950 census, 5,738,911. Mid-1960 U.N. estimate: 6,482,000.

Towns. 1940: Lourenço Marques (capital), 69,861; Beira, 12,988.

Trade

	1949	1960
Exports:	965,599,000 escudos ($33 million)	2,099,250,000 escudos ($72 million)
Imports:	1,750,563,893 escudos ($60 million)	3,646,257,000 escudos ($122 million)

Exports: cotton, 27%; copra, 18%; sisal, 13%.

Currency. As in Portugal: 80.50 escudos = one pound sterling. Approximately 29 escudos to $1.00

ANGOLA (PORTUGUESE WEST AFRICA)

A Portuguese colony under a governor-general.

Area. 481,351 square miles, including the detached tract of Cabinda.

Population. 3,738,010 (census of 1940); 3,665,829 Africans; 44,083 Europeans; 28,035 mixed; 63 others. Total in 1950 (census), 4,145,266; in 1960 (census), 4,832,677.

Capital. S. Paulo de Luanda.

Trade

	1949	1960
Exports:	1,793,012,000 angolars or Portuguese escudos ($62 million)	3,587,418,000 angolars or Portuguese escudos. ($123 million)
Imports:	1,337,024,000 angolars or Portuguese escudos ($46 million)	3,767,864,000 angolars or Portuguese escudos. ($130 million)

Exports (1960): coffee, 31%; diamonds, 14%; maize, 9%.

Currency. See Portuguese East Africa.

FEDERATION OF RHODESIA AND NYASALAND

Constituted 1953, dissolved 1963.

Trade

	1961
Exports:	£213,812,000 ($599 million)
Imports.	£154,562,000 ($433 million)

Exports: copper, 59%; tobacco, 18%; asbestos, 4%; tea, 2%; chrome ore 2%.

SOUTHERN RHODESIA

A self-governing colony of the British Commonwealth, part of the Federation of Rhodesia and Nyasaland 1953–1963.

Area. 150,333 square miles.

Population. 1,794,000 (1946 estimate); 3,140,000 (mid-1961 estimate). 1946: 1,704,000 Africans; 82,386 Europeans; 7470 Asian and colored. 1961: 2,900,000 Africans; 221,000 Europeans; 17,300 Asian and colored.

Towns. Salisbury, 89,000 Europeans; Bulawayo, 53,000 Europeans in 1961.

Land tenure

Tribal settlements (native reserves)	21,127,040 acres
Native purchase areas	7,859,942 acres
Crown lands available for settlers	32,685,659 acres

Livestock. European owned: 1,188,101 cattle; 108,064 sheep; 37,155 pigs; 18,431 goats (1949). African-owned: 1,954,000 cattle; 136,000 sheep; 405,000 goats (1960).

Trade

1949 Later trade figures included in Federation.

Exports (domestic):	£29,621,299 ($80 million)
Imports:	£54,585,817 ($153 million)
Re-exports:	£4,901,490 ($13 million)

Exports, tobacco, 39%; gold, 18%; asbestos, 13%; chrome ore.

Currency. As in Britain, pounds, shillings, and pence.

NORTHERN RHODESIA

A British colony in South-central Africa, part of the Federation of Rhodesia and Nyasaland 1953–1963.

Area. 288,130 square miles.

Population. 1,740,000 (estimate of 1950). 21,907 Europeans; 1117 Asians, 804 colored (census of 1946). 36,000 Europeans; 3100 Asians and colored (estimate of 1950). Estimate of June 30, 1961: Europeans, 74,000; Africans, 2,400,000; others, 9500.

Capital. Lusaka.

Trade

1948

Exports: £28,129,623 ($79 million).

Imports: £16,098,874 ($45 million).

Later trade figures included in Federation.

Exports (1949): copper, 85%; zinc, 6%; lead, 4%.

Currency. As in Southern Rhodesia.

NYASALAND

A British protectorate, part of the Federation of Rhodesia and Nyasaland 1953–1963.

Area. 36,686 square miles (land).

Population. 2,400,000 (1950 estimate); 2,831,700 (1960 estimate). About 9300 Europeans and 11,100 Asians in 1960.

Capital. Zomba.

Trade

1949

Exports: £4,689,733 ($13 million).

Imports: £5,041,627 ($14 million).

Later trade figures included in Federation.

Exports: tobacco, 67%; tea, 25%; cotton, 5%.

Currency. As in Rhodesia.

REPUBLIC OF SOUTH AFRICA

Became a republic and withdrew from the British Commonwealth on March 15, 1961; previously as the Union of South Africa or Unie van Suid-Afrika a self-governing dominion of the British Commonwealth.

Area

Cape of Good Hope	278,465 square miles
Natal	33,578 square miles
Transvaal	110,540 square miles
Orange Free State	49,866 square miles
Total	472,359 square miles

Population

	1946	1960
Europeans or Whites	2,372,690	3,067,638
non-Europeans or non-whites	9,045,659	12,773,490
Total	11,418,349	15,841,128

Non-Europeans in 1946 included 7,831,915 Bantus; 285,260 Asians; 928,484 others.

Towns. 1960: Johannesburg, 1,096,541 (389,690 white); Cape Town, 722,487 (279,404 white); Durban, 655,370 (194,276 white); Pretoria, 415,989 (202,664 white); Port Elizabeth, 270,815 (94,085 white); Germiston, 204,605 (84,419 white); Bloemfontein, 140,924 (61,213 white); East London, 114,589 (48,725 white); Pietermaritzburg, 95,124 (39,472 white).

Pretoria is the seat of government, Cape Town the seat of legislature.

Land use

	1949	1957
Land in farms:	214,777,497 acres	206,707,500 (whites only)
Number of farms:	177,242	103,059 (whites only)

Crops. Maize, wheat, potatoes, kaffir corn, oats, barley, fruits, sugar cane, tobacco.

Livestock. In 1949: horses, 346,594; cattle, 12,241,925; sheep, 31,907,749; goats, 5,528,820. In 1959: cattle, 12,326,000; sheep, 37,852,000; goats, 4,953,000.

Minerals. In 1949: coal, 27,600,000 tons; asbestos, 70,917 short tons; manganese ore, 644,831 long tons; gold, 11,705,048 ounces; diamonds, 1,494,527 carats; copper, platinum, chrome ore. In 1960: coal, 42.1 million tons; asbestos, 175,869 tons; manganese ore, 1,316,132 tons; iron ore, 3,385,000 tons; copper, 50,847, tons; chrome ore, 851,000 tons; gold, 21,383,019 ounces; silver, 2,226,204 ounces.

Trade

	1949	1960
Exports, excluding gold:	£153,624,896 ($430 million)	R789,350,848 ($1205 million)
Imports, excluding gold:	£314,579,015 ($757 million)	R1,111,394,912 ($1556 million)

Exports: gold, 44%; wool, 14%; diamonds, 4%.

Currency. Formerly, South African pound, normally equivalent to one pound sterling. Since 1961, Rand (formerly 10 shillings), divided into 100 cents.

SOUTHWEST AFRICA

A territory administered by the Union of South Africa. The old mandate from the League of Nations was a Class III mandate which laid down that the territory should be governed as an integral part of the territory of the mandatory power. The South African government never recognized the authority of the United Nations over Southwest Africa.

Area. 317,887 square miles.

Population. 1946 census: 37,858 Europeans; 53,172 colored; 269,569 Africans. Census of 1960: 73,154 whites; 451,908 Africans and colored.

    Capital. Windhoek, 35,890 (1960).

Trade	**1949**	
Exports:	£14,863,702 ($42 million)	later included in South Africa
Imports:	£13,069,816 ($37 million)	

Currency. As in South Africa.

BASUTOLAND

A British protectorate. Regent: Constantine Bereng Seeiso, for whom Ma'Ntsebo, widow of the late Paramount Chief, acted until February 1960, during his minority.

Area. 11,716 square miles.

Population. Census of 1946: 563,854: including 1,689 Europeans, 274 Asians, and 602 colored. In addition, about 35,000 Basutos were working in the Rand mines and 75,000 elsewhere. At the census of 1956 there were 641,674 persons (1,926 Europeans). Mid-1960 U.N. estimate: 685,000.

Capital. Maseru.

Currency. As in South Africa.

BECHUANALAND PROTECTORATE

A British protectorate. Each group of tribes is ruled by its chief.

Area. About 222,000 square miles.

Population. Census of 1946: 2325 Europeans; 1804 Asians and colored; 292,754 Africans. Census of 1956: 3173 Europeans; 248 Asians; 676 colored. Mid-1960 U.N. estimate: 350,000.

Currency. As in South Africa.

SWAZILAND

A British protectorate. Chief Mswazi II succeeded in 1939.

Area. 6,705 square miles.

Population. Census of 1946: 3204 Europeans; 6 Asians; 735 colored; 181,269 Africans. Census of 1956: 5919 Europeans; 1378 colored; 229,744 Africans; total, 237,041. Mid-1960 U.N. estimate: 259,000.

    Capital: Mbabane.

Currency. As in South Africa.

MADAGASCAR AND DEPENDENCIES (RÉPUBLIQUE MALGACHE)

Since 1960 an independent republic within the French community, formerly a French colony under a high commissioner.

Area. Approximately 227,500 square miles.

Population. 4,350,700 (estimate of 1950, including the Mayotte and Comoro Islands), including 44,517 French and 19,912 other Europeans. Census of 1960: 5,184,000, excluding Comoro Islands but including 74,000 Europeans.

Towns. Tananarive, 174,153 (1950) 206,324 (1960); Tamatave, 28,747; 48,627 (1960); Majunga, 32,163; 51,687 (1960).

Trade

	1949	1960
Exports:	7,369 million francs ($29 million)	18,489 million francs ($74 million)
Imports:	11,789 million francs ($47 million)	27,657 million francs ($111 million)

Exports: coffee, 30%; meat; hides; vanilla; rice; cloves, sugar.

Currency. Madagascan franc (franc CFA) = 2 French old francs.

RÉUNION (ÎLE DE LA RÉUNION)

An Overseas Department of France.

Area. 970 square miles.

Population. 242,343 (1946); 336,000 (estimate 1960).

Capital. St. Denis, 36096 (1946); 41,863 (1960).

Trade

	1949	1960
Exports:	2248 million francs CFA ($9 million)	8,989 million francs CFA ($36 million)
Imports:	2873 million francs CFA ($12 million)	12,902 million francs CFA ($52 million)

Exports: sugar, 77%; rum, 11%; vegetable oils, 9%.

Currency. One franc CFA = 2 French francs.

MAURITIUS

A British colony under a governor with an executive and legislative council. Dependencies: Rodrigues, 42 square miles; also other small islands.

Area. 720 square miles.

Population. 419,185 (1944); 501,415 (1952); 639,000 (mid-1960 U.N. estimate); dependencies, 13,468 (1944); 15,085 (1952); 19,000 (mid-1960 estimate).

Capital. Port Louis, 107,020 (1959).

Trade

	1949	1959
Exports:	163,075,201 Mauritius rupees ($34 million)	282,210,191 Mauritius rupees ($59 million)
Imports:	153,139,958 Mauritius rupees ($32 million)	286,851,725 Mauritius rupees ($60 million)

Exports: sugar, 96%; rum, 3%.

Currency. The Mauritius rupee, like the Ceylon rupee, is divided into 100 cents. Linked with sterling at one shilling and sixpence per rupee. One rupee approximately 21 cents U.S.

ATLANTIC ISLANDS

St. Helena. British colony; 47 square miles; 4700 people (1949), 4644 (1959).

Ascension. Dependency of St. Helena; 34 square miles; 162 people (1949), 418 (1959).

Tristan da Cunha. British; habitable area 12 square miles; 248 people (1949), 292 (1959). Evacuated in consequence of outburst of volcanic activity 1961, reoccupied in 1963.

Cape Verde Islands. Portuguese; 1557 square miles; 181,286 people (1940), 148,331 (1950); 201,549 (1960).

Madeira. Administered as district of Portugal.

Canary Islands. Administered as part of Spain.

Index

Thorn woodland, 112
Tibesti Mts., 56, 254
Tibu, 259
Ticks, 162
Tidmarsh, C. E., *Farming in S. Africa,* 110
Tigre, 348
Timber, 376
 and wood, 194, 195
Timbuktu, 134, 259
Tin, 194, 195, 368, 369, 395, 406, 474
Tinfields, 184
Tinley, J. M., *The Native Labor Problem of S. Africa,* 432
Tin ore, 193, 308, 449
Tin working, Nigeria, 316
Tirailleurs, 318
Tobacco, 117, 141, 142, 194, 246, 307, 310, 394, 419, 423, 454, 465, 485
Tobruk, 264
Togoland, 28, 318
 division of, 34
 former British, 39, 281
 statistics, 508
 French, 39
Togo (République Togolaise), 279, 314, 328–329
 statistics, 506–507
Toiches, 338
Toit, A. L. du, *The Geology of S. Africa,* 479
Tordesillas, Treaty of, 16, 377
Tororo, 394
Tothill, J. D. (Ed.), *Agriculture in the Sudan,* 346
 Agriculture in Uganda, 412
Touggourt, 255, 262
Tourism, 126, 485
 possibilities in Ethiopia, 352
Trace elements, 170
Trachoma, 164
Tractors, 370
Trade winds, 442, 485
Trading posts, European, 7
Transhumance, 220, 336
Transpiration, 112, 173, 189
Transportation, midcentury, 184–187
Transportation changes, 1950–1963, 187
Trans-Saharan bus services, 187
Transvaal, 106, 171, 462
Transvaal Bush Veld, 449, 463, 464–465
Transvaal Republic, 430
 establishment, 21
Trapnell, C. G., and Clothier, J. N., *Soils, Vegetation and Agricultural Systems of Northwestern Rhodesia,* 109, 428
Treaty of Paris, 1814, 283, 315
Trek, Great, 21
Trewartha, Glenn, T., 130
"Triangular Traffic," 14
Tribal meeting places, 173
Tribal organization, disruption of, 136, 147 *et seq.,* 188–189, 370, 437

Tribal system, 146
Tripoli, 259, 264
Tripolitania, 264, 265
Tristan da Cunha, 61, 483, 487–488
Tropical Africa, 10, 43, 87, 154, 193
Tropical Africa, transportation, 173
 exports, 1957, 194
Tropical climate, effect on health, 83–84
Tropical prairie soils, 89
Tropical savanna climate, 74–75
Tropical soils, 100–104
Trunk roads, 185, 187
Trypanosoma gambiense, 159
 rhodesiense, 159
Tsetse fly, 141, 159–61, 271, 394, 420
Tshopo hydroelectric plant, 193
Tsumeb mine, 474
Tuareg, 138, 258
Tuberculosis, 163
Tubman, President W.V.S., 293
Tunis, 117, 237, 249
 Gulf of, 237
Tunisia, 30, 81, 129, 232, 234, 237, 248–249, 262
 statistics, 501–502
Turks, 210, 339
 in N. Africa, 232

Ubangi R., 360, 363
Ubangi Shari, 373
Udi plateau, 96
Uganda, 26, 129, 160, 161, 195, 384, 391, 392–395
 1893, 339
Uganda Protectorate, 391
 statistics, 512
Ujiji, 7, 23, 24
Umtali, 419
Underdevelopment, 7
Undifferentiated Highlands, 79
UNESCO, 110
Union minière du Haut Katanga, 368
Union of South Africa, 431 *et seq.*
United Africa Co., 26, 408, 409
United Africa Party, 433
United Arab Republic (U.A.R.), 201, 209
United Nations in Congo, 362
United Nations Trusteeships, 34, 375
United States air bases, Libya, 266
United States Navy, 293
Universities, 153
 in E. Africa, 392–393
University Colleges, 188
 in Africa after World War II, 392
University of E. Africa, 153
University of Ghana, 302
University of Khartoum, 346
University of London, 392
Upper Egypt, 213, 218, 230
Upper Karoo, 457 *et seq.*
Upper Nile Provinces, 342
Upper Senegal and Niger, 324
Uranium ore, 368

Uranium oxide, 449
Urban growth, 421
Urbanization, 210
Usambara, 403
Usumbura, 372
Uvarov, B. P., 166

Vaal R., 21, 57
Valley of a Thousand Hills, 443
Vanadium, 474
Vanderbijl Park, 450
Van der Merwe, C. R., 104, 107
Vanderplank, J., 466
Van Dongen, I. S., 428
Vanilla, 497, 498
Vasco da Gama, 6, 16
Vegetable products, exports in 1957, 194
Vegetables, 196, 219, 245, 310, 352, 420
Vegetation, 108 *et seq.*
 classification (Shantz), 110
Vegetation and Soils of Africa, 88, 106
Vegetation map of Tanganyika (Gillman), 114
Vegetation of W. Africa, natural, 277
Veld, High, 78
Vereeniging, 196, 449, 450
 Treaty of, 1902, 430
Vespucci, Amerigo, 17
Victoria, 374
Victoria, Lake, 25, 51, 60, 177, 228, 391, 393, 404
 area, 55
Victoria Falls, 58, 119, 415
Victoria Falls Bridge, 177, 183
Victoria Nile, 228
Victoria West, 460
Village store, 189, 191
Vineyards, 246, 247, 249
Viticulture in Cape Region, 451, 454
Volcanic activity, 51
Volcanic cones, 51
Volcanoes, extinct, 382
Volta hydroelectric project, 193
Volta R., 299
Volta River Project, 299
Voortrekker Monument, 438
Voortrekkers, 475
Vridi Canal, 327
Vultures, 352

Wadi Halfa, 213, 333, 335
Wad Medani, 344
Wakefield, John, 409
Walvis Bay, 473, 474
Wankie, 368, 418, 420, 422
Warm temperate coastal strip soils, 105–106
Warner Beach, 468
Warriner, D., *Land and Poverty in the Middle East,* 231
Water, raising, 217
 underground, 460
Water-borne disease organisms, 162–163
Water control, 170